FLIGHTWISE

VOLUME 2

AIRCRAFT STABILITY
AND CONTROL

FLIGHTWISE
VOLUME 2

AIRCRAFT STABILITY
AND CONTROL

Airlife
England

Copyright © 1997 Christopher Carpenter

First published in the UK in 1997
by Airlife Publishing Ltd

British Library Cataloguing-in-Publication Data
 A catalogue record for this book
 is available from the British Library

ISBN 1 85310 870 7

Typeset by Wearset, Boldon, Tyne and Wear
Printed in England by Hartnolls Ltd, Bodmin, Cornwall.

Airlife Publishing Ltd
101 Longden Road, Shrewsbury, SY3 9EB, England.

Foreword

In his first volume, subtitled *Principles of Aircraft Flight*, Chris Carpenter describes the fundamentals of aerodynamics in non-mathematical terms. He explains the physics of subsonic, transonic and supersonic flow before analysing the various approximate methods and concepts that aerodynamicists use to get quantitative estimates for design purposes. To attempt this task without seeking refuge in the jargon and shorthand of mathematics is a difficult task but in the event a most rewarding one.

In his second volume Chris attempts the even more difficult task of explaining how aircraft can maintain stability and yet be manoeuvred and controlled with pin-point accuracy anywhere in the Earth's atmosphere. Anyone who has seen a small aerobatic aircraft being 'thrown all over the sky,' or watched a modern jet fighter at an air display, or travelled in a large airliner seemingly oblivious of the atmospheric disturbances surrounding it, must have wondered how the dual aims of stability and control are achieved. Once again, the approach is mainly non-mathematical and although this inevitably lengthens the discussion, the benefit is a clear understanding of the clever design and engineering that makes such varied flight patterns possible.

The range and scope of the book is also impressive. The traditional topics of static stability, dynamic stability, control systems and manoeuvring are fully covered but the book goes on to explain the way in which artificial stability, stability augmentation and modern avionics in general, have transformed the ability of modern aircraft. The book ends with a look at the future and a guide to the direction in which some of the current research aircraft may be leading. With stealth, vertical take-off and landing, vectored thrust and many other features having such a profound effect on stability and control, this is a stimulating section with which to end a most welcome second volume in the *Flightwise* series.

Professor J. L. Stollery, CBE,
Dsc(Eng), FEng.

Contents

Preface

This is the second of two books entitled *Flightwise*, whose aim is to present the principles of aircraft flight in a non-mathematical but intellectually rigorous manner to a readership for whom most of the existing literature on the subject is either superficial or steeped in weighty mathematics. The style of the *Flightwise* books is conversational, based on my approach to teaching the subject which I have found to be well received. The books start from the premise that the reader is intelligent and inquisitive but has no scientific or mathematical background beyond the ability to manipulate and understand simple algebraic formulae, and even such formulae are very few and far between.

The first volume, entitled *Flightwise – Principles of Aircraft Flight,* covered the essential low and high-speed aerodynamic principles of aircraft sustention and drag. Slowly but in a very focused fashion, it built vertically, drawing in and establishing *en passant* all the physical concepts and theories that were necessary for each next stage of its logical development, and never deviating far from such essentials. By this means it aimed to establish a sound professional understanding of the underlying concepts upon which aircraft are designed and to dispel many of the trite and over-simplistic explanations that abound in popular writings on the subject.

The present volume moves on to deal with aerodynamic stability and the means of controlling aircraft flight in the three dimensions of the atmosphere. It is structured in the form of a sandwich, the 'filling' being contained between an opening chapter which looks at the historical development of the awareness of the importance and necessity of full three-axis control backed up by adequate aerodynamic stability, and a closing chapter which looks at the state of the art today and the way in which the future would appear to be moving. The intervening chapters continue the Volume 1 approach of drawing in and explaining in depth all supporting concepts and mechanical and dynamic theory just before their point of use, first of all for stability in Chapters 2 to 7 and then for control in Chapters 8 to 14.

The structure is distinctly linear and progressive, but liberal forward and backward cross-referencing is provided to avoid the need for verbose repetition whilst appreciating that students do not learn everything at a first reading. Being a sequel to Volume 1, a knowledge and understanding of much of the material covered in that volume has had to be assumed as a starting base, but back-references to that volume, when given, are as suggested, rather than essential, foundation reading. On occasions, material pertinent to both volumes has been substantially drawn from Volume 1 and reproduced.

It is a great pleasure to be able to acknowledge the very heart-warming support, encouragement and advice that I have received whilst preparing this volume. I am particularly indebted to Professor J. L. Stollery of Cranfield University's College of Aeronautics, who was an invaluable teacher and personal tutor to me as a student some years ago, for his advice and encouragement and for kindly writing a foreword for each volume. Next may I express my very deep and sincere appreciation to Mr Clemens Zhender, a Swiss lawyer and Private Pilot's Licence holder, who approached me enthusiastically after reading Volume 1, and who kindly agreed, as an archetypical student representing the intended readership of *Flightwise*, to read the draft of Volume 2. He has provided me with corrections and very helpful comments which have been incorporated. I am also indebted to Mr John Gibson, a highly experienced retired aeronautical engineer from British Aerospace, Warton, for putting me right over some details of aircraft handling.

Most importantly, I owe a big debt of gratitude to Hoverspeed Ltd, who at my request kindly invited me to their base at Dover, to experience large hovercraft operations on the English Channel for a full day. Especially I am grateful for the kindness of Hoverspeed's Senior Captain, Linton Heatley, and his flight crew, with whom I crossed the Channel six times during that day on the flight deck, and on the strength of whose guidance and elucidation I was able to write the 'hovercraft' section of Chapter 11.

May I reiterate some acknowledgements from the preface to Volume 1? Again I thank all the staff of the College of Aeronautics at Cranfield University, for presenting me with an excellent grounding in the subject of aerodynamics and flight mechanics. In Volume 1 I drew special attention to the contribution made by Professor John Spillman, but in the present context of aircraft stability and control particular thanks must be given to Dr Mike Cook, my principal teacher in these subjects. He was a most patient, thorough and rigorous lecturer and tutor, whose personal guidance and course notes have been a sustained source of inspiration to me throughout the writing of this volume. Whilst I have been engaged in writing this book, he has been producing a new and authoritative in-depth textbook, also on aircraft stability and control. If any readers of *Flightwise* should move on to studying the subject in greater depth, I know from my experience of his very high quality teaching that his book will be one to be highly recommended.

Finally my thanks go to all my colleagues in the Engineering Department of the University of Warwick for freeing me to take sabbatical leave (again!) to write this book; and to all of the students whom I have had the privilege of teaching, who are without doubt the greatest source of inspiration of all.

Chris Carpenter
Weston-on-Avon
England

CHAPTER 1
The Challenge of Mastering the Air

INTRODUCTION

There be three things which are too wonderful for me, yea, four which I know not: The way of an eagle in the air; the way of a serpent upon a rock; the way of a ship in the midst of the sea; and the way of a man with a maid.[1]

Just as the mystery of the eagle's ability to defy gravity intrigued the writer of this biblical proverb, so today we may watch with incredulity as an enormous, heavily laden Boeing 747 airliner lumbers down the runway and launches itself into the air. But the proverb-writer's wonder goes deeper. Whilst the serpent has the knack of gliding lithely along the most tortuous of paths at great speed, the eagle is free in its three-dimensional ocean to guide itself gracefully wherever the spirit leads, to change course suddenly and swoop on its prey, and to come to rest on a rocky crag with pin-point accuracy and utter elegance (Figure 1.1). The ship in the midst of the sea not only obeys the master's hand at the helm, but also seems to scoff at the attempts of the ocean waves to upset its equilibrium, as it restlessly rolls, tosses and pitches, always returning to the right way up. So also the eagle appears unperturbed as it soars unwaveringly in a strong gusty wind. Likewise, amidst the intensity and dynamism of human relationships, similar elements of mastery and sympathetic dominance may have been observed by the proverb-writer in the case of a man with a maid. I wonder which of the four was the writer's afterthought!

My earlier book *Flightwise – Principles of Aircraft Flight* focused on the first aspect of this wonder of flight, discovering how the tremendous forces necessary for flight may be produced as a result simply of movement of an aircraft through the air, and how these forces may be tailored and optimised to satisfy our requirements. But such considerations are on their own insufficient to facilitate the design of a flying machine which is to be consciously directed along a chosen three-dimensional flight-path in the air, whilst at the same time resisting the attempts of variable disturbances of that air to deflect it from the chosen path, or to upset it from its orderly flight orientation and equilibrium. In this book we will investigate these two closely related aspects of aircraft flight, which are referred to as control and stability.

[1]Proverbs 30:18,19, Old Testament, Authorised Version.

Figure 1.1 '... the way of an eagle in the air ...'

Aircraft stability and control has today reached a very advanced state of sophistication. Although the fundamental principles have for a long time been well understood and thoroughly mastered, significant advances are still being made, especially with the assistance of (but by no means substitution by) computer technology. But even though nearly a century has passed since the Wright brothers' epic first sustained controlled powered flight on Thursday 17 December 1903, at Kill Devil Hills near Kitty Hawk, in North Carolina, USA, it is humbling to observe that for a full century before that man was, in a very real sense, on the very brink of mastering the air. In fact, it was considerations of stability and control which, throughout this period and even for a substantial time after the Wright brothers' historic flight, proved to be the constant stumbling-block over which many other attempts at flight faltered and came to grief.

Just as today we take for granted the ease of doing arithmetic thanks to the invention of a zero and place notation and can scarcely imagine the difficulty of the ancient Romans in doing their sums without recourse to these concepts, so the world of aeronautics is today inclined to take for granted the principles of aircraft stability and control which the earlier pioneers had to grapple with for such a very long period. These principles are by no means simple; even today they are seriously misunderstood by a very substantial proportion of people in aviation, and fallacious explanations abound.

Before we attempt to establish a structure for our thinking on these matters and to clothe it with some flesh, let us take a brief look through one or two selected windows at the history of man's striving for flight, as it unfolded throughout the nineteenth century and well into the twentieth. The chief source for this survey, which occupies the remainder of this chapter, is Charles H. Gibbs-Smith's book *Aviation – An Historical Survey*, (second edition, 1985) published by the Science Museum. That book is strongly recommended as providing a totally enthralling, comprehensive and authoritative insight into the subject that we can here only touch on briefly.

The purpose of including this historical prelude before our deeper studies which follow is more than merely to provide an interesting introduction to the book (although I trust that it will achieve that end). Rather, it is to bring into sharp focus the central and crucial position that aircraft stability and control considerations must occupy if one is to be successful when designing any flying machine. Potentially, man could have been flying much earlier than he was, if only more of the pioneers had taken on board this fundamental axiom of flight. A sense of the pivotal importance of the subject should also provide us with welcome motivation for properly getting to grips with its concepts and methods later on.

CAYLEY – THE TRUE INVENTOR OF THE AEROPLANE

Since the earliest times man has always aspired to imitate the birds in flight. Until the dawning of the modern scientific era in the last couple of centuries, his attempts to fly had concentrated on two basic needs: firstly, that of overcoming gravity and rising up into the air, and secondly, that of propelling himself and his vehicle through that air. Tentative approaches to tackling these aims included wind-borne kites, rocket propelled bird models, helicopter-style airscrews and the flapping of wings like the tantalising birds, but it was only lighter-than-air craft in the form of hot-air and hydrogen balloons that were to have any success at conquering the first challenge, that of sustention. The excitement of seeing the first manned balloon flight was to have a profound influence on one ten-year-old Yorkshire boy, George Cayley. The balloon's success prompted considerable experimentation (on the whole, abortive) into the concept of producing thrust for propulsion by means of an airscrew, an idea borrowed from earlier helicopter-like toys and models, and even a foray into the realms of jet propulsion (by Montgolfier). Although rudimentary steering devices (sometimes reminiscent of ship's rudders) were now and then conceived of for flying vehicles, it may have been tacitly assumed that steering would not be a problem, just as a carriage driver does not consciously need to give more than an indication of the required direction to the horse.

Although in the eighteenth century flight remained firmly in the realm of fancy, the development of military ballistics and of windmills was giving rise to the birth of aerodynamics as a new subject of investigation and research. So the time was ripe for the emergence of a capable scientist and thinker who was also fired with an aeronautical imagination and with a vision of the potential of flight. It was George Cayley, born in 1773 in Scarborough, Yorkshire, later baronet Sir George, who was to fulfil this rôle and come to be generally regarded (with the hindsight of the present century) as 'the true inventor of the aeroplane and one of the most powerful geniuses in the history of aviation'[2] and also as the founder of the science of aerodynamics. He was undoubtedly one of the giants of the history of aviation and other technology, unparalleled in his prowess since his celebrated predecessor Leonardo da Vinci of some three hundred years earlier, with whom he shared many qualities. Apart from devoting most of his life to aeronautical research and writing, he was the inventor of the tension-spoked bicycle wheel (which he used for the undercarriage of one of his gliders), the hot air engine and the 'caterpillar'-tracked vehicle, and he also carried out research in fields as diverse as acoustics, land reclamation, railway equipment, lifeboats, ballistics, artificial limbs, theatre architecture, optics and electricity. He founded the Regent Street Polytechnic Institution in London, and carried out research into scientific education. He was also the Whig member of parliament for Scarborough for a short time, a devout Unitarian, leisure-time poet and devoted husband and father. He died in 1857 where he had lived and carried out most of his work, at Brompton Hall, Scarborough, at the age of 83.[3]

George Cayley's aeronautical achievements were profound and visionary, theoretical and practical. Not only was he the first to rationalise the distinction between the forces of thrust and of lift and to establish the four-force model of lift, weight, thrust and drag as introduced in Chapter 2 of *Flightwise – Principles of Aircraft Flight*, but also he was the first to observe that a wing's lift was created in greatest

[2]Charles Dollfus.
[3]*Encyclopaedia Britannica* 1971 edition.

part by the reduction of pressure on the upper surface, and that a cambered wing would give more lift than a flat one. He thus revealed the concepts of the modern aerofoil. But most significantly in our present context, he clearly identified and provided for the needs both of aircraft control, to direct the path of flight as required, and of full three-axis stability (defined in Chapter 2), to prevent undemanded deviations from that path. His systematic and carefully published papers have led directly to all subsequent research and development in aviation. Much of the theory developed later in this book derives from that initially formulated by Cayley, some 70 to 80 years before the world's first sustained powered flight.

Not only was Cayley a theorist, but he also brought his ideas to fruition by building several successful heavier-than-air aircraft. As early as 1804, aged 30, he made the first proper aeroplane of history. It was a 5-foot long model glider with a kite-form wing set on a pole at a 6-degree angle of incidence; it had a tail unit attached by a universal joint – to act as a combined rudder and elevator control – and, most importantly, a moveable weight to adjust the position of the centre of gravity (Figure 1.2). Five years later he built a full-size glider with a wing area of 200 square feet which, after successful unmanned test flights, was flown for short distances with a young boy on board. Although rudimentary, through his novel concepts of providing stability by means of vertical and horizontal tail surfaces, combined with his awareness of the significance of the position of the aircraft's centre of gravity, Cayley had laid down the basic principles and ground rules of flight, which are still directly applicable to the conventional fixed wing monoplane aircraft form that is ubiquitous today.

These successes were followed by a series of other gliders over many years, sometimes flown free, sometimes towed, sometimes carrying a young boy (probably to demonstrate the airworthiness of the craft rather than to act as a pilot). Ultimately, at the age of 76, putting his faith in a triplane design, fixed tail unit and a separate elevator-cum-rudder, at first fixed but later intended to be pilot-operated, Cayley was ready for a man-carrying flight. But, for reasons that we are left to speculate about, he never himself flew one of his aircraft.

Figure 1.2   Cayley's sketch of his first model glider, 1804

Instead, his reluctant coachman was required to fly the glider across a small valley for this, the first successful man-carrying gliding flight in history. Sustained manned flight would appear to have been within the grasp of the aspirants at long last!

So why was it that, for the next 50 years or so, Cayley's magnificent lead was not followed, and the promised dawn of aviation did not materialise? A major reason was undoubtedly that the only mechanical powerplants so far developed were steam engines, and these were far too heavy for flight in relation to the limited amount of power that they were able to produce. Cayley was fully aware of this problem, and, despite his own brief foray into the development of the expansion air engine in about 1805, he acknowledged that powerplant development had a long way to go before it would meet the needs of aviation. It was for this primary reason that all of Cayley's aircraft were gliders. Having understood the four-force principle of lift, weight, thrust and drag and how it could be modified for gliding flight[4], Cayley wisely carried out all his flight experimentation using the gliding principle, realising that it was substantially the same in essence as level powered flight, and that the theory would require minimal adaptation when suitable power sources became available.

But Cayley's concentration on gliding flight was also motivated by a much more profound rationale. Before Cayley's inspirational insight and accomplishments, all attempts at flight had been stifled by a preoccupation with the necessities of sustention and propulsion. Having never got that far, it had scarcely occurred to the punters that, if they were to get airborne, the physical security of firm contact with the ground would at once vanish, and there would be no inbuilt restraint to prevent toppling over forwards, backwards or sideways, or to keep the vehicle correctly orientated along its flight path. Furthermore, variations in the required direction of flight (up, down, left, right) could not merely be hinted at, as with a horse drawing a carriage, and the aircraft would not have a mind of its own capable of imitating the apparently effortless steering of a bird in flight. It required a new sort of insight into the reality of flight to realise that the stability and controllability of a flying machine could not be regarded merely as afterthoughts, but that they were fundamental and crucial design requirements for the achievement of (i) getting airborne safely, and (ii) staying up there for any length of time. Such an insight was the hallmark of Cayley's genius. But, as history repeatedly shows us, this

---

[4]This is discussed in Figure 3.3 and the related text in Chapter 3 of *Flightwise – Principles of Aircraft Flight*.

was not a natural way of thinking for most people, even otherwise brilliant technologists, and the mentality that consigned control to the realms of afterthought was to have a very serious delaying influence over the successful mastery of the air.

Cayley's concepts of stability could very satisfactorily be tested (at least to a limited extent) by means of unmanned gliders, just as today we may play around with paper darts and aeroplanes. The fact that his boy passengers appear to have come to no harm on their brief flights suggests that Cayley had, indeed, mastered the rudiments of stability. But to test out his methods of controlling the flight path was going to require a pilot, and so the unwilling cooperation of the coachman was seen to be an essential precursor to validating Cayley's ideas. Had Cayley (like his predecessors) concentrated solely on getting a machine to raise itself *upwards* from the ground, he would never have progressed sufficiently to reach the brink of allowing a human pilot to demonstrate the use of controls in actual flight, and so he would have remained firmly on the ground like so many before (and after) him.

CHAUFFEURS AND AIRMEN

Chroniclers of the history of flight, aware of the influence that two opposing schools of thought have had on the development of aviation throughout the nineteenth and early twentieth centuries, have coined two words to distinguish and characterise them. First of all there was the 'chauffeur'. He was the aspiring aeronaut who conceived of the flying machine simply as an extension of the horse and carriage, or later of the motorcar; a vehicle rather like Father Christmas' sleigh, that could be driven around the sky above the rooftops, unconstrained by the inconvenience of following roads, and from which he could look down on the *hoi polloi* with an aloof air. The chauffeur lacked (or stifled) the foresight and scientific understanding to see beyond the fundamental needs of sustention and propulsion, and so kept banging his head against a brick wall by trying fruitlessly to achieve flight through brute force.

In contrast, there was the 'airman'. His inspiration for flight was not just to achieve a luxury means of locomotion. Rather, he was the dreamer who saw 'the way of an eagle in the air' as something tantalising and enticing in its own right, and aspired to be able to imitate it, to take on a mantle of three-dimensional freedom, so as to be able to twist and soar with the birds. It had long been realised that this was not achievable by man's own physical strength, through donning feathers and flapping arms, and so a flying machine had to be devised. But this flying machine had to become an extension of the very airman himself, and he would be the mind and the heart of the flying machine. He would become at one with the birds.

Cayley was the first of the true breed of 'airmen' following a succession of 'chauffeurs' over many generations. However, with one or two notable exceptions, the 'chauffeur' mentality was to continue to dominate the quest for sustained flight for many decades to come. It could not, and did not, succeed in delivering the goods. So, if Cayley had got it right (as we now know to be the case), and if he had indeed laid down the fundamentals of the theory of flight for posterity in his high quality publications, why did he have so little influence on the pattern of aviation development over the subsequent years? Why did aviation not emerge rapidly at this time from its doldrums?

More than anything else, the answer to this question lies in the underlying culture of Cayley's time. It is clear from his own words that Cayley himself recognised that he could not persuade the scientific world to take the idea of mechanical flight seriously. In 1809 he wrote of 'the art of flying, or aerial navigation as I have chosen to term it for the sake of giving a little more dignity to a subject bordering upon the ludicrous in public estimation'. The aviation eccentrics, showmen and charlatans who were his contemporaries, had caused the subject of flight to be consigned to the status of farce or science fiction in public perception. 'A prophet is not without honour, save in his own country, and in his own house.'[5]

OTTO LILIENTHAL

We could enumerate at length the contributions and achievements of other great pioneers of this period, not least such figures as Alphonse Pénaud, Samuel Pierpont Langley and Octave Chanute, but although highly significant in the progress towards sustained manned flight the contributions of these and other such great men do not mark specific major turning points along the road.

However, the performance of one leading actor on the stage, Otto Lilienthal (1848–96), was to have a very profound influence on the Wright brothers, and so deserves inclusion here. Even though he did not set up a landmark of any one specific major new development, Lilienthal was the first man in the world to launch himself into the air and fly, and was by far the most prolific maker and flyer of gliders of his century. As with so many characters in the history of aviation before and since, he (along with his brother Gustav) was blessed with an innate interest in flying which was aroused during childhood at his home in the Germano-Polish territory of Pomerania, where he and his brother enthusiastically engaged in youthful flying experiments with flapping wings. In 1869, after two of his three years studying at Potsdam and Berlin to become a professional engineer, he and his

[5]Matthew 13:57, New Testament, Authorised Version.

brother progressed to experimenting with a six-wing ornithopter (flap-ping-wing flying machine) suspended against a counter-weight. Curiously, he remained devoted to the wing-flapping idea all his life (particularly for propulsion), believing that it was with the powered ornithopter that man would ultimately triumph. But he was wise enough to realise that experimentation with fixed-wing gliders was the best preparation for powered flight of any form.

Lilienthal built a total of 18 different aircraft (plus replicas of some), all of which, with the exception of the first two and the last, he flew successfully and repeatedly as gliders. Two were equipped with a 2 horsepower carbonic acid gas motor intended to drive flapping wing-tip propelling devices modelled on the wing-tip feathers of birds, but he only flew these aircraft as gliders. His aims in all his many gliding flights are best reflected in his own words:

> One can get a proper insight into the practice of flying only by actual fly-ing experiments ... The manner in which we have to meet the irregulari-ties of the wind, when soaring in the air, can only be learnt by being in the air itself ... The only way which leads us to a quick development in human flight is a systematic and energetic practice in actual flying experi-ments.

Thus Lilienthal, one of the breed of true 'airmen', through his glid-ing exploits concentrated his efforts on achieving reliable lift and full controllability of a stable aircraft. Achieving stability by means of a fin, tailplane and wing dihedral[6] following the principles of Cayley, he controlled most of his gliders by use of the hang-glider concept, in which the pilot hung by his arms and could swing his body in any desired direction to shift the centre of gravity. Apart from a few strange and usually abortive experiments with the use of aerodynamic controlling devices, Lilienthal contributed little to the development of effective methods of controlling an aircraft, although shortly before his death he did leave some written evidence that he was beginning to give these matters some thought. However, it was not primarily in this area that he excelled. Rather, he enters the annals as one who epito-mised the 'airman' attitude, regarding pilot and craft as one, and achieving great results through continuous, persistent practice at flying and controlling his gliders.

Lilienthal was known to remark that 'Opfer müssen gebracht wer-den' (sacrifices must be made), and so it was fitting, if tragic, that his prolific gliding career was cut short when, at the age of 48, he was killed in a flying accident. His glider stalled in a gust, one wing

---

[6]Dihedral refers to the wings being inclined upwards from root to tip. This is a stan-dard way of achieving stability against rolling deviations from level flight, as explained in Chapter 6.

dropped, and the glider side-slipped into the ground, the impact breaking his spine. He was buried with the epitaph 'sacrifices must be made' engraved on his gravestone. However, thanks to the timely development of greatly improved photographic techniques at the start of his flying career, Lilienthal was the first aviator in history to have his achievements extensively recorded for posterity in some excellent photographs, which were widely published at the time in popular magazines. Consequently his prolific experimentation was to have an influence on subsequent aviators disproportionately greater than his limited contributions to the scientific theory of flight might have warranted. As a great experimenter, he is rightly regarded as the key figure in aviation during the last decade of the nineteenth century.

STABILITY OR CONTROLLABILITY?

It should not be thought that stability and control were purely the province of the 'airman', or that the philistine 'chauffeurs' were unconcerned about such matters. From about the time of Cayley onwards the concepts of aircraft stability and controllability began to polarise into two distinguishable subjects. Learning from the persistent occurrences of early machines toppling over one way or another as soon as they left the ground or launching platform, experimenters in the late eighteenth century began to concentrate on building craft which were inherently very stable, and thus Cayley's influence was at least partially beginning to show.[7] However, although an unmanned flying model cannot have too much stability – indeed a high degree of stability is virtually essential – this principle does not logically carry over when attempting to put a pilot-controlled machine in the air. The more stable the machine is, the more it will naturally resist any attempts by the pilot to guide it on to a new flight path. Stability and controllability are to a certain degree incompatible with one another.

By the end of the nineteenth century, stability had come to be regarded as an absolute essential for safe, successful flight, a philosophy which closely conformed with the 'chauffeur' school of thought, and thus so much inherent stability was being incorporated into new aircraft designs that there was no chance of effectively controlling their flight. Thus the very achievement of stability had become a stumbling-block to the successful development of a flying machine that could be fully controlled and guided along a chosen path, and great astuteness and vision were needed to reach beyond this mind-set. It

---

[7]This trend was paralleled by equally intense efforts to secure an engine of satisfactory power:weight ratio; but that is another story.

was Wilbur and Orville Wright who were to reach out objectively and overcome this obstacle to progress.

WILBUR AND ORVILLE WRIGHT

So who were these young Wright brothers, and what was it about them that earned them one of the most prestigious places in the technological history of the world? Wilbur (1867–1912) and Orville (1871–1948) were the sons of a United Brethren Church bishop, and lived in Dayton, Ohio, where they built up a modest business manufacturing and selling bicycles. Both were enthused with the idea of flight from early childhood and read everything that they could find on the subject, including *McClure's Magazine* which the Wright household subscribed to. In 1894 that magazine contained an article on the work of Otto Lilienthal, which was excellently illustrated with dramatic photographs of Lilienthal flying his gliders, and it appears to be this, followed by Lilienthal's flying accident and death two years later, that were the sparks which rekindled the brothers' smouldering childhood fire of enthusiasm.

Like the proverb-writer at the start of the chapter, Wilbur became absorbed by the flight of birds, but unlike the former he was to apply a keen analytical mind to what he perceived. An observation that he made at this time encapsulated the most important feature that was to characterise the brothers' future work:

> *My observation of the flight of buzzards led me to believe that they regain their lateral balance when partly overturned by a gust of wind, by a torsion of the tips of the wings.*

Wilbur's rapidly maturing interest and his study of all the technical papers on flight that he could lay his hands on quickly induced Orville to become as enthusiastic as his brother. Together they developed the latent qualities which, within a relatively short time, were to transform these two young bicycle manufacturers into outstanding engineers and inventors. They launched into experimental research in 1899 by building a biplane kite to test the theory of wing-warping that Wilbur had arrived at through observation of the buzzards.

The Wright brothers were not merely 'more of the same', the next players to enter the scene of aviation history; they were different in kind from their predecessors. They were deep thinkers, and their approach to the task of achieving powered, sustained, controlled flight was based on a sound scientific and philosophical attitude coupled with determination tempered with great patience. They did not even start by brainstorming how they should proceed, but rather they first of all stepped backwards a couple of paces, to review thoroughly and objectively the course of the slowly unfolding saga of flying history up to that time, before allowing themselves to become inextricably bound up in it.[8]

As a result of this review process, they came to perceive and to understand the two radically different concepts of aviation unconsciously held by the pioneers, represented by the 'chauffeur' school and the 'airman' approach. They were able to identify that the 'chauffeurs' had become so preoccupied with inherent stability that they were neglecting control and manoeuvrability in the air, or were at best treating these vital matters in a dangerously cavalier fashion. The 'airmen', on the other hand, though at first nurtured on the same concept of inherent stability, had been learning through the attendant problems of practical gliding experimentation to adopt a more dynamic approach to control and stability – but they had by no means solved all those problems. Unfortunately the 'airman' approach, though potentially more likely to achieve results, was inherently more dangerous, and the first 'airmen' flew at continual risk to their lives, as demonstrated by (the relatively few) tragedies such as the death of Lilienthal. If the 'airman' approach was to be adopted, and if the Wright brothers were to survive to see their quest through to a successful outcome, they realised that it was essential that they should pursue their aims with thoroughness in their planning, meticulous attention to detail and high quality workmanship, taking due account of the needs of safety at every turn.

They had thoroughly studied the theory; they had astutely grasped the historical perspective of their situation; they were now ready to plan their campaign. The strategy that they decided to adopt was both revolutionary and daring. They decided that, since stability was proving to be a rival to controllability, they would deliberately make their aircraft unstable, both in pitch and in roll. They would provide it with effective and sensitive aerodynamic controls that the pilot would manipulate at all times. Thus the pilot's deliberate steering action, up and down and left and right, was to substitute for the lack of stability. This would mean that any temporary lapse of concentration or any mistake made by the pilot would be likely to have disastrous consequences, but on the plus side it should mean that the pilot would have full authority over the motion of the aircraft at all times, which was what the 'airmen' had all been searching for. It was the lack of such full-authority control that had denied men success in their attempts at flight up to that time.

To design an aircraft without stability in roll simply involved not

[8]This philosophy is the same as the attitude with which I very much hope that readers will approach both this and the previous volume of *Flightwise*. If one takes time to understand the fundamental underlying principles of a subject, the details will look after themselves, and problems and questions can be tackled as they crop up.

providing the wings with the dihedral that had become standard practice, and so all of the Wright brothers' aircraft were designed with straight wings, (i.e. horizontal, not inclined upwards towards the tips), or even with a little bit of droop ('anhedral') to emphasise the point. To render the aircraft unstable in pitch, the Wright brothers at a stroke boldly dispensed with the rear horizontal tailplane, the use of which had been established by Cayley and confirmed ever since as the 'right' way to build an aeroplane.

On their own, these two actions would of course have meant that the aircraft would be unflyable, but the strategy was made complete by adding ingenious means of providing aerodynamic control in both of these motions, which could be constantly adjusted by the pilot. For roll control, they adopted the same approach as Wilbur had observed in the buzzard, which was to twist the wing-tips on demand so that either tip could be made to produce a different amount of lift from the other to induce a rolling motion. This device, which became known as wing warping, was one of the major hallmarks of the Wright brothers' success, and was to characterise and to set apart their aircraft from all others, even for a number of years after their successful first flight.

Having dispensed with a tailplane, the Wrights instead placed a new adjustable horizontal control surface on an extension out *in front* of the wings, to be operated by the pilot. This device has given rise to the term 'canard configuration', *canard* being the French word for a duck, although the connection between the two is not at all clear. I prefer to think that the name derives from its alternative meaning, that of a joke or an extravagant hoax, because anyone with the least sensitivity for the way in which an aircraft or a dart or an arrow or a bird flies through the air knows intuitively that the tail has to be at the back. The idea of flying tail-first appears patently absurd! However, the use of the canard (termed 'horizontal rudder' by the Wrights) was to prove successful, and was the second significant hallmark of the Wrights' achievement.

Stepping out of the story for a moment, it is interesting to observe that, once sustained flight had been mastered, designers reverted to putting the tail at the back (the norm today). Nevertheless canard foreplanes have in recent years had a surprising comeback, and are now to be seen on a variety of types from light aircraft to state-of-the-art fighters. Contrary to common belief, the use of canard foreplanes does not imply that the aircraft is inherently unstable in pitch, and it is perfectly possible to build a very stable aircraft of this design, as we will discover in Chapter 4. The reasons for its renewed use today are not dissimilar to those for which the Wrights introduced the concept, and we will come across canards in various contexts in later chapters of the book.

Having formulated their basic design strategy in 1900, the Wright brothers set to work building, developing and experimenting at a prodigious rate, with a series of nearly a thousand perfectly controlled glider flights in 1902. In the following year they turned to designing and building their first powered machine which they called *Flyer 1*. On 17 December 1903 in front of an assembled group of witnesses and a well-placed camera to record the event, the brothers between them made four flights, the longest lasting 59 seconds and covering half a mile. In only three years, relying entirely on their own resources, Orville and Wilbur had achieved the world's first powered, sustained and controlled flight.

Their rate of progress was the more remarkable for two additional reasons. Firstly, they were to discover that all of the aerodynamic data that they had inherited from Lilienthal and others was seriously in error, and so they set to work with their usual meticulous thoroughness and established a new database, by carrying out aerodynamic experiments using a bicycle to provide airflow, and also by building and using a wind-tunnel to test a range of aerofoils. Secondly, they discovered that, contrary to their expectation, all the available internal combustion engines were still too heavy in relation to their power output. So, undaunted, they designed and built their own petrol engine from scratch.

At long last the air had been conquered – and not by a mere never-to-be-repeated hop, but by a sustained, controlled, powered flight in an aircraft taking off from and landing on level ground. Rapidly the Wrights developed their skill and modified and improved their design, so that by the end of 1905 they had developed their *Flyer III*, in which they routinely carried out banked turns, circles and figure-of-eight manoeuvres, staying airborne typically for half an hour at a time, sometimes until they ran out of fuel, and flying for distances of several miles.

During this development period, they faced and tackled many difficulties and set-backs. The most significant technical problem that beset them arose from the use of wing-warping to control the aircraft in roll, since this also produced an unwanted rotation about the vertical axis, the equivalent of what is today called adverse aileron yaw. This was compounded by the associated problem of the stalling of the lower wing-tip when trying to bring the aircraft out of a banked turn, and it resulted in a number of crashes. Aircraft controls cannot be treated in isolation from each other, and often using a control to rotate an aircraft about one axis also has a secondary effect of causing it to rotate about a different axis. To cut a long story short for now, the ultimate solution lay in installing a pilot-operated vertical control surface at the back (a rudder) through which the pilot could control the yawing motion independently of the rolling motion. It was this eventually successful combination of wing-warping and adjustable rudder, which they patented, that was the Wright brothers' most profound contribution to aircraft controllability, and thus ultimately to successful flight.

FROM PRIDE AND PIG-HEADEDNESS, GOOD LORD DELIVER US

> *From all blindness of heart; from pride, vain-glory and hypocrisy; from envy, hatred and malice, and all uncharitableness, Good Lord, deliver us.*[9]

We saw earlier how the ascendancy of the luminary George Cayley failed to set the world alight, that despite his insight and achievements mankind was not ready to benefit from his influence, and that flight remained in the doldrums. Now in the twentieth century, with the technological revolution speeding on apace in all areas of life, and with the air having at last been mastered by two airmen of great insight, skill, determination and integrity, surely progress would be rapid, making up for lost time?

But that was not to be. Indeed, the events of the five years immediately following the Wrights' achievement turned out to be a débâcle of immense proportions, and an enigma almost defying explanation.

Once Wilbur and Orville had mastered the technique of coordinating the controls, there was nothing to hold them back, and they became prodigious airmen, increasingly agile and at ease in their newly discovered element. But whilst the local farmers became blasé about the frequent appearance of an aeroplane flying overhead, the rest of the world carried on unperturbed and unaffected, dismissing the brief garbled reports of the exploits of these two young upstarts from Dayton as nothing more than hysterical claims reminiscent of so many before them. Consequently, up to the end of 1907, apart from the flights of the Wright brothers, all other attempts at flight were mere faltering hops which could be timed in seconds, with only one flight briefly exceeding a minute, and the distances flown measured in hundreds of metres. This extraordinary state of affairs deserves some investigation, since the explanation relates directly to the issues of aircraft stability and control, which it is our purpose to understand and to come to grips with.

Who were the actors, or the potential actors, on the aviation scene at this time? Despite the fact that the Wrights were American, there was not a strong American tradition of aviation pioneering. Scanning the history of aviation since antiquity rapidly reveals that a great

[9]The Litany, Book of Common Prayer.

majority of the contributors to the story hailed from one or another part of Europe and it was here, particularly in France, that the main frenzied thrust to achieve successful flight was being made at the turn of the century.

I use the word frenzied deliberately. With the rapid and successful development of technologies such as electricity, telephones and wireless telegraphy, photography and cinematography, and particularly mechanised land and sea transport towards the end of the nineteenth century, it was regarded by the French as a matter of national honour to ensure that they should be the first to conquer this one remaining challenge of heavier-than-air flight, thus maintaining their long tradition in the aerial field and upholding their own perceived pre-eminence. Thus at the start of the twentieth century very substantial resources were being brought to bear to support this drive for mastery of the air, and a whole group of eminent, experienced Frenchmen of undoubted talent ostensibly dedicated to the pursuit of aviation were drawn together to tackle the challenge. So when news of the alleged achievements of the Wright brothers reached these men, they were not in a mood to accept what they were hearing. As a result of their national pride they withdrew behind a mantle of chauvinistic ambition intent on rivalling and defeating this potential opposition, and to a man they pursued this cause by stubbornly refusing to believe their ears.

Since the hard evidence could not easily be totally dismissed, some attempts were made at building imitations of the Wrights' sophisticated *No. 3* glider. The fullest details of this glider including a comprehensive lecture, scale drawings and fully illustrated technical reports had been presented to the Aéro-Club de France. The members had been given information regarding, though not the reason for, the simultaneous use of wing warping and rudder, the central key to the Wrights' success, and so were fully equipped to build a successful replica. However, the task appears to have been approached petulantly, perhaps more with a hope that they would *not* succeed than that they would, in order to discredit the reports of their rivals' success. They did not adhere to the design details, but produced slapdash, unscientific imitations of the Wrights' aircraft, abandoning systematic thoroughness and scientific analysis. In particular, they totally dismissed all evidence of the need for control in roll, and played down or even eliminated the wing-warping feature on the grounds that it was too dangerous. Needless to say, these gliders were failures, and maybe these men considered themselves vindicated, saying 'I told you so'.

But their attitude was also very cavalier when building aircraft to their own designs. They greatly underestimated the complexity of designing, building and flying an aeroplane, and unlike the Wrights they paid no attention to formulation of basic problems and methodically going about their solution. One feature of their efforts was that they would flit about from one design concept to another, producing and discarding a proliferation of useless and virtually untried aircraft prototypes, rather than ever concentrating on one concept (even if not ultimately the best) and working patiently towards perfecting it.

The contrast between the attitude of the Wrights and of these would-be aviators in France once again brought into very sharp focus the distinction between the 'airman' and 'chauffeur' schools of thought. The latter group were utterly dominated by the 'chauffeur' ideal of driving an aerial motorcar rather than of riding a winged horse. They relied on brute force for lift and thrust to get airborne, and considered the 'driver' to be simply someone relatively detached from the process who would initiate small changes of course in a highly stable machine. Actually flying their aerial automobiles was regarded as a mere triviality which would quickly be mastered once they had persuaded the things to fly straight and level. Thus no one spent more than an aggregate of a few minutes in the air, in any of the types that they built at this time. By comparison, the Wrights with their 'airman' attitude put in hundreds of hours of flying time over thousands of flights, so that they learnt to become an integral part of the machine that they were operating.

TURNING POINT

Thus the period from 1903 to 1908, potentially a period of great aviation development following the lead of the Wright brothers, turned out to be a fiasco, during which the ill-directed efforts of the French potential aviators achieved virtually no true flights of note. They still held tenaciously to their instinct for maximum stability, and totally disregarded the notion of aircraft control having a rôle to play in keeping an aircraft safely aloft.

During this period, there emerged one Henri Farman, a notable exception to the 'chauffeur' mould described above. He was English born, but French-speaking, being domiciled in France. He was well aware of the importance of the man–machine bond through his experience as a motor-racer, so that when his interests turned to aviation he naturally approached the challenge from the 'airman' point of view, and hence made much more progress than his contemporaries. He did not design his own aircraft, but started his flying career in a stable 'box-kite' biplane built by the Voisin brothers with forward elevator and tail unit containing the rudder, but with no form of control in roll. As was to be expected, this aircraft had had no more success than achieving about half a dozen brief hops, but Farman set to work flying it and modifying it intensively. By 1908, he had become the most successful and famous of the European pilots, but he still had not adopted any form of roll control, and so his potential for achievement was still very limited.

In October 1907 Farman won the Archdeacon Cup for the first powered flight of over 100 metres, with a straight flight of a staggering (to the Europeans!) distance of 771 metres during which he was airborne for nearly a minute. Subsequently he began to experiment somewhat falteringly with turning flight, and flew a circular path, remaining airborne for over a minute. This was the first flight ever (apart from those of the Wrights themselves) to exceed the 59 seconds achieved by Wilbur Wright on his first flight on 17 December 1903. (Orville had had a previous flight on that same day of 12 seconds.) Thus Farman became the obvious front runner (indeed the *only* European runner) for the big competition, the Grand Prix d'Aviation, which he was to attempt on 13 January the following year.

The year 1908 dramatically marks the end (or if you prefer, the consummate beginning) of our story of the history of flight. Let us bring together in our mind's eye and compare the events of two special dates in that year: 13 January and 8 August. On that January day, France was to witness its first major triumph ('la mémorable victoire') as Henri Farman made his attempt to win the Deutsch-Archdeacon Prize of 50,000 francs, offered to the first man to fly a kilometre circuit consisting of rounding a post placed 500 metres away from the start and returning. Farman successfully flew the prescribed circuit and, owing to his having to make a very wide turn on rudder alone (having no roll control), he probably covered 1500 metres in all. He also entered the European record books by being airborne for 1 minute 28 seconds, and this was by far the longest and most impressive flight yet made in Europe.

Meanwhile, the Wrights had secured agreement to have their machines built in France, and an official acceptance test was also at last to be made before the US Army authorities. In May, Wilbur, after getting himself back into practice at the controls, travelled to France to prepare a new, improved flying machine that the Wrights had had shipped there, and which was awaiting him in store, in readiness for a planned public demonstration flight on 8 August. The spectators on that day were suspicious, sceptical and in many cases downright hostile, and included those who, in their own uncertain hopes, were the only aviators in the world.

The demonstration was brief and, for Wilbur, routine. He took off, made two graceful circles and landed smoothly: he was in the air for only 1 minute 45 seconds, but those 105 seconds were to revolutionise world aviation in a totally electrifying way (Figure 1.3). The entire

Figure 1.3   The Wright A aircraft which revolutionised European aviation by its manoeuvrability in 1908

audience was totally stunned and overcome with amazement at Wilbur's effortless mastery of his aircraft and of the air, as he gracefully banked and turned and circled, the like of which they had never even conceived of before. Mixed with their utter astonishment were many outbursts of adulation and praise, exclamations of dismay at having their own impotence publicly revealed, and – to their credit – sincere repentance and abject apology, as they at last fully and publicly acknowledged the injustice they had perpetuated in refusing to accept the truth.

TAKE-OFF

There was no turning back. From that day onwards, aviation moved only forwards, in a more steady and respectable manner, although of course the 'chauffeur' attitude could not be eliminated overnight and remained for many years an impediment to more rapid progress. The importance of the pilot's mastery of his machine was never again doubted, and proper control systems were implemented and developed. The Wrights' design policy of instability meant, of course, that their machines were very demanding to fly, and required substantial skill and total concentration from their pilots, and this was not ultimately a very satisfactory state of affairs, especially for training novice pilots. Consequently there was a move towards a more practical type of vehicle, with greater development potential than the Wright concept, and with inherent stability – something which the pioneers could understand and were comfortable in pursuing – but never again was stability to dominate at the expense of full three-axis controllability.

The 'airman' exercising his authority through adequate aerodynamic controls, assisted by natural inherent stability, had triumphed, and the way ahead was prepared for the aeroplane as we know it today.

CHAPTER 2
Stability Concepts and Definitions

INTRODUCTION

In Chapter 1 we have seen the very fundamental place that concepts of stability and control need to occupy in the mind of the aircraft designer, if he is to succeed in designing a successful flying machine at all. Although we have been deliberately imprecise so far about our definitions of the two terms, we have seen that they refer to distinct but strongly interdependent ideas. From an analytical point of view they both depend on exactly the same mathematical 'equations of motion', but different things are done with those equations depending on whether we are looking at stability or control.

We have also seen in Chapter 1 that the concepts of stability seemed to have become firmly established long before the pioneers had a proper grasp of the need for effective control. Although the Wright brothers dramatically demonstrated that this approach was, at least in the immediate short term, misguided, it did occur naturally, suggesting that the most logical order for studying these two concepts is to consider stability first. Some authors who deal with control before stability do so because they present an over-simplistic and misleading view of aircraft control (leaving many fundamental questions unanswered), so that they then feel that they need to warn their readers that stability is 'very difficult', and it is relegated to brief superficial treatment as an afterthought. As with most subjects, however, the perceived degree of difficulty depends almost entirely on the level of understanding of the fundamental concepts that is acquired before one attempts to apply those concepts to real-life situations. Stability is no more inherently complicated than control, and the equations (which we will not be looking at in detail in this book) have to contain additional terms for control work compared with stability work. We therefore tackle stability first.

Our thinking about stability can conveniently be classified into a number of subdivisions, although they all interact with each other to a certain extent. In Chapters 4 to 7 we break down the subject into these subdivisions for a closer look, but here and in the next chapter our purpose is to develop a familiarity with stability's language and underlying principles.

THE GENERAL CONCEPT OF STABILITY

'Stability' and 'stable' are greatly overused words. They are often used in everyday English to imply the notion of something being firmly established and immovable, and may be applied in a very broad range of situations. We may refer to a stable government, a stable structure, a stable medical condition, a stable chemical substance or a stable relationship. In reality, however, none of these things is immovable or invariant; each is dynamic, and so the word has a deeper nuance. It actually means that the dynamics of the situation are such that, if something happens that would tend to upset the *status quo* of the subject in question, then that upset is short-lived and the initial state tends to be restored promptly. The word should not, therefore, be used of a medical condition to imply that the patient is getting better, but only that he or she is neither getting better nor worse.

As with many other words, some of which, such as force, work and energy, have been introduced in *Flightwise – Principles of Aircraft Flight*, stability is a word that has a very precise meaning in science. It can never be used to refer vaguely to a complex object or situation such as the four examples in the previous paragraph. Likewise, to talk about an aircraft *in toto* being stable or unstable is unscientific and totally meaningless. Rather, we may refer only to the stability (or otherwise) of a certain *parameter*, which means some quantity which can be expressed in precise physical units and can be measured and given a numerical value.

Consider a rather contrived example of a hot brick suspended from a fixed beam by a cord and free to swing to and fro when nudged or disturbed by a gust of wind. The position of the brick pendulum at any instant may be conveniently specified as the angle in degrees between the cord and the vertical. Its position thus measured is stable, since it automatically tends to revert to the starting value (0°) following each disturbance away from this value, once the cause of the disturbance is removed. The temperature of the brick at any moment, on the other hand, is not stable, since it will keep cooling and nothing occurs as a result of this cooling process which makes it warm up again to its previous temperature. Eventually the temperature will itself reach a stable condition when the brick has cooled to the temperature of its surroundings, for then, should any temporary external influence cause its temperature to change a little, when the influence is removed the brick will revert to the ambient temperature by natural heat transfer to or from its surroundings.

Just as we cannot refer to the stability (or otherwise) of the brick *per se*, so we cannot talk about the stability of an aircraft. In fact, what we are talking about in that case is, in the most general sense, the stability of the aircraft's motion (rather than, say, its temperature or its weight). But as we shall shortly see, this encompasses a whole wealth of parameters, since the motion occurs in all three dimensions of space, and in each we shall have to consider whether we mean distance, speed or acceleration, since all of these are needed to describe its motion. Furthermore, we have to treat the aircraft as more than a mere particle, a small concentrated mass like a golf ball whose orientation is of no great concern to us. An aircraft is a large structure, and the way it points and the way up it is are of very great importance for many reasons. Just as there are three mutually perpendicular directions (or axes) *along* which we must consider its motion, so we must consider the *rotation* of the aircraft *about* these three axes. Once again, we have three levels of parameter to consider: amount (angle) of rotation, rotational speed and rotational acceleration. Then, when we have got to grips with these six possible parameters, we have to consider whether we can safely treat each of them in isolation from all of the others, or whether any of them will be influenced by others.

STATIC AND DYNAMIC STABILITY

We have seen that a parameter is said to be stable if it tends to recover its original value automatically following a disturbance from that value. However, the nature of this recovery is different in different circumstances. If you nudge the brick so that it swings a little on its cord, then when it swings back through the 0° position it will not immediately stop there but will overshoot, and a sequence of oscillations will occur. On the other hand if, after the brick has cooled to the temperature of its surroundings, it is briefly heated by playing a Bunsen burner flame over it, then when the flame is removed the brick will eventually just revert to its ambient temperature, and there is no conceivable reason why it should overshoot this temperature and become colder than the ambient temperature, even for a moment.

These two types of stability demonstrate two distinct ways in which we may regard the subject. They are loosely referred to as dynamic and static stability respectively. Although not amenable to precise definitions, a parameter is said to be statically stable if there is an *initial tendency* inherent in the system for that parameter to revert to its starting value. Only in such circumstances is it possible to speak at all of the system's dynamic stability, since the latter refers to the nature of the oscillations (if any) which follow after the initial recovery to (or towards) the initial value. If a parameter is statically unstable, questions regarding its dynamic stability are meaningless and cannot be posed.

STATIC STABILITY

Let us first of all firm up on our ideas of static stability. Although old hat and simplistic, there is no better way of doing so than by looking

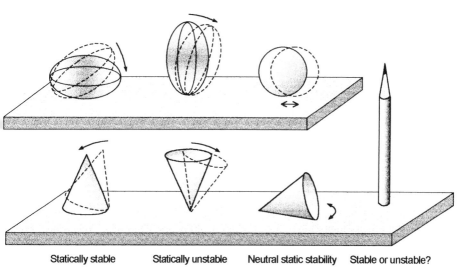

Statically stable   Statically unstable   Neutral static stability   Stable or unstable?

Figure 2.1   Examples of static stability and instability in common objects

at a diagram of familiar objects which clearly demonstrate the concepts (Figure 2.1). If the rugby ball lying on its side or the cone sitting on its base is tipped a little and then released, each will revert to its starting position, and its angular displacement, the parameter which measures its position, is said to be statically stable.

If the rugby ball is standing on its end, or the cone balancing on its tip, then clearly the tiniest disturbance will be enough to make the angular displacement from the starting position grow and keep on growing, and the ball or cone will topple over. In fact, no nudge may be necessary at all (especially in the case of the cone), and it may be impossible to balance the objects in this position. The ball or cone's position is statically unstable.

Now if the ball or the cone is laid on its side (or the rugby ball is replaced by a soccer ball) and the ball or cone is rolled a little way from its starting place and then released from rest, it will neither move further away from its starting position nor return towards it, but just stay placidly in its new position. The stability of the starting position and new position are both statically neutral, i.e. neither stable nor unstable.

As food for thought, a pencil has been placed on the lower shelf in Figure 2.1, standing on its flat base. Would you say that its position was stable or unstable? Clearly a very small nudge will be sufficient to knock it over, but it is quite possible to stand a pencil up in this way.

The answer is that the pencil's position is marginally statically stable, but that that margin of stability is so small that to all intents and purposes we might just as well say that it is unstable. This last example illustrates very clearly the care with which we need to use our terminology, since the ideas of stability are not always very precise. As we shall see later on when considering an aircraft's longitudinal stability, certain aircraft which have been designed without a tailplane (sometimes known as a horizontal stabiliser) have had a marginally stable attitude in pitching motion, but this margin may be exceeded through an uncomfortably small disturbance, making it effectively unstable and thus the design unacceptable.

In discussing the examples in Figure 2.1, we have been infuriatingly pedantic about our use of terminology, in order to adhere to our earlier insistence that only a parameter, and not a physical artefact, may be considered as possessing or not possessing stability. Furthermore, we have repeatedly included the qualification 'statically' in front of the words 'stable' or 'unstable'. It is hoped that these points have now been emphasised enough, and in future we can allow ourselves to revert to a much more casual way of using such words wherever the context makes it clear precisely what we are talking about. Though language must always be afforded the greatest of respect, it must remain our servant and not become our master.

A fundamental aim of the *Flightwise* books is to encourage the reader to be continually asking 'why?' at every turn. When we consider the stability of an aircraft, we shall thus not only look at *how* required effects are achieved, but shall also seek explanations of *why* the techniques work, and what are the underlying physical principles. It will therefore be good practice here to look again at the examples in Figure 2.1, and to ask *why* the rugby ball is stable on its side but unstable on its tip.

One way to tip the rugby ball up from lying stably on its side is to pull upwards on one end of the ball. As a result, the ball takes up the dotted position, and it is clear from this that its centre of gravity (which is at the centre of the oval) finishes up higher than it started. If the lifting force is now removed from the end of the ball, the force of gravity pulling downward on the ball at its centre of gravity is free to pull that point downward again, back towards the starting position. Exactly the same is true in the case of the cone on its base, which may be lifted initially at the left-hand edge of the base; then since its centre of gravity has been raised it will fall back into its starting position when released.

In the case of the unstable, balanced ball and cone, the result of even the smallest initial tipping force will be to lower the centre of gravity – the centres of the dotted outlines are clearly lower than the centres of the outlines in the starting positions. Thus the disturbing force is here merely helping gravity to pull the centre of gravity downward, making the object topple, and if the disturbing force is removed gravity will continue its work in the same direction. On the other hand, when either the round ball or cone on its side is rolled a bit, the centre of gravity neither rises nor descends, but merely moves horizontally. Gravity has no component acting horizontally, and therefore has no effect on the rolling motion whatsoever. Finally, the pencil's centre of gravity rises in opposition to gravity for just a very brief part of its motion – roughly until a diagonal line drawn on it becomes vertical – and thereafter it begins to fall, aided by gravity.

Thus in the stable cases a disturbance raises the centre of gravity and restoration is produced by the natural effect of gravity pulling back down on the object. In the unstable cases an initial departure lowers the centre of gravity, and the inherent downward force of gravity causes further departure rather than restoration.

MOMENTS AND ROTATIONAL MOTION

Although *Flightwise – Principles of Aircraft Flight* dealt very extensively with forces, only fleetingly was it necessary to introduce the concept of a moment, which is the turning effect of a force, and that was when considering the pitching effects of transonic flow over an aircraft, in the middle of Chapter 11. But now in our study of stability and control the moments produced by forces will be a central and constantly recurring theme. Later on we shall firm up on our ideas about moments, but it will be useful at this point to introduce the concept in the context of basic static stability, while still looking at the examples of Figure 2.1.

We said that the force needed to cause the rugby ball initially lying on its side to tilt *could* be an upward force on one end. However, the tilt could equally well be produced by a *downward* force on the other end. Likewise, it would be more natural to tilt the cone by pulling *sideways* on its apex rather than lifting it by the lower edge. In each case the effect, as we have seen, is to *raise* the centre of gravity, and so the directions of the forces have somehow got a bit mixed up with each other. Let us look more closely at the cone, reproduced in Figure 2.2, to see what is going on.

In Figure 2.2(a) we will take it that we have supplied just enough horizontal force P at the apex to tilt the cone to the position shown, and that we are now holding it steady in that position. (There is either a little peg on the ground surface or enough friction to prevent the bottom right point of the rim of the cone from moving to the right.) The cone is now perfectly motionless in all respects. It is clearly not

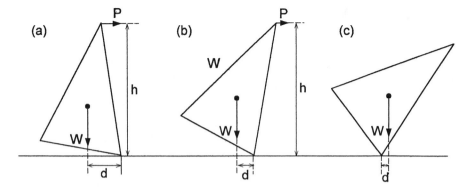

Figure 2.2   Moments on a cone leaving the stable position

accelerating upwards nor sideways, and so by Newton's First Law there are no resultant forces acting in any direction on the cone *in toto* (i.e. regarding it as a particle). But now we must rethink Newton's First Law so that we can apply it (or something very like it) to the other possible form of motion, that of rotation.

We can no longer regard the cone simply as a particle, as its size, shape and orientation and the positions of the forces on it are now very significant to the way it behaves. Instead, we have to treat the cone as a *rigid body*. 'Rigid body' is another of those phrases and words introduced into technical vocabulary (like 'particle' and 'smooth') in order to be able to model the real world in an orderly fashion, making appropriate simplifications by which one can disregard unwanted side-effects (hopefully relatively small) which would distract from analysing the major items under consideration. A rigid body is simply an object which is assumed not to distort even the tiniest little bit from its original shape. If the cone were hollow, as would appear to be the case from looking at Figure 2.1, then it is quite possible that the forces in Figure 2.2(a) might cause the cone to buckle a little at the point of contact with the ground, so that all distance measurements would be slightly corrupted. But if the cone were solid and made of wood or metal, then the rigid body assumption would probably be very sound, and we could take it that any small distortion that might occur would cause only negligible errors in the answers that we get.[1]

When we later come to consider a complete aircraft, we shall make

---

[1]Technically, a rigid body is defined as a body such that the distance between each and every pair of points in it remains constant.

the assumption that it is a rigid body. But though this may be satisfactory for a solid cone, it would seem to be of extremely dubious validity when applied to such a large structure, with long slender members such as wings and fuselage. In fact you will know, if you have watched the wings from the passenger cabin of an airliner flying through turbulent air, that the wings and engine pylons bend quite significantly. Indeed they are designed to do so, since it is only thus that they can absorb the very large load variations that they must experience. Furthermore, in Chapter 11 of *Flightwise – Principles of Aircraft Flight*, in the subsection 'Roll Control Problems', it was shown that the twisting of wing-tips resulting from the large, localised aerodynamic forces that arise in transonic flight can have very significant (and quite alarming) effects on the controllability of the aircraft. The consequence can be that when the pilot attempts to roll his aircraft one way, it will actually roll in the opposite direction! However, although it may be necessary to depart from the rigid body assumption when considering certain specific aspects of aircraft design such as these, it provides a necessary, and fortunately very satisfactory, starting point for an analytical study of aircraft stability and control, and we will scarcely need to consider departures from that assumption within the scope of this book.

Coming back to earth, our cone is to be regarded as a rigid body, and it is being held stationary in the position of Figure 2.2(a) by a force P acting horizontally at the apex. The cone has rotated, and is free to rotate, about the bottom right point of the rim which we have said is immovable, and so this point may be regarded as a pivot. If we wanted to be able to work out how big the force P would have to be in order to raise the cone to its tilted position, we should need to know some rules about how forces behave in relation to rotational motion, since obviously the sizes and positions of the forces are relevant to the answer, as are the shape of the cone and the angle through which it is raised.

We were reminded just now of Newton's First Law, which tells us that, regarding the cone as a particle, the resultants of both the vertical forces and the horizontal forces are zero since there is no acceleration in either of those directions. (If you are unfamiliar with Newton's laws, may I strongly urge you to brush up on the subject, as a proper understanding is absolutely essential for all that is to come.[2]) But now that we are concerned with rigid body rotation rather than linear motion, and since the forces affecting the rotation act in a number of different directions at once, we are clearly going to need to rethink

---

[2]A useful source might be Chapter 2 of *Flightwise – Principles of Aircraft Flight*.

this basic principle. Can we apply something like Newton's First Law to this sort of rotational motion?

Yes we can, very easily. To do so we use a directly equivalent parallel Newton's First Law which has been derived for the rigid body rotation situation. All we have to do is to define an equivalent rotational quantity or concept for each of the familiar linear quantities and concepts that appeared in the original First Law, and then state it again, unchanged except for substituting the new equivalent quantities for their old counterparts.

Newton's First Law of Motion briefly says 'no force, no acceleration', or more completely it can be stated like this:

> **If**[3] **all of the *forces* acting on a *particle* are such that they exactly balance each other out and their resultant is zero, then the *particle* will have no *acceleration*. No *acceleration* means that, if at rest it will remain at rest; and if moving at a certain *speed* in a certain *direction*, it will continue to move with the same *speed* in the same *direction*.**

When we have replaced all the words which are printed in italic in the above law with their direct equivalent quantities for rotational motion, we shall have generated the parallel Newton's First Law for rotational motion. We already know that we must replace 'particle' with 'rigid body', and we will leave aside 'force' for the time being. 'Direction' must fairly naturally be replaced with 'rotational direction', implying clockwise or anticlockwise.[4] That leaves us with the kinematic quantities 'acceleration' and 'speed' to consider.

If we break down acceleration into its elemental parts, we find that we must call on some more fundamental quantities, those of time, distance and speed. Now time is time and seconds are seconds both in the linear and the rotational systems, and so no change is needed here. Instead of distance (typically measured in metres), the rotational equivalent is angle, which means amount of turning. Now angles are measured either in units of degrees or radians, and in order for the system to work properly and consistently[5] it is essential that the more mathematically pure unit of the radian is used to measure angles. A radian is an angle measurement which is defined as the ratio of two lengths, and this is conveniently absolute and dimensionless, whereas

---

[3]More strictly we should write 'If and only if ...' here, since the law also applies backwards, a fact that we use shortly. (Mathematicians abbreviate this to 'iff'.) But we will stick with 'If ...' for simplicity.

[4]This is in fact an oversimplification, but it will suffice for present purposes.

[5]The principle of a parallel system that is being introduced here is far more powerful than is needed just to cope with Newton's First Law. In fact it deals completely with translating all the axioms and equations of the mechanics of particle dynamics into an exactly corresponding set for rigid body rotation.

the size of a degree has been initially arbitrarily chosen[6]. As a rough guide, one radian is equivalent to a little less than 60°, the angle of an equilateral triangle. Angles may have positive and negative values corresponding to clockwise and anticlockwise directions (not necessarily in that order – the convention used must be stated) just as distances may be positive or negative to signify movements in opposite senses along the same direction line.

Having defined rotational time and the rotational equivalent of distance, we can immediately derive the definitions of the other quantities that we need. Rotational speed is defined as the rate of change of angular position, or the angle rotated through divided by the time taken; its units are radians per second. Rotational acceleration is the rate of change of angular speed, or the change in angular speed divided by the time taken, and is expressed in radians per second per second or radians per second squared. But since radian measure is defined in terms of a ratio of two lengths, (e.g. metres per metre) the length units cancel out, so that radian measure is a dimensionless quantity with no units. Consequently rotational velocity and rotational acceleration are normally expressed simply as s^{-1} (per second) and s^{-2} (per second squared) respectively, which can be a little confusing since there is nothing in the unit to tell you that you are dealing with angular quantities.

In passing, a little caveat may be timely. It is most important not to confuse the concept of angular acceleration with that of centripetal acceleration. The former is the rate at which the rotational speed is changing, and the latter is a *linear* acceleration directed towards the centre of rotation. If a particle, or a point on a rigid body, is moving along a circular path at a constant speed, it has zero angular acceleration, but it still has a positive centripetal acceleration towards the centre.[7]

We have dealt with all the italic words in Newton's First Law except for force, and so we must now consider what is the rotational equivalent of a force. It will be simplest to begin by giving it a name, even though we don't yet know what it means, and so without beating about the bush let us give it its proper name straight away, and declare that the rotational equivalent of a force is a *moment*. We can now

---

[6]The division of a full rotation into 360 degrees probably arose in the first place because it is approximately the angle through which the Earth rotates around the Sun in one day, since there are about 365 (which is not far off 360) days in a year. Furthermore, 360 is a very convenient number, since it can be exactly divided by a great many smaller numbers.
[7]Centripetal acceleration is explained near the end of Chapter 2 of *Flightwise – Principles of Aircraft Flight*, under the heading 'Forces in Curved Motion'.

re-write Newton's First Law in its equivalent rotational form by sub-stituting the new rotational words for all the italic words. Italic has been used for the substitutions.

> If all of the *moments* acting on a *rigid body* are such that they exactly balance each other out and their resultant is zero, then the *rigid body* will have no *angular acceleration*. No *angular acceleration* means that, if at rest it will remain at rest; and if moving (i.e. rotating) at a certain *angular speed* in a certain *rotational direction*, it will continue to move with the same *angular speed* in the same *rotational direction*.

Now let's refer back to Figure 2.2(a), and remember that the cone is being held at rest. It is thus a rigid body which has no angular acceler-ation, and by interpreting the above law in reverse we can see that this implies that all the moments acting on it exactly balance each other out, and their resultant is zero. There are only two things in the dia-gram which are trying to make the cone rotate about the pivot point, and those are the gravity force W (the weight acting at the centre of gravity) and the applied force P. So clearly moments depend on forces, and the moments – the turning effects – of these two forces must be exactly equal and opposite so that their combined effect or resultant is zero.

Intuitively we can see that the distances marked as h and d must have something to do with it. If P were applied at the top of a light rod sticking up from the cone's vertex so that h were greater, we would clearly require a smaller force P to hold the cone steady. If the cone were broader-based so that d were greater, then for the same weight W we would need a larger force P. Similarly, a door handle is posi-tioned near the edge of a door furthest from the hinge line, since a much greater force would be needed to open and close the door if the handle were close to the hinges. It would seem that the moment of a force depends not only on the size of the force but also on how far from the pivot axis it is acting[8]. In fact, from experience gained by tak-ing measurements, we can be more precise and state that the turning effect of a force acting on a rigid body is *directly proportional* both to the magnitude of the force and to the perpendicular distance between the line of the force and the pivot axis. And since we haven't yet defined the word moment, we will simply declare the constant of pro-portionality to be unity, so that the definition becomes:

> The moment of a force is the product of its magnitude and the perpen-dicular distance between the line of action of the force and the pivot axis.

---

[8]The pivot axis in Figure 2.2 is the line through the pivot point perpendicular to the paper, since rotation occurs in the plane of the paper.

Now since the cone is at rest and the resultant moment is zero, it follows that the clockwise or overturning moment of the force P must be equal to the anticlockwise or restoring moment of the weight W. Thus

$$Ph = Wd$$

and if any three of these quantities were known the other could be found. Exactly the same principle applies when balancing a see-saw with a heavier person on one end than on the other: the product of weight and distance from the pivot must be equal in each rotational direction, so the heavier person must sit closer to the pivot. The principle is not limited to two forces, and there may be any number of forces in any directions. Provided the sum of moments of all the clockwise-tending forces is equal to the sum of the moments of all the anticlockwise-tending forces, the resultant will be zero, and so there will be no rotational acceleration.

We began our discussion about the static stability of the cone by considering linear forces, but realised that, since we were considering the rotational motion of a body, the particle approach was limited in its scope. Now that we have defined the moment of a force and have established the all-important *Principle of Moments* (which is what the rotational equivalent of Newton's First Law is usually called), we can adequately and effortlessly conclude our discussion of the three parts of Figure 2.2. In diagram (a) the cone is clearly stable since the upsetting moment Ph is having to oppose the restoring moment Wd, and if P were removed or reduced the moment Wd would win and the cone would fall back. In the situation at (b), however, the cone has tilted further, and although W is unchanged its moment arm d has become reduced. Consequently the restoring moment is weakened, and although the cone is still stable, we might say loosely that it is now 'less stable' than it was – although we have made no attempt to describe stability as a quantifiable concept. But the concept seems reasonable in view of diagram (c), in which we see that the centre of gravity has now passed right over the pivot axis, and d has moved to the other side of the pivot axis. Consequently the moment of W, which was previously anticlockwise and restorative, is now clockwise and if unchecked will topple the cone unstably. As with the toppled pencil, we have passed out of the stable regime into an unstable regime.

Before leaving the Principle of Moments, let us make sure that we are not being too parochial and restrictive in our understanding of it. When considering the force system on a complete aircraft flying at a constant speed in straight, level flight, namely constant lift, weight, thrust and drag, we can apply Newton's First Law twice[9]. Firstly, since the aircraft is flying level one needs little persuasion to accept that the lift must be exactly equal to the weight. However, most people are far less prepared to accept the fact that the thrust is exactly equal to the drag! If the aeroplane is to keep going, they surmise, it is obvious that the forward force must be greater than the rearward force – or else it would slow down. Furthermore, those massive engines on big airliners today produce a colossal amount of thrust – far greater than the relatively small drag force that a modern, highly streamlined airliner would produce!

Wrong on both counts! An aeroplane flying at a constant speed in straight, level flight is certainly not accelerating upwards or downwards, nor forwards or backwards, nor sideways – in fact it is not accelerating, full stop. Newton's First Law says that, if a body is not accelerating, then the resultant of all the forces acting on it must be zero (because an unbalanced force causes an acceleration, by Newton's Second Law). Thus if thrust were greater than drag, the aeroplane would be flying forward at an ever-increasing speed. If thrust were *less* than drag, it would slow down. But only when thrust *equals* drag will the forward speed remain constant. The phrase 'in equilibrium' is commonly used to refer to any object in the 'no force, no acceleration' situation of Newton's First Law. To be in equilibrium, the object does not have to be at rest – *viz.* the cruising aeroplane – but just not accelerating; and then all the forces are exactly balanced out.

The rigid bodies that we have been considering have all (except for Figure 2.2(c)) been at rest and not rotating in the situations we have considered, but that is not a necessary condition for the principle of moments to apply, any more than a particle has to be at rest for Newton's First Law to apply to it. Consider, for example, a road wheel of a car travelling at a constant speed on a straight level road. The wheel is rotating at a constant angular speed and has absolutely no angular acceleration. Consequently the Principle of Moments may be applied to it, which tells us that the sum of the moments turning the wheel one way (e.g. in the way it is actually rotating) is exactly equal to the sum of the moments opposing that motion. The actual agencies producing these moments, and the magnitudes of the moments, are different depending on whether the wheel is a driven wheel or not, but in either case, although rotating, the wheel is in equilibrium and the resultant of the moments is zero. Similarly the Earth is spinning at a

---

[9]This topic is covered at length in Chapter 2 of *Flightwise – Principles of Aircraft Flight.*

constant rate of one rotation every 24 hours[10], and there are no moments acting on it so that it has no angular acceleration.

DYNAMIC STABILITY

Dynamic stability is all about oscillations on either side of the starting value of the parameter under consideration. The stable cone of Figure 2.1 is likely to fall back and immediately to come to rest sitting fairly and squarely on its base; the unstable cone balancing on its tip and the neutrally stable cone on its side don't return to their starting positions at all. So questions of dynamic stability never arise in the case of the cone. Nor do they arise when considering the unstable and neutral balls in Figure 2.1.

On the other hand, the stable rugby ball on its side *is* likely to oscillate for a while when released after being disturbed. In this case the oscillations will quickly be damped, as usually happens in simple statically stable systems. But more complicated situations do sometimes arise, where other things may happen instead, and if you have had experience of driving a car towing a caravan, you may be uncomfortably aware of some of the alternative possibilities.

So let us consider the stability of the lateral (i.e. sideways) angle that a caravan makes with a car towing it along a straight road, when a gust of wind causes the caravan to swing temporarily to one side. When the gust has passed, the caravan will naturally be drawn back by the towing car to the starting position where the angle is zero, and so the system is statically stable. However, that may not be the end of the matter, and it is possible for oscillations – possibly catastrophic – to ensue. Let us consider the various possibilities by referring to the set of graphs in Figure 2.3 which illustrate all possible dynamic stability eventualities of any statically stable parameter, such as in our case the lateral angle of the caravan.

The horizontal axis refers to time, and its origin at the left represents the instant when a disturbance is removed and the parameter is free to recover towards zero under the static stability of the system. The vertical axis represents the stability parameter under examination, and extends above and below the origin to accommodate values on each side of zero. Since in the interests of generality we need not be specific about the nature or the units of the stability parameter, we have arbitrarily defined the magnitude of the initial disturbance as one unit. This provides us with a consistent basis on which to make comparisons of the various graph curves.

---

[10]Actually the Earth rotates once in every 23.93 hours. This is because it must rotate not 360° but about 361° each day (24 hours), to compensate for about one degree of movement each day in its orbit around the Sun.

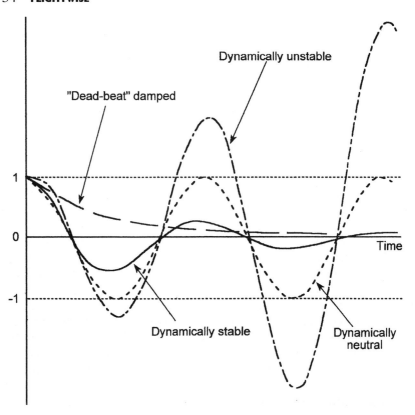

Figure 2.3   Dynamic stability possibilities of a statically stable parameter

The rugby ball on its side represents the most usual and invariably desirable situation, that of dynamic stability. It is represented by the continuous curve in Figure 2.3, in which the *amplitude* (i.e. the amount by which the parameter departs from zero on each side) is seen to reduce on each successive swing, so that the curve eventually flattens out completely when all traces of the disturbance have disappeared. Now this frequently corresponds with the behaviour of a caravan with no so-called stabiliser[11] attached to the coupling to the car. Following a gust of wind caused, perhaps, by being overtaken by a large lorry, the caravan will swing to one side, and then will swing from side to side by a lesser amount on each swing, returning to an undisturbed situation until another gust. The amount by which the parameter decreases on each successive oscillation, and consequently the number of observable oscillations before they die out, depends on a character-

---

[11]A stabiliser is usually a device which provides resistance by friction to any altering of the lateral angle between car and caravan.

istic of the system which is both technically and casually referred to as *damping*.

The driver of a well-designed, well-balanced and properly loaded car/caravan outfit, or one using an effective stabiliser, may well not experience these oscillations at all, since the motion is so heavily damped that the parameter never actually overshoots the zero position after the initial disturbance. This situation is represented by the long-dashed curve in Figure 2.3, and is loosely referred to as 'deadbeat' stability since no oscillations ensue. This type of response should still be regarded as dynamic stability even though no actual overshoots occur, since it still represents a system's dynamic response over a period of time following an initial disturbance within a statically stable system.

So far the caravan's behaviour is probably regarded as good or acceptable. However, there are a great many factors which substantially affect the dynamic stability of a caravan, and the subject is not at all simple. For a start, the lateral angle is not the only parameter that must be considered, and pitching and rolling motion will be equally important. All of these depend on the relative weights of car and caravan, the internal weight distribution of each, the geometry of the wheelbase, the tow-ball position of each, and the effectiveness of any stabiliser used. They also depend on driving conditions such as whether the outfit is going uphill or downhill, whether it is accelerating or decelerating, how fast it is going, whether it is going straight or round a curved path, the wind speed and direction, the road surface conditions and driver's level of skill.

So it emerges that the dynamic stability of such a system is an infinitely more complex situation than that of the rugby ball on its side. Although the 'laws of nature' might appear to suggest that any oscillation can only die away and not increase after the initial disturbance, this turns out to be not necessarily the case, and the complex interaction of so many influences may result in other dynamic responses. The short-dashed curve of Figure 2.3 illustrates a situation which may prevail, in which the oscillations refuse to go away but just stubbornly persist at the same amplitude as they started with. For the caravan outfit driver, if this occurs it can be extremely nerve-wracking, since he or she knows that some action is needed which will restore a dynamically stable situation. The trouble is that the two things which the driver has most direct control of, speed and acceleration, may actually tend to work in opposition to each other, especially if going downhill. Instinctively going at a slower speed would seem to be a likely cure, but to reduce speed the driver has to slow down using the brakes, which invokes a system of decelerating forces which may actually make the situation worse! Attempting to restore the dynamically stable situation by means of corrective use of the steering wheel may be theoretically possible, but it is very likely that the driver will apply the 'corrective' actions at just the wrong moments, making the situation worse rather than better. In aircraft parlance, such events are known as 'pilot-induced oscillations'.

The outcome of such responses may be to alter the dynamic stability balance so that dynamic instability occurs as shown by the chained line curve of Figure 2.3. Here, oscillations about the starting position do occur, but their amplitude, instead of reducing with time, actually increases on each swing. Clearly the outcome of such a motion, if continued, will be catastrophic, since the oscillations will eventually become so large that the basic static stability is overcome (as with the pencil in Figure 2.1) and the caravan will wrap itself right round the side of the car: catastrophic indeed. We have here the wholly undesirable situation of static stability with dynamic instability.

When considering the dynamic stability possibilities illustrated in Figure 2.3, it is useful to be able to describe the situations rather more precisely than just by saying whether they are dynamically stable, neutral or unstable. We would like to be able to put numbers to them, and we can see that there are essentially two characteristics of all the curves – the *frequency* and the *damping* of the oscillations (except for the 'dead-beat' damped case in which frequency has no meaning) – that lend themselves to some form of measurement.

Damping is an indication of how quickly the oscillations will die away (if die away they do). Although a mathematical analysis of dynamic stability does indeed produce a number which measures this damping, it is a dimensionless number whose numerical value does not bear any obvious direct link with what is being measured, beyond the fact that a larger number means more heavily damped, or more rapidly convergent[12], than a smaller number. Furthermore, a zero value of damping refers to the dynamically neutral situation in which the amplitude neither grows nor reduces; a negative value implies that the motion is dynamically unstable and thus divergent; the larger the negative value, the more rapid the divergence. Beyond this qualitative approach, we will not use damping values in the present book, leaving that to more in-depth studies of the subject.

Frequency, on the other hand, proves to be a very useful parameter, since frequencies of distinctly different orders of magnitude occur in aircraft stability considerations, and also since changes to the geome-

---

[12]Convergent or converging means that the parameter in question departs less and less from a single value as time progresses, until it becomes indistinguishable from that value. In other words, it is another word for dynamically stable. Diverging or divergent means the opposite, and applies to a dynamically unstable situation.

try or mass distribution of an aircraft may have significant effects on the frequency of particular types of oscillation. The frequency of an oscillation is simply the number of complete oscillations, or cycles, that occur in a given unit of time, invariably a second, and so the unit of frequency is cycles per second. In the *Système International* (SI) metric system of units, this unit is given the name of hertz after the German physicist of that name, and the abbreviation H, following the SI convention of abbreviating (but not initialing) units named after individuals with a capital letter. A very useful and closely related concept is *period*, or *periodic time*, which refers to the time taken for one complete oscillation to occur. An oscillation having a frequency of 4 H completes four oscillations in 1 second, and so its period or the time taken to complete one oscillation is a quarter of a second. A frequency of one fifth of a cycle per second corresponds to a period of 5 seconds. Thus the relationship between frequency and period is that each is the reciprocal[13] of the other.

No time scale has been shown in the graph of Figure 2.3 for the sake of generality. However, to give ourselves an idea of the typical magnitudes of frequencies that we are dealing with, I suppose (off the top of my head) that the frequency of the oscillating rugby ball on its side might be about 2 cycles per second. For the caravan situation an oscillation might typically take 2 or 3 seconds to complete, (best observed by following someone else's caravan!) so that the frequency would be a half or a third of a hertz. Note that all of the oscillations in Figure 2.3 have the same frequency and period as each other, since they all cross the horizontal (time) axis at the same points as each other, and that in the time range shown just over two full cycles occur. (A complete cycle may be regarded as from one point of maximum amplitude (say the start point) to the next point of maximum amplitude on the *same* side of the zero position.) If the entire figure (to the last peak) were to span a time range of 10 seconds, then the frequency of all the oscillatory curves would be 2 ÷ 10 or 0.2 hertz, and the period would be 5 seconds. In aircraft stability work we shall typically be concerned with certain oscillations which have periods of round about 1 second, and other much slower oscillations with a periodic time of approaching a minute. Fortunately these typical aircraft frequencies are well within the range that we can observe with the naked eye, whereas frequencies of many tens, thousands or millions of hertz occur in other branches of Physics.

---

[13]The reciprocal of a number x is $\dfrac{1}{x}$.

AIRCRAFT STABILITY AXES

The study of aircraft stability limits itself to analysing the motion of the aircraft as a whole, and so we will regard it as a rigid body. If we did not make this assumption, we would find ourselves deviating into considering such things as the increase in the length of a supersonic aircraft – Concorde is about 6 inches longer in the cruise than on the ground, due to kinetic heating and thermal expansion – and the twisting of wing-tips under aerodynamic load. Such considerations may have a measurable effect on the aircraft's stability characteristics, but will here be disregarded in the interests of establishing a manageable system of analysis. Thus we are concerned wholly with the *movements* of a rigid body.

Aircraft are free to move in each of the three dimensions of space, and so before we can specify the parameters which we want to consider we must define some sort of reference frame within which our measurements may be understood. The best way of defining such a reference frame for our purposes is as a set of three mutually perpendicular, or *orthogonal*, axes, so that any point may be uniquely specified by its distances from the origin of these axes in the directions of each. One might start by using an existing axis system with which we are familiar, namely North–South, East–West, and Up–Down. But although this might be OK for an aircraft flying due North at a constant height, it would make our life unnecessarily difficult for any other, more typical, situation in which the aircraft's position in all three axes may be continuously changing, (e.g. an aircraft flying East-South-East and descending).

Since we shall use as the basis of all our considerations an aircraft flying in a straight line, it is usual in stability work (though not the only possible approach) to start by defining one of our three axes as the aircraft's line of flight, whatever direction that may be. At the same time as defining this axis we need to define an origin, and it is customary (for very sound reasons that will be made apparent later on) for the centre of gravity of the aircraft to be defined as the origin, so that the axis set will move with the aircraft. This first axis, called the longitudinal stability axis, can thus be defined as the line through the aircraft's centre of gravity parallel to the direction of the aircraft's flight, as shown in Figure 2.4. It is important to note that the direction of this axis is the same as the direction of the free stream airflow (sometimes called the 'relative wind') that is being experienced by the aircraft, and it is also that of the velocity vector of the aircraft's centre of gravity.

Having defined this axis as described above, we now regard it as 'fixed' in the body of the aircraft, so that when the aircraft is disturbed briefly by a rotation in any direction the axis will be rotated with it,

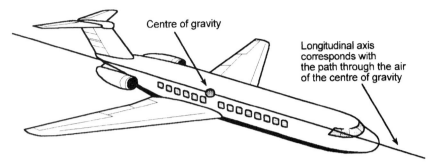

Centre of gravity

Longitudinal axis
corresponds with
the path through the air
of the centre of gravity

Figure 2.4   Definition of longitudinal stability axis

and may temporarily not coincide with the relative wind. We are thus defining an axis system in which we can *describe* the aircraft, rather than one *within which* the aircraft moves.

Bear in mind that, although this axis turns out to be a line through fixed front and rear points of the fuselage, it is not defined as such. To clarify this point, think what difference it would make if we had started to apply our definition of the axis with the aircraft flying at a lower forward speed. If flight is to be maintained along the same flight path, the total lift of the wings must not be changed, and the only way to achieve the same lift at a lower speed is to increase the angle of attack of the wings. Since the wings are rigidly attached to the fuselage, this implies that the nose of the aircraft must be pitched up relative to its position at the higher speed, this pitching occurring about the centre of gravity. But the new longitudinal stability axis still corresponds with the flight path (i.e. the path of the centre of gravity), and so this axis has *not* been pitched up. It will therefore now emerge lower at the nose and higher at the tail of the aircraft than it did before.

Since the longitudinal axis is also the direction of the free stream airflow, the angle between this axis and the mean chord-line of the wing is the wing's angle of attack. This angle is designated by the symbol α (Greek 'alpha') and will be used in addition to the other angles that are introduced a little lower down. Care should be taken not to confuse α with θ, to be defined shortly. Note that, using the above definition of the longitudinal stability axis, the axis will emerge from nose and tail at different points at different flight conditions of the aircraft, and will therefore only be applicable for one given flight condition. This will have no effect on our considerations in this book, but must be borne in mind if you will be going on to study the equations of motion of an aircraft.

Having defined one axis, we define the other two based on the first.

Each will pass through the centre of gravity as origin, and each will be at right-angles to the first. We might be tempted to say, just go for a horizontal line and a vertical line, but it is not quite so straightforward. That would not do if the aircraft were climbing or descending, since the vertical axis would not be at right-angles to the longitudinal axis. Furthermore, though flying straight, the aircraft's wings might not be level for some reason, and then a horizontal axis is not the most convenient arrangement. As with the longitudinal axis, we would like to fix the other two axes into the aircraft so that they pitch and roll with the aircraft.

When trying to define what is called the lateral axis, we run into a difficulty. We can start by saying that it is a line through the centre of gravity at right angles to the longitudinal axis, but somehow we also need to say that it points roughly in the direction of the wings. Since wings are scarcely ever straight but may have a dihedral angle (upward inclination from the root) and/or sweep and/or taper and/or other geometric features, such a vague statement will not do. To resolve this dilemma, it is instructive to step back for a moment and to note a very useful and important feature of nearly all conventional fixed-wing aircraft, and that is that they possess one plane of symmetry. Certainly the top is not the mirror image of the bottom, nor is the front the mirror image of the rear; but to a very good approximation (in most cases) the left is a mirror image of the right, and there is a plane of symmetry slicing the aircraft 'vertically' (provided it is in level flight or on level ground) fore-and-aft through the centre of the tail fin and the fuselage. Furthermore, unless the aircraft is flying crabwise (which in the normal course of events it isn't), the longitudinal axis as previously defined lies in this plane of symmetry. Since there is only one line that can be drawn through a given point and perpendicular to a given plane, we may now immediately define the lateral axis as the straight line through the centre of gravity perpendicular to the aircraft's plane of symmetry, as shown in Figure 2.5.

That brings us to the third axis, which is called the normal axis, since it is defined simply as the line through the centre of gravity normal to (or perpendicular to) the longitudinal and lateral axes (Figure 2.5). Only if the aircraft is flying straight and level will the normal axis be vertical, but it is always in the aircraft's plane of symmetry.

Before considering what quantities we are going to be measuring along these axes, there remains one task, and that is to decide upon the sign conventions to be used for positive and negative directions along each of these axes. It is at about this stage in the process of preparing the ground that I have sometimes found students to begin to get just a little apprehensive and fidgety, as they start to imagine (wrongly, I am pleased to say) that there is going to be an awful lot of

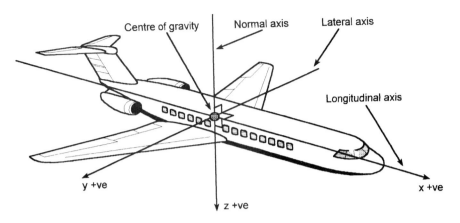

Figure 2.5 **Definitions of other stability axes**

rote-learning of conventions and symbols and other essential but cumbersome paraphernalia. Although I will admit that there is a fair amount of this paraphernalia, especially if you intend to take the subject beyond the level of this book, I promise and assure you most emphatically that rote-learning of random information is most definitely not part of the game. If it were so, I would most decidedly not be a player myself, since rote-learning to me is a *bête-noire*. If you will be guided, I hope to lead you by the hand to show you how to recall when needed, rather than remember, the conventions and terminology by application of logic and basic knowledge of the English alphabet, of left and right, of clockwise and anticlockwise, and of the sense in which a conventional screw thread or corkscrew advances, rather than by feats of memory.

Along each axis we need to define one of the two possible directions as positive, the other being negative. Let us start with the longitudinal axis, where any choice other than 'ahead is positive' would be patently absurd, so this is the convention that we adopt. However, for the other two axes there is no such obvious choice, and so we need a little rule to recall the conventions that are always used. Imagine yourself sitting in the pilot's seat in the aircraft, facing forward, and apply the simple rule 'clockwise is positive'. First of all, turn your head clockwise, i.e. to the right so that you are looking out towards the starboard wing-tip. You are now looking outwards along the lateral axis in the positive direction. Now face straight ahead again, point your arm in the positive lateral axis (right) direction, and apply the rule 'clockwise is positive' again. This time imagine rotating clockwise about the longitudinal axis, or if you prefer, rolling off your seat to the right, without relaxing your right arm. You are now pointing in the positive direction along the normal axis, which is straight downwards relative to the aircraft. The three positive directions are indicated on the three axes of Figure 2.5.

Were you surprised by the choice of downwards for positive in the normal axis? There is actually a very good reason for this. In a two-dimensional system we usually call the axes x and y, and to get from pointing in the positive x-direction to defining and pointing in the positive y-direction you must turn 90°, in *any* direction. However, if your perspective is limited to one side of the piece of paper containing the x–y plane, then you will say that this statement is patently not true, and you must turn anticlockwise! But if you were to go round to the back of the piece of paper and it were tracing paper so that you could see the axes through it, the direction of turn would be reversed, without redefining or redrawing the y-axis. If you were not restricted to the plane of the paper at all, then the positive-y direction could be in *any* direction in a plane normal to the x-axis. There is thus no need for a convention in general, although there is when working on one side of a sheet of paper.

For a three-axis system it is convenient to bring in the letter z to define the third axis. Since we are now working in three dimensions, we can no longer be restricted to the plane of a piece of paper, and so the direction of rotation through 90° from the x-axis positive direction to the y-axis positive direction is arbitrary. However, given these first two, the direction of the positive z-axis is no longer arbitrary, just as, in the two-dimensional system, given the surface of the piece of paper to work on, the y-axis direction is no longer arbitrary. Two people using opposite conventions for the z-axis direction will not be able to share formulae and equations with each other, since all z values will have been entered with opposite signs, and the resulting expressions will be distinctly different.

Therefore a convention is needed, and the rule for it is based on the familiar (perhaps even intuitive, at least for a right-handed person) direction of rotation of a corkscrew or of a screwdriver driving in a conventionally threaded screw. As the corkscrew or screwdriver is rotated clockwise, so it advances the screw away from the operator; turning anticlockwise withdraws the screw towards the operator.

In aircraft work it is customary to define the longitudinal axis as the x-axis, the lateral axis as the y-axis and the normal axis as the z-axis, as in Figure 2.5. Now if you were to drive a screw in the direction of the z-axis, the screwdriver would have to rotate clockwise, turning from positive-x towards positive-y, in order for the screw to advance in the positive z-direction. (Note the 'clockwise is positive' rule coming in again.) But you do not have to start with x, since the set of symbols x, y and z behave cyclically like this: ⟳. If instead you rotate the screwdriver clockwise from the positive y-direction towards the positive z-direction, the screw will advance in the positive x-direction; and rotating from z to x advances in the y-direction. This is known as a right-handed set, and is the usual convention used for defining the positive directions of three orthogonal (i.e. mutually perpendicular) axes. It is a little unfortunate that it results in positive-z being downwards in our case, which is unnatural, but it is worth living with this annoyance in order to have a conventionally sound system that supports the mathematics well.

AIRCRAFT STABILITY PARAMETERS

Each of the kinematic quantities distance, speed and acceleration can be defined in each of the three axis directions, and in addition we can define all the rotational equivalent quantities of angle, rotational speed and rotational acceleration, *about* the axes, (i.e. regarding the axes themselves as pivot lines). That gives us 18 quantities, to which we must also add the cause parameters. These are force in the linear directions and moment in the rotational directions, resulting in another six parameters. There are in addition various other quantities which we have not yet met which relate to the rotational equivalent of mass (for the rotational equivalent of Newton's Second Law), and so we could very quickly amass a vast set of symbols, which would be rather daunting.

It is not our intention to develop the full mathematical model of aircraft stability, and so we shall be spared a rigorous definition of all these terms. However, we have a considerable amount of fairly deep discussion ahead of us regarding the interactions between forces and moments and their various kinematic effects, and so it will serve us well to provide symbols for those quantities that we shall meet often, so that we can get used to using them as shorthand, thus saving a lot of repetition of long words and phrases.

We have already defined distances along the stability axes as x, y and z respectively, and that convention we will keep for convenience of reference. We shall sometimes need to use the rotational equivalents of distance, i.e. angles, and so we must allocate symbols to these. Angles are usually given Greek letters as symbols, and so we shall need a convenient group of three such letters (just like the convenient English triple [x, y, z] for distance). So please swallow hard, and accept that the trio of Greek letters used, in this order, are [ϕ, θ, ψ], which are spelled out as 'phi', 'theta' and 'psi' and pronounced 'fy', 'theeter' and 'p-sy' respectively.

The first of these, ϕ, must represent an angle of rotation about the first axis, the x-axis. Again, imagine yourself sitting in the pilot's seat looking forward, i.e. along the positive direction of the longitudinal axis. ϕ measures angles about this axis, and so it refers to the amount that the aircraft is banked over from its starting position at any instant. We apply the ubiquitous sign convention that 'clockwise is positive', so that a bank to the right corresponds to a positive value of ϕ. Remember that the axes are fixed in the aircraft, and so since we are referring to a rotation of the aircraft, the axis framework itself rotates from its starting position, the angle being measured from the undisturbed position.

The second symbol, θ, represents an angle rotated about the y-axis, the lateral axis, and thus refers to the nose pitching up or down. For the sign convention, once again look out along the positive y-axis (i.e. out along the right wing) and clockwise, i.e. nose-up, is positive. The third symbol, ψ, stands for rotation about the z-axis, the normal axis, and is called the yaw angle. Again, looking along the positive direction of the axis (downwards) a positive yaw is clockwise, corresponding to a swing of the nose to the right. These, along with the symbols defined beneath them, are shown in Figure 2.6.

It is primarily these angles that we shall be using as the aircraft stability parameters. However, just as with the rugby ball and the caravan it was the oscillatory motion that particularly interested us rather than the specific value of the angle of disturbance at any moment, so with aircraft we shall much more frequently be involved with rates of change of distance and angle, in other words speed and rotational

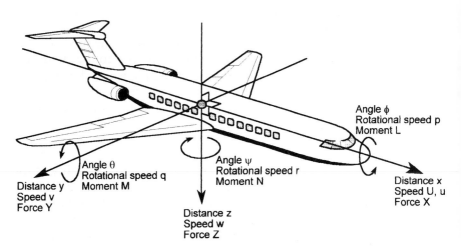

Figure 2.6   Stability parameter conventions

speed. Speeds in the directions of the three axes are given the symbols u, v and w (the triple of letters coming immediately before x, y and z in the alphabet), and rotational speeds about the three axes the symbols p, q and r respectively, the same sign conventions applying as before.[14] Note that since v refers to the speed in the y-direction and not the forward direction, confusion can arise if capital V is used for the forward speed of the aircraft. Therefore in stability work U is used instead for the undisturbed forward speed, but we will continue to use V for the aircraft's flying speed where no confusion can occur. Capital letters refer to the steady initial speed values, (thus V and W are both zero in symmetrical flight – can you see why?) and lower case u, v and w are used for the so-called 'perturbation' values that get added to U, V and W following a disturbance.

Now we must deal with the forces and moments. Strangely, the forces in the three directions x, y and z are given the corresponding capital letter symbols X, Y and Z respectively, representing the resultant force in each direction. Notice that positive X is forward, and so drag turns out to be a negative force and thrust is positive. Likewise (in level flight) weight is positive and lift is negative, since positive Z is downwards. By Newton's First Law, in unperturbed steady straight flight each of X, Y and Z is zero.

Finally, and very importantly, we need a suitable triple of letters, easily remembered, for the moments of forces about each of the three axes. Since M is conventionally and appropriately used to represent a moment, a suitable triple of letters which easily trips off the tongue is L, M and N, and these are used to represent the moments about the x, y and z axes respectively. The positive directions are defined in the same way as the directions of the angles and rotational speeds, using the 'clockwise is positive' convention. Thus a positive value of L is a rolling moment which is trying to tip the left wing up and right wing down; a positive M is a pitching moment trying to tip the nose up; and a positive N a yawing moment trying to turn the nose to the right. It is convenient that the basic moment symbol M happens to refer to pitching, since this is the one that we will be concerned with in the very important and crucial subject of longitudinal stability, to be discussed in Chapter 4.

SPEED STABILITY

Chapters 4 to 7 are given over entirely to looking at the stability of the various rotational motions that an aircraft is subject to, about the three axes. We would not be honest if we did not examine briefly

---

[14]Sometimes $\dot{x}$, $\dot{y}$, $\dot{z}$, $\dot{\phi}$, $\dot{\theta}$ and $\dot{\psi}$ are used instead. There is a minor technical difference, which need not concern us here.

whether there were other motion parameters whose stability is of interest and importance, and in particular we should look at the linear motions (distance and speed) in the directions of the three axes. It so happens that any linear motions that occur in the y and z directions are closely tied up with the rotational motions that we will be looking at later, and so they do not require special treatment on their own.

There is one parameter, however, whose stability is of particular importance to a pilot when flying an aircraft, which comes outside the scope of our later discussion of rotational motions, and that is the aircraft's forward speed. One of the things that is impressed on every novice pilot, and which strikes home as a major difficulty if he or she is already an experienced car driver, is the need to maintain a constant forward speed, and the difficulty of doing so. This need for speed constancy is not just a novice's problem but is a requirement of all pilots, demanding constant attention. For this reason, it would be very valuable if the speed of the aircraft could be statically stable, which would mean that any undemanded change in speed would automatically trigger an inherent feature that would make the speed tend to revert to its undisturbed value without bothering the pilot.

The basic principles underlying speed stability rest in the nature of aircraft total drag, which has been dealt with extensively in *Flightwise – Principles of Aircraft Flight*. Chapter 12 of that book deals in particular with the topic of induced or lift-dependent drag, and includes a section on the subject of speed stability in the context of induced drag. To understand fully what is involved, we would need to have covered the topic of how to vary an aircraft's speed and height, which is discussed later in Chapter 10 under the subheading 'Cruising', especially the paragraphs relating to Figure 10.7. It is therefore possible at this juncture to give only a rather superficial overview of the situation.

Figure 2.7 demonstrates that the pilot of an aircraft has a substantial choice over how much total drag his aircraft experiences, simply by flying at different speeds, and furthermore that each possible value of total drag may be experienced at either of two different speeds in the normal operational range. Before we had introduced the idea of lift-induced drag, there was only the profile drag, which we have seen varies with the dynamic pressure and hence with the square of the speed, and so the slower one flew the less drag there would be. But with the introduction of induced drag, that picture was changed, and the graph showing total drag first of all falls to a minimum value as the airspeed increases, before eventually rising again. To fly with minimum drag, the pilot must adjust his controls so that the aircraft is operating at the lowest point of the total drag curve, at the speed called the minimum drag speed.

Now, on the face of it, it would appear obvious that the minimum

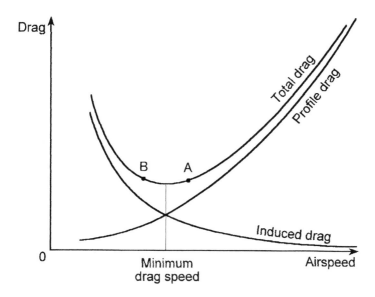

Figure 2.7   **Minimum drag speed and speed stability in level flight**

drag speed would be the most efficient speed to fly at. In fact, it can be shown that to fly for the greatest *specific air range* (which means the greatest distance on a given amount of fuel), the best point to operate at is actually slightly to the right of the minimum drag speed point. (It is actually at the point where a tangent from the origin meets the total drag curve, since at this point the ratio of drag:air speed is minimum.) If, however, the pilot wishes to fly for maximum *endurance*, so as to stay airborne for as long a time as possible without necessarily getting anywhere at all, then the minimum drag point is the best theoretical point for him to operate at.

In practice, however, the pilot will normally choose to fly a little to the right of the minimum drag point, whichever type of objective he has, since it is far less hard work for him (and hence safer) than operating at the bottom or to the left. To see why this is, let us assume that the pilot is cruising straight and level at a steady speed (so that the thrust equals the drag), and that he is intending to operate at point *A* on the total drag graph, a little to the right of the minimum drag point. Let us suppose now that the throttle is correctly set up for the thrust to equal the drag at *A*, but that the pilot's pitch control is being held slightly too far back for precise level flight at *A*. The result – but not the immediate result, as explained later in the text around Figure 10.7 – is that the speed drops from that at *A*, and thus (from the graph in

Figure 2.7) it is clear that the drag reduces a little. But the thrust is unaltered, and so it now exceeds the drag, and there will therefore be an automatic tendency to recover to the point *A*. If the control column were slightly too far forward, the speed would increase, drag would exceed thrust, and again the speed would tend to recover to point *A*. Therefore operating at point *A* has the great advantage that the aircraft possesses *speed stability*, so that with no interference from the pilot the aircraft will always have a tendency to settle back to its undisturbed speed.

Now let us see what transpires if the pilot elects to cruise at point *B*, just to the left of the minimum drag point on the cruising total drag curve. If an incorrect pitch control setting (too far forward) causes a small increase in speed, this will be accompanied by a small *reduction* in drag, so that (with no movement of the thrust control) thrust is now greater than drag, and the aircraft will continue to accelerate away from its original speed. The speed will continue to increase (unless the pilot intervenes by throttling back) until the minimum drag speed is exceeded, and then the speed will become stable as it was at *A*. On the other hand, if from point *B* the speed decreases by a little because the pitch control is held slightly too far back, the drag will increase and will exceed the thrust, and so the speed will continue to fall. In order not to lose lift and thus height, the pilot will have to pull back further on the pitch control, thus increasing the angle of attack of the wings, and hence the lift coefficient. This causes an increase in the lift-induced drag, and so the progress up the left-hand limb of the total drag curve continues. The top left end of the total drag curve corresponds to the stall point, and so ultimately if no thrust correction is made the aircraft will stall.

A pilot can fly 'hands-off' in a condition of speed stability such as at point *A*, but at a point such as *B* with speed instability it is possible to fly only by making constant adjustments to the thrust control, which is very demanding of the pilot's time and concentration, and may lead to an inadvertent stall if the pilot's attention is distracted.

CHAPTER 3
Forces, Moments and Rigid Bodies

INTRODUCTION
In *Flightwise* we aim to make challenging topics appear both under-standable and intriguing, by looking first at the essential fundamental principles so that no development step gets overlooked, and by bring-ing in additional concepts and methods as and when (and only if) they are required. In order to be equipped to tackle aircraft longitudinal stability, we must first of all pick up on our earlier discussion of moments that we commenced in Chapter 2 and extend it to a fairly sophisticated level of abstract modelling. We will then be properly armed to tackle the matter in hand, and in the process we shall meet a number of interesting and unexpected ideas.

THE STABLE CONE
In our discussion of the forces and moments on the cone near the beginning of Chapter 2, we regarded the bottom right corner of the cone in Figure 2.2(a) as a fixed pivot, making it very natural to take moments about that point. By so doing, we were able to disregard the reaction force of the ground and the force exerted sideways by the peg or by friction, since these forces would act through the pivot point and would therefore have no turning effect about that point – you cannot open or close a door by pushing or pulling on the hinge line.

But this meant that we were looking at only part of the overall pic-ture. We will go back now and consider the entire set of forces on the cone, and this will lead us to the discovery of some very important axioms that will be essential to us when considering the longitudinal static stability of an aircraft. The cone in its equilibrium position of Figure 2.2(a) is reproduced in Figure 3.1, but now we leave out the ground line, and replace the effect of the ground and peg (or friction) with the reaction forces that they exert on the cone.

The overall reaction force of ground and peg (or friction) on the cone must act through the point of contact. It is convenient to con-sider this reaction force split into two perpendicular components, one vertical (the normal reaction of the ground) labelled R and one hori-zontal (the friction or peg force) labelled F. Since the cone is totally in equilibrium we may apply Newton's First Law both in the vertical and the horizontal directions, and this tells us that the resultant force in each of these directions is zero. Thus, even though the pairs of oppo-site forces are not in line with each other, the normal reaction from

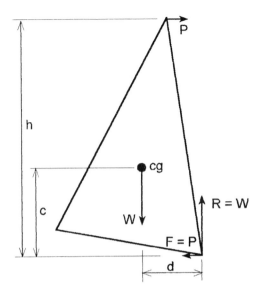

Figure 3.1   Forces on a cone in equilibrium

the ground R must exactly equal the weight W and the horizontal restraining force F must equal the pulling force P. There are no other forces acting on the cone.

When we took moments about the point of contact with the ground, the principle of moments gave us the equation $Wd = Ph$, or, if we regard clockwise as positive, $Ph - Wd = 0$. But now there is no obvious reason for that choice of moment centre, so let us experiment with other possibilities. What happens, for instance, if we take moments about the centre of gravity? In this case the weight force W acts through the moment centre, so that it has no turning effect, but all three of the other forces F, P and R do. In order to be able to specify the perpendicular distance from the centre of gravity to the lines of action of the forces P and F, we have introduced the symbol c to represent the height of the centre of gravity above the ground. Applying the Principle of Moments about the centre of gravity, regarding clockwise as positive, we now have:

$$P(h - c) + Fc - Rd = 0$$

Substituting P for F and W for R and multiplying out the bracket gives:

$$Ph - Pc + Pc - Wd = 0 \text{ or } Ph - Wd = 0$$

which is exactly the same equation as we had previously when we took

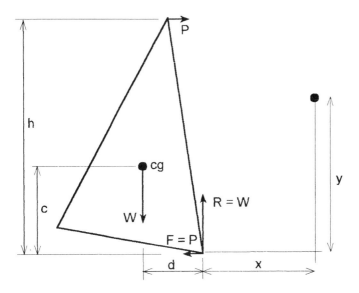

Figure 3.2   Cone with arbitrary moment centre

moments about the original pivot point. This is a surprising result, and it prompts us to ask the question, what happens if we choose another point instead, not a special point such as the so-called pivot point or the centre of gravity but any old point? Will we get the same equation again? To test this, let us redraw the figure before it gets too cluttered, and place an arbitrary point at a distance x to the right of the original pivot point and a height y above it (Figure 3.2). Immediately you will notice that this is not even a point on the cone – but who said it should be? We just want to explore what happens if we take moments about an arbitrary point, and outside the cone is as arbitrary as you can get![1]

Working out the distances from the point to the lines of action of the forces is a little more tricky now, so the algebra gets rather more cumbersome. Again taking clockwise moments as positive, we observe that each of the forces P, R and F provide positive contributions and W has a negative effect. The principle of moments gives:

$$P(h - y) + Fy + Rx - W(d + x) = 0$$

---

[1]Although outside the cone, the point must be regarded as fixed to the cone so that, if the cone moves in any way, the point moves with it. But this does not arise in the present static situation.

Multiplying out the brackets and making the same substitutions as before gives:

$$Ph - Py + Py + Wx - Wd - Wx = 0$$

Now all the terms containing x or y cancel out, leaving us with $Ph - Wd = 0$, which is exactly the same equation as we had before. Also we observe that this result contains no reference at all to the values of x and y, so that, whatever point we choose to take moments about, we shall get exactly the same equation. Can we conclude, then, that it actually doesn't matter what point we take moments about, and that the answer is always the same?

A FORCE ON A SLIDING SLAB

Before jumping hastily to conclusions, let us look at a system that will help in understanding what is going on. We will take a sheet of a heavy material, (steel, say) and cut out of it a random-shaped slab, which we place flat on a horizontal surface on which it can slide freely without any friction at all. We could come close to this with very smooth ice, or an air bed which supports the slab by the hovercraft principle. By applying forces to this object only in the horizontal plane we effectively have a two-dimensional system, since the weight of the slab acts at right angles to the plane and hence has no effect whatsoever in the plane. But its mass *does* have an effect, as we shall see.

The principles that we shall be examining in this chapter are not in fact *quite* restricted to a two-dimensional system. If that were to be the case, they could not be applied to a three-dimensional aeroplane, and it is for that purpose that we are developing them here. But we will look again at this point at the end of the chapter, and in the meantime restrict our thinking to a two-dimensional body for ease of handling. The present discussion quite definitely does not apply in general to any three-dimensional body.

If we apply a horizontal force F to the slab, such that its line of action passes through the slab's centre of gravity which is shown by the black dot in Figure 3.3, the whole slab behaves as if it were a particle and accelerates along the straight line of the force. Because by definition the centre of gravity is the point where all the mass can be thought of as being concentrated, the force F does not have any rotational effect on the slab at all. The force F is actually distributed through the material of the slab to act on every point on the slab, but all the bits of F acting to one side of the centre of gravity cancel out with all the bits acting on the other side, and their resultant moment is zero.

When we work out (by adding vectors circus-elephant style as

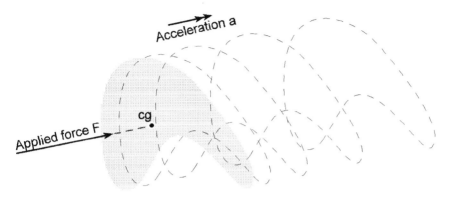

Figure 3.3   The motion of a rigid body subjected to an applied force through the centre of gravity

explained in Chapter 2 of *Flightwise – Principles of Aircraft Flight*) the resultant of a distribution of forces on a body resulting from an airflow over the body, the answer contains three elements: the magnitude of the resultant force, its direction, and the position on the body at which it acts, which together with the direction is called its line of action. If the applied force *F* in Figure 3.3 were the resultant of aerodynamic forces on the object, then there would be no guarantee at all that this resultant would pass through the centre of gravity – indeed, it would be highly unlikely to do so. So let us now investigate what happens in a more typical situation (Figure 3.4) in which the force does not pass through the centre of gravity. Imagine pulling horizontally on a cord attached to the heavy slab on an ice rink, so that the line of the cord does not pass through the slab's centre of gravity. How will the slab behave? One instinctively feels that the slab will move in the direction of the force but at the same time will turn round a bit. If the force-line passes close to the centre of gravity, the motion will be predominantly linear, but the further the force-line acts off-centre the more the slab will rotate.

Let us try to rationalise what is happening by considering one thing at a time. When applying Newton's Laws to linear motion, we have always worked on the assumption that the object being acted upon could be regarded as a particle. Indeed we did so with the cone in the previous section, when showing that $R = W$ and $F = P$. If this is justified in the situation of Figure 3.4, the linear acceleration will still be *a* (as in Figure 3.3) in the direction of the applied force, and as before it will be the acceleration of the centre of gravity, since we are regarding the slab's whole mass as being concentrated at that point. In Figure 3.4 the centre of gravity is shown accelerating along a straight line

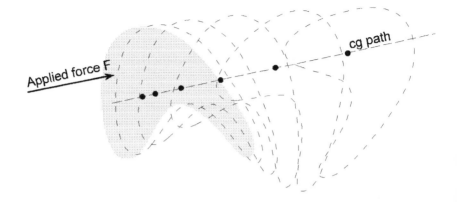

Figure 3.4   The motion of a rigid body subjected to an applied force not through the centre of gravity

which is parallel to the applied force, but this is no more than a hunch at present, and it demonstrates our hope that the straight path of the centre of gravity is unaffected by anything else that may be happening.

The main change from Figure 3.3 is that the mass of the slab is now no longer uniformly distributed on each side of the applied force. In fact, the part of the slab on the force side of the centre of gravity (i.e. above in the figure) is getting a greater share of the force's effect than the part on the other side (below), and is consequently accelerating at a greater rate, so that the slab has a clockwise rotational acceleration in addition to the presumed linear acceleration of the centre of gravity. It would be wishful thinking at this stage to presume that this rotation was *about* the centre of gravity, but if we were correct in this and the previous speculation it would enable us to split the slab's motion into two parts which could be dealt with separately: (i) the straight-line motion *of* the centre of gravity, and (ii) the rotational motion *about* the centre of gravity.

We can systematically test out our two hypotheses by making use of a subtle trick. Figure 3.5 shows a single instantaneous snapshot of the slab being acted upon by an applied force F which does not act through the centre of gravity. We apply an additional pair of forces P and Q through the centre of gravity, such that they are each parallel to and equal in magnitude to F, but act in opposite directions to each other. Clearly P and Q completely and exactly cancel each other out, and together can have no effect whatsoever on the motion of the slab, so that we are at liberty to insert them into the diagram without fear of corrupting the previous system. We will use the letter d to represent

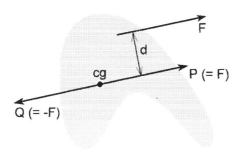

Figure 3.5   Slab with applied force *F* not through centre of gravity; forces *P* and *Q* have no effect

the distance between the line of action of *F* and that of the *P–Q* pair.

Now, instead of treating *P* and *Q* as a pair, let us think of *P* as a solo force and regard *Q* and *F* as working together. On its own *P* can be regarded as the linear force providing the slab with its linear acceleration. Since it acts through the centre of gravity, it has no moment about that point, and so its effect is simply to provide the linear acceleration *of* the centre of gravity that we considered in Figure 3.3. So, since *P* has no rotational effect about the centre of gravity let us now ignore *P* and turn our attention to *Q* and *F*. They form a pair of equal and opposite forces which are not collinear with each other, and they alone must now be regarded as the cause of any rotational motion. We would therefore like to be able to work out the moment that this force pair exerts on the slab.

To do so raises the old question, what point should we take moments about? A sensible suggestion might be the centre of gravity, since it is *about* this point that we would like to show that the rotation occurs, so let us do so and see what we get. Now *Q* acts through the centre of gravity, and so has no moment about it, which leaves just *F*, whose clockwise moment is simply *Fd*. Thus the moment of the pair of forces *F* and *Q* about the centre of gravity is *Fd*. (Note that we are not here applying the principle of moments, because the system is not in equilibrium; the clockwise moment *Fd* produces a rotational acceleration.)

Let us see now what happens if we take moments about some other point instead, and let us be bold and choose a completely random point (which need not be on the slab at all but will move with the slab) such as the point A in Figure 3.6, which is at a perpendicular distance *b* from the line of action of *Q*. (The force *P* has been omitted in Figure 3.6, since we are no longer concerned with it.) The clockwise moment of the force pair *F* and *Q* about A is $F(b + d) - Qb$, which after multiplying out the bracket gives $Fb + Fd - Qb$. Since $F = Q$,

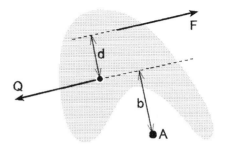

Figure 3.6   Non-collinear force pair *F* and *Q* acting on slab

$Fb - Qb = 0$, and so the clockwise moment of the force pair about A is Fd, just as it was about the centre of gravity. Furthermore, the distance b does not appear at all in the answer, and so the position of A is immaterial. Thus the moment of the force pair F and Q may be worked out about *any* point, always giving the same answer which is [either one of the forces (remember they are equal)] times [the distance between their lines of action].

COUPLES

Pairs of forces such as F and Q in Figure 3.6 are of very great importance, and are given the special name of *couples*. A couple is simply a pair of forces which are equal in magnitude, opposite in direction, but do not act along the same straight line. Being equal and opposite, they always have a zero linear resultant so that, in so far as Newton's First and Second Laws of *linear* motion are concerned, they have no effect and can be completely ignored. But being non-collinear, they always produce a moment, whose magnitude is [one of the forces] times [the distance between their lines of action]. As we have seen, it makes absolutely no difference what point the moment is calculated about, and so the moment of a couple is a property purely of the couple itself, and not of the positions of its constituent forces[2]. As an example of couples that we have already come across, we see in Figure 3.2 that P and F form one couple acting on the cone with a clockwise moment Ph, and W and R form another with an anticlockwise moment Wd. As we saw, since the cone is in equilibrium, the resultant of the moments of these couples is zero, so that $Ph - Wd = 0$, and so the system consists just of two equal and opposite couples which are mutually can-

---

[2]Sometimes you may meet the expression 'a pure couple'. However, this does not signify any additional property, but the tautologous use of the word 'pure' is probably simply meant to emphasise the fact that there is no linear resultant, or to obviate any confusion between a couple and the moment of a single force.

celling. So the answer to the question posed at the very end of the section on the cone is, no, it does not matter what point moments are taken about in this situation, since the force system consists only of couples. For later reference, we will now state our first important axiom:

> **Axiom 1. The moment of a couple is independent of the point about which moments are taken.**

We have shown that P acts on the centre of gravity giving it a linear acceleration, and that the F–Q couple causes a rotation, but it remains to be seen whether this rotation occurs about the centre of gravity or some other point. Certainly we did not have to take moments about the centre of gravity, and furthermore a glance back at the positions of the forces F and Q in Figure 3.5 might lead one to think that the slab would rotate about some point other than the centre of gravity – probably a point halfway between the forces – and if this were the case the centre of gravity itself would progress in a circular path around the centre of rotation. However, this cannot be. If it were, it would imply that the straight line motion of the centre of gravity caused by P would have a circular motion superimposed on it, so that the centre of gravity's movement would no longer be in a straight line. By Newton's Second Law we know that a sideways force is needed to deflect a mass from its straight line path, but neither the F–Q couple (which has no linear resultant sideways or in any other direction) nor the force P (which acts solely along the straight line path of the centre of gravity) can provide any such deflecting force. Therefore the centre of gravity must move in a straight line, and any rotation that occurs must be about the centre of gravity.

We have now demonstrated categorically a very useful fact that we will state as our second axiom:

> **Axiom 2. At any instant, the motion of a two-dimensional rigid body can be split into two completely independent motions which are superimposed one upon the other: (i) a linear motion *of* the centre of gravity, and (ii) a rotational motion *about* the centre of gravity. A resultant linear force (regardless of its line of action) only affects the linear motion *of* the centre of gravity, and a couple will affect only the rotation *about* the centre of gravity, without disturbing it from its straight path[3].**

---

[3]Note that the phrase 'linear motion of the centre of gravity' does not imply that the centre of gravity is necessarily moving in a straight line or at a constant speed. Motion can include acceleration, either in the direction of motion or normal to it (centripetal acceleration), or any combination. But such accelerations are still linear (or to be strictly honest, we ought to say 'rectilinear'), as opposed to rotational. Hence the caveat in Chapter 2 (in the section 'Moments and Rotational Motion') not to confuse centripetal acceleration with rotational acceleration.

In one important respect, the application of the principles of forces and moments to the longitudinal static stability of an aircraft is actually simpler than the example that we have been considering. Whereas we have been thinking about accelerations of the slab, when we turn our attention to aircraft longitudinal static stability we will be concerned with the situation in which there are *no* linear or rotational accelerations. Furthermore, the rotational speed will also be zero (although that will not be the case when we look at longitudinal dynamic stability). When we were considering the effect of a force on a slab in Figure 3.4, we cheated a bit. As soon as the slab begins its doubly accelerating motion, the very situation that we have carefully set up with regard to the slab's orientation and the position on it at which the applied force acts will change, so that the system can strictly be considered only for a brief instant, and not as long as the series of dotted snapshots in the figure would suggest. But for our present purposes we are more interested in the forces and couples themselves than in the accelerations that they would create if unopposed. Since for our present studies we only need to apply the ideas to equilibrium situations, we simply require (in our example) an equal and opposite force to balance P and an equal counteracting couple to balance the Q–F couple. But the complete set of equations of motion for full analysis of aircraft dynamic stability and control are based on Newton's Second Laws for linear and rotational motion, in which accelerations are the order of the day, and so the concepts that we have established will come even more into their own if you will be going on to study such matters.

MAKING THE IDEAS MORE USEFUL

Following our introduction of the concept of a couple, it is convenient to rationalise and streamline a little the way that we draw diagrams involving forces and couples. Just as a force, a linear motion producer, is given its own symbol →, so a couple, a rotational motion producer, is given *its* own symbol, ↻. Just as the force arrow may be labelled with a letter, typically F, denoting its magnitude, so a couple arrow is usually identified with a letter, most commonly M, standing for the moment of the couple. The couple's arrowhead indicates its direction, clockwise or anticlockwise. To illustrate the use of this couple symbol, Figure 3.5 is redrawn at Figure 3.7 using a couple symbol for the F–Q couple. Note that, although the positioning of the force P is crucial, the couple symbol may be drawn literally anywhere at all on the diagram, since its value is independent of the point about which moments are taken, and the couple applies to the rigid body *in toto*.

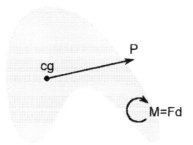

Figure 3.7   Figure 3.5 redrawn with couple symbol replacing the *F–Q* force pair

The force *P* and the couple *M* in Figure 3.7 completely represent the force system shown in Figure 3.4 without the distraction of the dotted outlines representing the acceleration. Hence we can see that any force such as *F* acting on a rigid body along a line of action which does not pass through its centre of gravity may be completely replaced by an equal parallel force through the centre of gravity (*P*) together with a couple, whose magnitude is the force times the distance it moves sideways. The direction of the couple is the direction of the rotation that *F* would cause about the centre of gravity.

This movement of a force to the centre of gravity with accompanying couple can also be reversed, so that a force through the centre of gravity may be put somewhere else on the object provided that the necessary couple is included. But even better, we can chain together two such force shifts; by following a movement *to* the centre of gravity with a second movement *away from* the centre of gravity to any new point, we can establish a powerful manipulative device which is completely independent of the position of the centre of gravity.

To illustrate this process, let us consider the sequence of steps shown in Figure 3.8, starting with diagram (a) which represents a force *F* acting on the slab along a line at a distance *a* from the centre of gravity. The steps simply apply (twice) the earlier trick of adding a pair of equal, opposite and collinear forces to the system which produces no change to the system's effect, and then regrouping the forces.

(a→b) A pair of opposite forces *P* and *Q* (each equal and parallel to *F*) are applied acting through the centre of gravity, as discussed with Figure 3.5 earlier.

(b→c) The pair of forces *F* and *Q* is replaced by a couple symbol. Note that this can be drawn *anywhere*, since it affects the entire slab. The result of this step gives us the system which demonstrates Axiom 2.

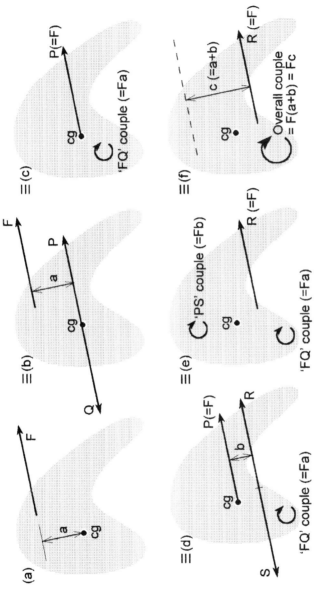

Figure 3.8 Sequence showing replacement of a force by the same force elsewhere plus a couple

(c→d) A new pair of opposite forces R and S, each equal and parallel to P (and hence to F) are applied to *any* random point of the slab at a distance b from the centre of gravity. As with the P–Q pair, they cancel each other out and have no effect, and so the motion of the slab remains unaltered.

(d→e) The pair of forces P and S is replaced by a second couple symbol. Once again it can be drawn anywhere.

(e→f) The two couple symbols are replaced by a single one which represents their combined effect, their sum. The distance between the final force R and the original line of the force F is the sum of the two distances a and b and is labelled c.

It is the overall transformation from diagram (a) to diagram (f) that is important. It means that we may shift a force sideways in accordance with the following axiom, without altering the effect of the force at all, and thus create a force and couple system that is more convenient for our purposes:

> **Axiom 3.** **Any force may be represented by an equal and parallel force acting at any other point on the object, together with a couple. The magnitude of the couple is the magnitude of the force times the distance it is moved sideways.**

In Figure 3.8(f) the force F has been moved sideways a distance c, and to compensate we have applied a couple of moment Fc in the direction that the original force would tend to rotate the body about any point on the new force's line of action. The opposite of this axiom is also true and useful and may be stated as a corollary thus:

> **Corollary to Axiom 3.** **A system consisting of a force and a couple may be represented by just a force, whose magnitude is the same as that of the original force and whose distance from the original force is the moment of the couple divided by the force.**

This axiom and its corollary can be used for any force or force and couple acting on a rigid body, even when there has been no reference whatsoever to the centre of gravity, regardless of whether the force is causing accelerations or the object is being restrained in equilibrium. In other words, we have stated a principle that is a property of forces and moments on their own, completely independently of the system of which they are a part.

APPLICATION TO AIRCRAFT

The discussion of this chapter has been firmly based on the idea of a two-dimensional system, but an aeroplane is very decidedly three-dimensional. However, it so happens that we have been restricting the scope of our discussion unnecessarily in the interests of simplicity, and it is capable of somewhat wider application. Any rigid body which has its mass (together with all the applied forces and moments) distributed symmetrically on each side of a plane (called a *plane of symmetry*) may be thought of as if it were concentrated in a slab in the plane of symmetry. It is as though all the mass elements and forces were projected, in matched opposite pairs, on to the plane of symmetry, and any effects that they would have outside the plane of symmetry are totally cancelled out.

Now a conventional aircraft has one such plane of symmetry, the plane which slices fore-and-aft through the centre of the fuselage and the tail fin and which contains the longitudinal and normal axes. Therefore for the purpose of studying longitudinal, or pitching, stability, we may project the entire aircraft (particularly the wings) into this plane and treat it just as if it were a two-dimensional slab whose shape is the side view of the aircraft. Furthermore, it will suit our requirements for the next chapter if we assume that the wing is unswept, untapered, untwisted and has no dihedral, so that every cross-section of the wing will project on to the drawing of the fuselage in exactly the same position as every other one. In reality this is rarely the case, and so the aerodynamicists have to define suitable average values and positions for the important wing features.

We have now established the necessary ground rules, and can proceed in the next chapter to take a close look at the longitudinal static stability of an aircraft.

CHAPTER 4
Longitudinal Static Stability

INTRODUCTION

If you have ever assembled a cheap toy balsa-wood model aeroplane consisting of flat wing and tailplane to be slotted into a slightly thicker piece of wood constituting the fuselage and fin, the next thing you probably did was to try launching it by hand from shoulder height to see whether it would fly. Invariably (before proper adjustments were made) it would either swoop up into the air, stop and plummet tail first, or it would immediately tuck its nose under and plunge down to the ground, or come back and hit you in the midriff. As a young child I remember being intrigued by a similar problem regarding the paper darts and aeroplanes we used to make: you could bend up or down flaps torn into the paper at the back of either the wings or the tailplane, and could thus produce a range of different effects. But for successful flight in either situation it was always necessary to make the front of the model somewhat heavier than the back, by means of thick folds of paper, paper-clips or, in the case of the balsa model, a small lead weight; other adjustments could then follow.

We have here the problem of longitudinal static stability, which, after tackling the fundamental question of how to achieve lift, is undoubtedly the first and foremost consideration of any aircraft designer. We have to configure our aircraft in such a way that, if it should pitch up, something about its design makes it immediately tend to pitch back down again in compensation; and *vice versa*. But how? What are the rules?

We saw in Chapter 1 that this problem was essentially solved by George Cayley nearly 200 years ago, a full century before the Wright brothers' successful mastery of flight. The elements of the solution bequeathed to us by Cayley are clearly seen in the sketch of his first model glider in Figure 1.2, namely a main lifting wing, a stabilising tailplane and a movable weight by which to locate the centre of gravity in the right position. But the figure cannot show the relative sizes and orientations of these features, nor the principles upon which such considerations must be based.

It was not because it was a trivial nut to crack that it was initially solved two centuries ago, but rather because its crucial importance to successful flight was recognised very early. Although it is the most fundamental of all aircraft stability considerations, longitudinal static stability is undoubtedly the most tricky to grasp, and probably of all aspects of aircraft stability and control, the least well understood by professing aeronautical folk. Furthermore, it is something which can very easily (and unwittingly) be affected, possibly adversely and even dangerously, by virtually anybody – even a well-intentioned passenger in a light aircraft!

MODELLING THE AIRCRAFT

Let us now start to frame the problem that we wish to solve. We wish to investigate the pitching characteristics of an aircraft that consists essentially of a pair of aerofoil section wings to provide lift, a well-streamlined fuselage to carry pilot and load, and a powerplant to provide forward motion and hence the airflow over the wing. Experience also suggests that it may need some sorts of secondary aerodynamic surfaces for providing control and stability, but we will leave these out at first, since it would be useful (and easier) to investigate the need for such things from scratch, without preconceived ideas or solutions. So let us consider a monoplane aircraft which is conventionally shaped except that it has no fin or tailplane. Since we will restrict our investigation to the pitching behaviour of the aircraft, let us assume that the thrust of the engine is in the free-stream direction (i.e. opposite to the drag) and that both it and the overall drag act through the centre of gravity, so that they have no pitching moment about that point. Furthermore, let us assume that all of the lift is produced by the wings and none by the fuselage.

There are now only two forces left on the aircraft which could influence the aircraft's pitching behaviour: one is the wing lift, and the other is the weight. If we further specify that the aircraft is in straight level flight, the lift will be equal in magnitude to the weight.

With these fairly drastic (but by no means unreasonable) simplifications, we can reduce the situation to a very simple diagram illustrating the problem that we wish to investigate. The fuselage can be completely dispensed with, and the aircraft can be simply represented by an aerofoil section. Horizontally acting forces are irrelevant to our purposes, and so the only forces to be shown are lift (acting upwards) and weight (acting downwards). Figure 4.1 shows the complete model of the aircraft on the basis of which we are now going to investigate longitudinal static stability. Remember that, although only showing the wing, the diagram represents the entire aircraft and not just the wing.

If your gut reaction to Figure 4.1 is a mixture of bewilderment and disgust at the suggestion that such a puerile and simplistic figure could form the basis of our study of what you have been told is one of the most difficult aerodynamic concepts to come to grips with, just recall one thing. When such figures have been met previously, the aerofoil

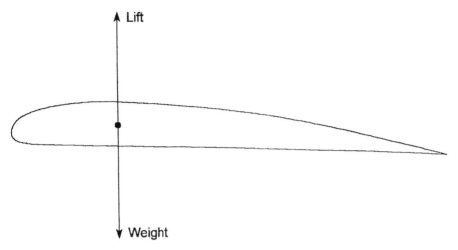

Figure 4.1 **Model of a tailless aircraft for studying longitudinal static stability**

and aircraft were being regarded as a particle, and to all intents and purposes the only point on it that existed was the centre of gravity. Now, however, we are into the business of rigid bodies, and so we have to start asking questions about *where* the forces act upon the body. Figure 4.1 shows both forces acting at the same point, but there is no justification for this, and of course they normally don't. Thus, although their resultant force is zero, in the normal course of events they produce a couple. The next step will be to examine for each of the two forces in turn where they act and what their position depends on.

Let us look first of all at the weight force, since that is the easier. The position of the weight force on the aircraft is totally independent of any aerodynamic influence, and depends purely and simply on the position of the aircraft's centre of gravity. In turn, the position of the centre of gravity depends only on the fore-and-aft distribution of the total mass of the aircraft. Clearly the aircraft must initially be so designed that its centre of gravity lies close to where the wing lift is acting, since to a first approximation they must be equal, opposite and collinear in order to balance out. Thus a long fuselage will normally extend roughly the same distance in front of and behind the wing, unless heavy engines are mounted at the tail, in which case more fuse-lage will project forwards to compensate. The designer has very great flexibility over where he places the aircraft's centre of gravity, but once the aircraft is built the scope for moving it is much more restricted.

It is often possible to alter the position of the centre of gravity of an existing aircraft very substantially by the way in which the load it is carrying is distributed. On a very lightweight two seat sailplane with tandem seating, there will be a substantial variation in centre of gravity position depending on whether it contains one or two people, and in which seats he, she or they are seated. On a light four seater touring aircraft, there will be a substantial difference in the centre of gravity position depending on whether or not the rear two seats are occupied, and whether luggage is stowed in the space behind the rear seats. In an airliner with a long fuselage and under-floor hold, the positioning of passengers and cargo is a major consideration when preparing the aircraft for flight. In some aircraft, including the supersonic Concorde but also some subsonic aircraft, the centre of gravity is very deliberately shifted a large amount fore-and-aft at different phases of flight by pumping fuel between tanks in the wings and tail. Under certain extreme requirements, a major centre of gravity shift may be achieved by placing heavy ballast such as lead or sandbags in the nose or the tail of the aircraft. Despite this flexibility, remember that the centre of gravity position is not affected in any way by the flying conditions of the aircraft: but, as we shall see, it does have a significant effect on those flying conditions.

CENTRE OF PRESSURE

The centre of pressure may be defined as the point where the line of action of the total reaction of the entire aerodynamic force distribution around the aircraft crosses the aerofoil chord line. As such it strictly includes the viscous force distribution (as discussed at the start of Chapter 3 of *Flightwise – Principles of Aircraft Flight*) but the viscous forces usually make a negligible direct contribution to the lift component of the total reaction. Note that the centre of pressure position is also influenced by the pressure distribution over the remainder of the aircraft, in particular the fuselage and tailplane. But since we are assuming the fuselage contribution to lift to be negligible and we have chosen to have no tailplane in our model, in the present case the centre of pressure is simply that of an aerofoil.

One of the first things that was discovered about the way aerofoils behave, much to the frustration of the early would-be pioneers of flight, was that the centre of pressure of an aerofoil actually moves forward and backward a substantial amount as the angle of attack, and hence the lift, is varied. It is clear then that if, in Figure 4.1, the centre of gravity is correctly placed to correspond with the centre of pressure at one particular flight condition, at any other flight condition with a different angle of attack the lift force will have shifted, resulting

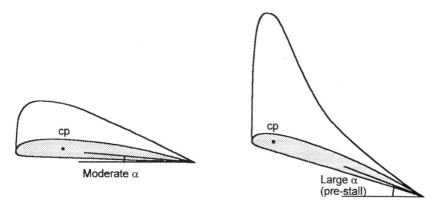

Figure 4.2 **Centre of pressure movement with angle of attack**

in a couple producing either a nose-up or a nose-down pitching moment. The fundamental longitudinal stability problem hence stems directly from the movement of the centre of pressure. Realising this inescapable fact, it was George Cayley who was the first person to make a proper study of the movement of an aerofoil's centre of pressure.

The reason for this shift in centre of pressure arises directly from the nature of the pressure distribution around the aerofoil at different angles of attack. The height at each point of the curves above the aerofoils in Figure 4.2. represents very approximately the lift component of the resultant of the top and bottom surface pressure forces at the corresponding point on the aerofoil chord. The left hand diagram shows the way in which lift is distributed in typical cruising conditions with a moderate angle of attack α of, say, 4°. The reason that the lifting effect is greater towards the front of the aerofoil than the rear is that the wing is thicker there, so that more speeding up of the airflow and reduction in static pressure occurs there than where it is thinner. The effect of this is then biased upwards (rather than being symmetrically dispersed about the chord) as a result both of the angle of attack and the camber of the aerofoil, which combine to point the trailing edge downwards relative to the free stream and hence produce the circulation required for lift.[1] The centre of pressure of this lift distribution may be typically a quarter to a half of the chord length behind the

---

[1]The principles underlying circulation and lift are fully discussed in Chapter 7 of *Flightwise – Principles of Aircraft Flight*.

leading edge, but remember that its position changes all the time with varying angle of attack.

The right hand diagram shows a typical lift distribution over an identical aerofoil whose angle of attack has increased to an angle close to its stalling angle, and this is when the lifting effect is at a maximum as discussed in Chapter 9 of *Flightwise – Principles of Aircraft Flight*. In this condition the airflow reaches a very high speed and consequently produces a very large suction as it rounds the leading edge. Thus the lift distribution is seen to peak very markedly over the leading edge region, so that the centre of pressure shifts a considerable distance forward from its previous position. If the angle of attack is further increased and a leading edge stall occurs, then the boundary layer separation over the leading edge prevents the very high speed and low pressure occurring there, and so the lift distribution peak suddenly collapses, and the centre of pressure rapidly moves rearwards again.

Our study of aircraft pitching behaviour will centre on the couple produced by the lift and weight force pair in Figure 4.1. Although the weight force remains constant and fixed in position[2], it is now clear that both the magnitude and position of the lift force vary appreciably. This means that, when it comes to calculating moments, there is not one variable to contend with but two (magnitude and position) each time there is a change in angle of attack. This would make the theory very cumbersome to handle, but fortunately there is available to us a very useful concept known as the aerodynamic centre, which we shall discover a little later and which will enable us to get round this problem. We will therefore not often meet the awkward concept of centre of pressure again, except to highlight its vagaries and unsuitableness for our purposes.

TRIM

There is one more essential piece of terminology that we must introduce into our vocabulary before we can proceed further, and that is the word *trim*. To say that an aircraft is trimmed is simply shorthand for saying that it is in rotational equilibrium. Thus the word can be applied in any of the three rotational directions of pitching, rolling and yawing. Although equilibrium strictly means no rotational acceleration, in this case it also means zero rotational speed, since we will assume that the aircraft starts off not rotating. If an aircraft is flying at

---

[2]We can safely ignore changes in aircraft weight due to fuel consumption, since although significant over a long time span we are only concerned with events which occur in a relatively very brief period of time. Likewise, once it is predetermined by design and loading, we regard the position of the centre of gravity as fixed.

all (i.e. nose-first, wings steady), it is a *sine qua non* that it must be trimmed about each of its three axes, since otherwise it would start tumbling about its centre of gravity in one direction or another. In particular, if an aircraft is longitudinally trimmed, the resultant pitching moment on it is zero.

The aircraft depicted in Figure 4.1 is shown longitudinally trimmed since the lift and weight forces are opposite each other and collinear. But if either the weight or the lift were acting at a different point so that the two were not collinear, the aircraft would not be trimmed, and we would have to do something about it. When we come to discuss what makes the aircraft longitudinally stable or otherwise, we shall have to keep coming back to consider whether it is also trimmed, since trim is an even more fundamental requirement for flight than stability. The Wright brothers' *Flyer* was not stable, but it had to be trimmed in order to fly at all.

If you are, or have rubbed shoulders with, an aircraft pilot, you may be feeling indignant that the previous two paragraphs fall short of the truth. Unfortunately over time there have arisen two slightly different definitions of the word trim as applied to aircraft (about any of the three axes), and nowadays pilots use trim to mean something additional to the aeronautical engineer's meaning of the word. Let us stick to longitudinal motion for now. It is clear from Figure 4.1 that for an aircraft to be trimmed is a highly elusive condition, and that trim is lost as soon as the centre of pressure moves at all. As we shall see later, when this happens it is necessary to recover the trimmed condition by providing a restorative moment to compensate for the lift-weight couple, and this trimming moment is provided by a secondary flying surface (tailplane or canard) at a considerable distance aft or forward of the centre of gravity.

The aerodynamic force on this trimming surface has to be frequently adjusted by the pilot through means of his controls, and it is extremely wearing for a pilot to have to maintain a constant pulling or pushing control force, just as a car driver finds it unsatisfactory to have to compensate constantly with the steering wheel if the car has a tendency to pull to one side. The pilot may also need to apply a constant rolling control input to compensate, say, for one wing being a little heavier than the other, and/or a constant yawing control input to compensate for one of two wing-mounted engines producing more thrust than the other. If the pilot's time and physical resources are constantly occupied by these trivial requirements, he is not free to concentrate on and carry out his other functions and duties.

From fairly early days in the history of flight, designers have solved this problem by providing an assortment of so-called trimming devices through which the control forces required to trim the aircraft can be applied automatically by aerodynamic means rather than by the pilot. All the pilot has to do is to make a once-only adjustment to the device by means of a subsidiary control whenever a change in flight condition demands it, and then his hands (and feet) can be free for other tasks. In Chapter 11 we will look at the methods that have been devised for this purpose, but for now we just wish to clarify the use of the word trim.

An engineer considers an aircraft to be trimmed if there is no resultant moment (about the axis in question) and thus the aircraft is in rotational equilibrium. The pilot, on the other hand, says that an aircraft is trimmed (about a given axis) if the moments are balanced out, and if *in addition* the aerodynamic trimming devices are adjusted correctly so that the pilot himself is not having to apply trimming moments through his controls.

STABILITY AND TRIM ANALYSIS

We are now ready to investigate how the stability and trim of the aircraft depend on the forces depicted in Figure 4.1 and their resultant couple when they are not collinear. The lift force (and consequently any pitching moment that it is responsible for) produced by an aircraft's wing depends on a number of variable quantities in addition to the aerofoil's shape and angle of attack, namely the speed of the airflow V, the density of the air ρ (which depends primarily on the altitude at which it is flying) and the plan area of the wing S. But we may eliminate the effects of wing area and flight condition (air speed and density) by using the dimensionless quantity called the aircraft's coefficient of lift C_L instead of its actual lift force. This quantity is a measure of the *lifting effect* of an aircraft's wing section, and is a number usually in the range between 0 (or a little below) and about 2 or 3. It is defined as:

$$C_L = \frac{\text{Lift}}{\frac{1}{2}\rho V^2 S}$$

Provided the shape of the aerofoil section does not change, the value of C_L is directly related to the aerofoil's angle of attack, and since this is the one thing that we will be varying C_L is ideally suited for our purposes. If you are not familiar with the concept of dimensionless aerodynamic coefficients and the definition of C_L, you may find it useful to read up a little about it before proceeding, and a possible source might be the end of Chapter 3 and much of Chapter 9 of *Flightwise – Principles of Aircraft Flight*.

By the same arguments, it will also be useful to use a dimensionless coefficient for all the pitching moments that we will be dealing with. Following the method of deriving such coefficients introduced in

Chapter 5 of *Flightwise – Principles of Aircraft Flight* in the section 'Simplifying Aerodynamic Coefficients' we may immediately define the coefficient of pitching moment C_M as:

$$C_M = \frac{\text{Pitching Moment}}{\frac{1}{2}\rho V^2 Sc}$$

where c is the mean chord length of the wing. Conveniently when defining our axes and terminology in Chapter 2 we found that it was the middle letter of the triple L, M and N for moments about the three axes which happened to be the symbol used for pitching moment. Thus in the present context although C_M is defined specifically as the *pitching* moment coefficient, the definition is in fact the same as the general definition for *any* coefficient of moment for a general aerodynamic moment M.

If one requires to study closely the way in which two particular quantities vary with each other and affect each other, sometimes the clearest way to see exactly what is going on is to use a graph or a number of graphs relating these two quantities together. The set of graphs that we will be looking at extensively for much of this chapter will bring out the essential details of the problem, and will enable us to investigate the answers to various questions which will arise. Since we have just introduced the two crucial parameters C_L and C_M, it will come as no surprise that this set of graphs has these two quantities for the variables on its two axes. The axes are shown in Figure 4.3 by way of introduction, with no graph, but the graphs that we will

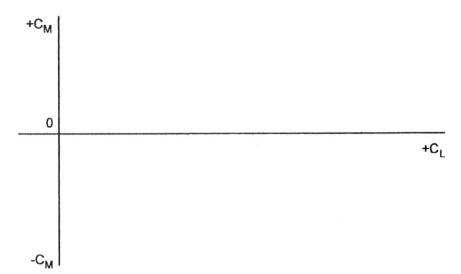

Figure 4.3   Graph axes for analysing longitudinal static stability and trim

subsequently develop using these axes will all refer to the basic aircraft model of Figure 4.1.

When contemplating a new graph, especially one in which the axes represent less than thoroughly familiar quantities, and which may possibly show these axes in different directions from when those same quantities have been met in other graphs (such as the C_L axis here), it is essential to take stock and think what the points and lines on this graph will mean. Therefore, in view of the importance of the series of graphs that are to follow, we will look at the axes alone in the first instance.

The horizontal axis is labelled C_L and extends a small distance to the left of the origin for negative (downward) lift values, but mainly extends to the right (positive). The horizontal component of the distance from the origin to any graph point will represent the lifting effect of the aerofoil, and this is directly related to the angle of attack. Moving to the right therefore means increasing the wing's angle of attack, and movement to the left implies that it is decreasing. Since the aircraft's weight and the flight conditions are constant, there can be one and only one value somewhere on the C_L axis which corresponds to the 'lift = weight' situation. For any point at which $C_L = 0$ (i.e. all points on the vertical axis) the aerofoil is producing no lift. If the aerofoil were symmetrical, this would imply zero angle of attack, but in fact the aerofoil in Figure 4.1 is cambered – this is very significant – so that a zero lift point would imply a slightly negative (nose-down) angle of attack.

Now to look at the vertical axis, which is labelled C_M standing for pitching moment coefficient. The usual graph convention is employed such that positive is upwards and negative downwards. From Chapter 2 (using the 'clockwise is positive' rule when looking out of the aircraft to the right, the positive y-axis direction) we recall that a positive pitching moment is nose-up and that negative is nose-down. Because in Figure 4.1 the aircraft has been drawn pointing to the left, nose-up happens to correspond with clockwise, which is handy. Although there is a graph axis for C_M, if an aircraft is to fly at all it must be trimmed, which means that $C_M = 0$, and so the only points on the graph which can have any meaning for a viable aeroplane will be points along the horizontal axis. Any points that get plotted anywhere else on the graph plane may be of some theoretical interest, but will not represent a flyable aeroplane, since it is not trimmed. Thus there is only one graph point, a specific point on the C_L axis, at which lift equals weight and the aircraft is trimmed. This is the only possible flight point at the prevailing flight conditions. One might well ask at this stage, how on earth can such a restrictive set of graph axes serve any useful purpose? Please bear with me!

Let us now investigate one rather special point on the graph. To do so we will employ the services of a wind-tunnel which is equipped with a standard balance capable of measuring the lift force and pitching moment that the airflow exerts on the aerofoil. When an aerofoil is mounted in a wind-tunnel, the centre of gravity position ceases to have any significance, since the forces and moments are now resisted by the mounting structure rather than by the aerofoil's weight. In a wind-tunnel, pitching moment is therefore not measured about the centre of gravity, but about some fixed and stated reference point – it might for example be the leading edge of the wing, but we do not need to know what point it is for the time being.

We mount the aerofoil in the wind-tunnel in such a way that we can adjust its angle of attack and can directly measure its lift force and pitching moment about the stated reference point. We now turn on the wind-tunnel, and adjust the wing's angle of attack until the lift force measured by the balance is exactly zero. Had the aerofoil section been symmetrical and uncambered, this would simply have meant that the wing's angle of attack would have been zero, but because we have a cambered aerofoil it actually means that we have to set the wing chord at a small angle of attack below the airflow. This negative angle is called the zero-lift angle of attack. So with the wing producing no lift at all we turn our attention to the pitching moment reading, and perhaps surprisingly observe that this is not zero but shows a nose-down (negative) pitching moment. The reason for this is that, although the resultant lift force is zero, the front part of the aerofoil is actually providing a downwards (negative) contribution to lift because of the tight curvature and high air-speed in the region of the underside of the leading edge, whilst the further aft parts are providing a small positive lift contribution. This is illustrated in Figure 4.4, in which the lift distribution envelope is drawn so that its height above or below the aerofoil chord line at any point represents the lift at that point.

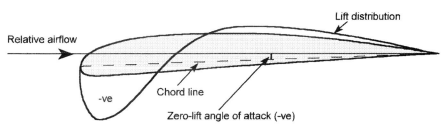

Figure 4.4   Lift distribution of a cambered aerofoil set at its zero-lift angle of attack

Figure 4.5   Plot of the zero-lift pitching moment for a typical cambered aerofoil

The negative lift region near the leading edge will have exactly the same area as the positive lift region over the further aft part of the aerofoil, so that their *lifting* effects cancel out and their force resultant is zero, whilst they produce a nose-down *couple* which is not zero.

What we have shown is that a cambered aerofoil, even when producing no lift, still produces a pitching moment, and that it is negative or nose-down. This is a crucially important feature of any cambered wing, and it has a major impact on the longitudinal stability and trim of an aircraft, as we shall see. It is given the name of *zero-lift pitching moment* and the symbol for its moment coefficient is C_{M_0}. Using the pitching moment balance reading and the appropriate wing size and airflow values, we now calculate the value of C_{M_0} using the definition of C_M given earlier. Using this value of C_{M_0} for C_M and 0 for C_L we plot and label the corresponding point on the graph, as shown in Figure 4.5.

It is interesting to step back at this point and ask the question, where is the centre of pressure in the present situation? Actually this is almost a daft question, since there is no resultant lift force and hence the question of where it acts really does not have much meaning. But we could ask, what was happening just *before* this situation of zero lift was achieved, as the angle of attack was progressively being reduced towards the zero-lift angle? We saw earlier that, as the angle of attack is increased towards the stalling angle, the centre of pressure moves progressively nearer to the leading edge, and if the angle is reduced the centre of pressure retreats. But how far does it retreat? All the way to the trailing edge? Or is that silly?

To answer this question, let us suppose that we have a situation in which the angle of attack has been reduced *almost* to the zero-lift angle; C_L is still positive but tiny, not far off zero, and the pitching moment is scarcely any different from C_{M_0}, i.e. nose-down. The pitching moment about the reference point that the wind-tunnel balance is using is the product of the lift force and its distance from this reference point. Now C_L has shrunk virtually to zero, and so the distance must have become really vast in order for their product to be the finite value C_{M_0}. In the extreme $C_L = 0$, and the only number that zero can be multiplied by to give any non-zero result (such as C_{M_0}) is infinity itself. So we find that the position of the centre of pressure moves right off the wing altogether, and migrates all the way to infinity.

Which direction has the centre of pressure gone? Well, at first we saw that it moved rearwards as the angle of attack was reduced. We also know that it is behind the wind-tunnel's pitching moment reference point, since positive lift is upwards and the pitching moment is nose-downwards. We thus conclude that, when a wing is set at its zero-lift angle of attack, the centre of pressure is at a distance of infinity behind the wing. So contrary to our thought that perhaps it was absurd for the centre of pressure to move as far back as the trailing edge, we discover that there is nothing to prevent the lift from acting at a point which is not on the wing at all – bizarre! Of course this strange state of affairs comes about because we are actually dealing with a force-couple system, and not just a linear force acting on a particle. The odd behaviour of the centre of pressure further reinforces our previous feeling that really the centre of pressure is not a very useful concept to talk about, and that we need a better approach.

Let us return now to the graph of Figure 4.5, on which we have so far plotted merely one point, the value of C_M when $C_L = 0$. We would like to investigate where points should be plotted as we gradually increase the angle of attack and hence C_L, but before we can do this there is one important question which we have so far only paid brief lip service to, and which requires an answer. Since pitching moments (and hence C_M values) depend not only on the lift force but also on the length of the moment arm, we must state precisely how we are defining our C_M values, which means that we must decide and state what point we are taking moments about.

The zero-lift pitching moment C_{M_0} is caused effectively by an equal, opposite and non-collinear pair of forces, an upward force from the positive lifting region in Figure 4.4 and a downward force from the negative lifting region, and the linear effects of these two forces cancel out to produce zero lift. Thus C_{M_0} is the moment of a *couple*, and so drawing on our first axiom of Chapter 3 we know that its value is completely independent of what point we take moments about. We were thus able to plot the C_{M_0} point in Figure 4.5 without first needing to ask what point the wind-tunnel balance takes moments about – it makes absolutely no difference to this value. But for any other point on the graph this will not be the case, since if C_L is not equal to zero its constituent parts no longer form a couple, and the moment value given by the balance will depend on the choice of point about which it reads moments.

Although the wind-tunnel balance takes its moments about some point fixed by its design, when we are relating our results to an aeroplane we would like to take moments about its centre of gravity. This is because, as we saw in Axiom 2 of Chapter 3, we can separate out the linear motion *of* the centre of gravity and the rotational motion *about* the centre of gravity. Any linear non-zero resultant force resulting from the lift being temporarily greater or less than the weight will have the effect of deflecting the path of the centre of gravity upwards or downwards, whilst its moment about the centre of gravity causes rotation only about that point, making it for our purposes effectively a pivot point. Furthermore, by taking moments about the centre of gravity, we have the added convenience of being able to leave out the weight force altogether from our deliberations, since it has no moment about any point on its own line of action.

We have a free hand in placing the aircraft's centre of gravity wherever we choose, so let us do one or two wind-tunnel tests to find out how the pitching moment coefficient behaves when measured about different possible centre of gravity positions. Unfortunately this will not usually coincide with the point that the wind-tunnel balance takes its moments about, so a mathematical conversion is called for, involving both lift and pitching moment, based on the principle of Axiom 3 of Chapter 3. From now on when referring to moments taken from the wind-tunnel balance, we will take it as read that this conversion has been carried out.

First of all, let us consider a wind-tunnel test which simulates the aircraft's centre of gravity (and hence moment centre) to be located exactly at the trailing edge of the wing. Before running the wind-tunnel, let us try to anticipate what we would expect to happen to the pitching moment coefficient as the angle of attack, and hence the coefficient of lift, is progressively increased from the zero-lift condition. We have seen that the pitching moment is initially nose-down (i.e. C_{M_0}), and as the lift force increases in magnitude, the centre of pressure moves forward from an infinite distance behind the wing, initially towards the centre of gravity position at the trailing edge. It is not obvious what happens overall to the pitching moment during this first phase, since the increase in lift would tend to produce an increasingly nose-down moment (being behind the trailing edge), but the moment

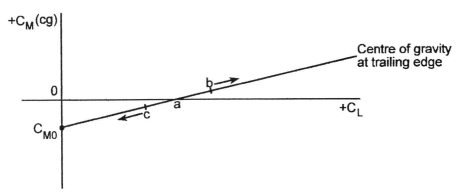

Figure 4.6   Graph of C_M(cg) against C_L with the centre of gravity at the trailing edge

arm is rapidly shrinking from infinity tending to give a smaller nose-down moment. However, once the lift force has passed the trailing edge and is within the wing chord, the trend is beyond doubt. Both force and moment arm progressively increase, so that the pitching moment (their product) becomes greater and greater in the nose-up, positive direction.

So having anticipated the results as far as we can, we now run the wind-tunnel test over a full range of C_L values up to near the stall, read and process the balance readings of lift and pitching moment about the trailing edge, and plot the results on a graph of C_M (now defined more precisely as C_M(cg)) against C_L as shown in Figure 4.6. We find that we get a straight line which slopes upwards from the C_{M_0} point (which is unchanged from its previous value).

Almost exactly the same result could be obtained by applying a mathematical method called 'thin aerofoil theory', which is based on the potential flow ideas discussed in Chapters 5 and 7 of *Flightwise – Principles of Aircraft Flight*. As in the case of the graph of C_L against α, we find that theory predicts a straight line for the present graph, and that wind-tunnel testing very closely agrees with the theoretical prediction up to just before the stalling angle. The upward slope agrees with our anticipated outcome once the lift force has passed the trailing edge on its passage forwards, and the straightness of the line shows that the trend was in the same direction even when the lift force was behind the trailing edge.

Let us look closely at the implications of the graph in Figure 4.6, which tells us how a tailless aircraft would behave if the centre of gravity were placed at the trailing edge of the wing. Since the graph slopes upwards from left to right, we see that somewhere it must cross the C_L-axis, giving us a *trim point* (the point labelled 'a') at which the pitching moment is zero, and thus at this point the aircraft is trimmed. Let us assume that this is the correct C_L value to give 'lift = weight' and that the aircraft is flying at this point on the graph.

If now due to a gust in the airflow or a brief control input by the pilot there is a small increase in angle of attack and hence in C_L, then the graph point moves a small distance to the right and up along the graph line to the point 'b', which means that the pitching moment is no longer zero but has a small positive value. This nose-up pitching moment will cause the aircraft's nose to rise further than it already has, so that the angle of attack and hence C_L will get larger still, and the aircraft will move even further up the graph to the right. The situation gets worse and worse, and if nothing is done about it the aircraft will rapidly move right away from the only acceptable flying point, the trim point. Thus the aircraft is *unstable* in pitch since there is no natural restorative effect back towards the *status quo* but rather the reverse. If the temporary disturbance had been such as to reduce C_L, then the corresponding movement on the graph would have been downwards and to the left, from point 'a' to point 'c', resulting in a nose-down pitching moment which, as before, would tend to amplify rather than ameliorate the initial disturbance.

Whilst some readers may be happy to accept this account of what happens, perhaps you are concerned that we have taken our eye off the aeroplane and are becoming too abstract by referring only to a graph line on a piece of a paper. What do we really mean when we say that the aircraft is at a point on a graph, when it demonstrably is not – it is in the sky! To meet this justifiable objection, let us recall Figure 4.1, the aerofoil representing the tailless aircraft with just lift and weight forces shown. A similar figure is redrawn three times in Figure 4.7, and the centre of gravity is marked with a pivot-like spot at the trailing edge. The weight force is omitted since it acts through this 'pivot' and has no pitching moment effect. At the trim point (a) of the graph in Figure 4.6 the lift produces no pitching moment, and so it can only be acting through the centre of gravity, i.e. at the trailing edge, as shown in diagram (a) of Figure 4.7, labelled 'trimmed'. (The letters a, b and c in Figures 4.6 and 4.7 correspond with each other.) Common sense tells us that in practice it is not possible (with no moment) for an aerofoil to produce lift at its trailing edge, which demonstrates that to place the centre of gravity as far aft as this is outside practical limits of acceptability for a viable aircraft. But the principles being illustrated (remembering that we used a wind-tunnel rather than a flying aeroplane to produce our graph results) *are* valid, since we have seen that, combined with a pitching moment, the lift force can in fact act even much further back than this.

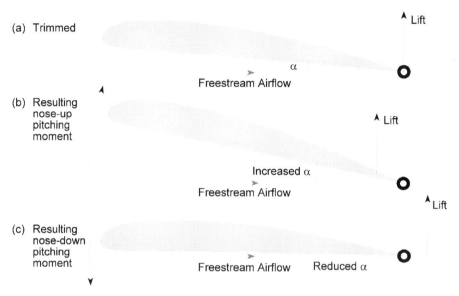

(a) Trimmed

Lift

α

Freestream Airflow

(b) Resulting nose-up pitching moment

Lift

Increased α

Freestream Airflow

Lift

(c) Resulting nose-down pitching moment

Freestream Airflow   Reduced α

Figure 4.7   Unstable aircraft, centre of gravity at trailing edge

Figure 4.7(b) shows the situation in which the angle of attack has been increased a little as a result of a temporary pitch-up of the aerofoil due to air turbulence. The centre of pressure and hence the lift force has moved forward so that it now tends to pitch the aerofoil further nose-up, resulting in an unstable departure from the trim point. (The magnitude of the lift force has actually increased a little as well, but this need not be considered in the present context.) On the other hand, if the initial disturbance had caused a reduction in α and C_L as in Figure 4.7(c), then the lift would have moved further aft (and reduced a little), tipping the nose further down and again producing an unstable rotation.

So we see that the graph line of C_M against C_L in Figure 4.6 represents an unstable aircraft because the centre of gravity has been placed excessively far back. We can discern that the aircraft is unstable simply from a glance at the graph, noticing that the slope of the graph is positive, or up to the right. Any C_M–C_L graph with a positive slope will indicate an unstable condition, since an increase in angle of attack is always accompanied by an increase in nose-up pitching moment making the angle of attack tend to become greater still; and *vice versa*. For those who are familiar with the concept of rates of change expressed in differential calculus notation, as introduced and discussed in Chapter 6 of *Flightwise – Principles of Aircraft Flight*, we may state that, if $\dfrac{\mathrm{d}C_M}{\mathrm{d}C_L} > 0$ then the configuration is unstable in pitch.

Having examined the effect of placing the aircraft's centre of gravity at the trailing edge of the aerofoil, let us now see what would happen if we were to place it at the leading edge. This time we cannot look at a set of diagrams similar to Figure 4.7, because for the aircraft to be trimmed the lift force would have to act through the leading edge, and since the centre of pressure never gets quite as far forward as the leading edge of an aerofoil this is clearly not going to be a practical possibility for an aircraft with no pitching moment. However, it will still turn out to be a useful step towards understanding the problem, since this and the previous case deal with two extreme situations between which the actual centre of gravity must clearly be placed.

There is of course no *mathematical* reason why we should not take moments of the lift force about any point that we choose. Furthermore, by using a wind-tunnel model rather than an actual aircraft we are able to investigate the behaviour of forces and moments that would occur on the aircraft which is represented, whilst at the same time not being constrained by other physical requirements of actual flight (such as trim in this case) which are not pertinent to the questions that we are asking at the moment. The restraining influence of the wind-tunnel balance allows us to do this in the wind-tunnel, even though it would not be possible in real flight. Applying the Corollary to Axiom 3, we simply shift the lift force to the chosen centre of gravity position (the leading edge) and combine it with the resulting pitching moment.

We cannot tell by simple inspection what results are likely to emerge this time. However, the previous wind-tunnel test results can be used again, but the conversion of the pitching moment values using the method discussed earlier will produce a new set of C_M values (except C_{M_0}). When the resulting data are plotted on the $C_M(\mathrm{cg})$–C_L graph, the graph turns out to be a straight line sloping *downwards*, as illustrated in Figure 4.8, which incorporates the previous results for the sake of comparison.

Although there is now no trim point (except at a negative C_L value if we were to extend the straight line to the left of the origin, i.e. the case of inverted flight which we will consider later), it is still instructive to investigate what happens when the wing is producing a C_L value corresponding to a typical point 'd' on the line, and a disturbance occurs in the airflow. If the C_L value temporarily increases a little, the graph point moves to the right along the graph line to a point 'e', and since the line slopes downwards the pitching moment is more negative than at 'd'. As a result, there is a downwards change in the

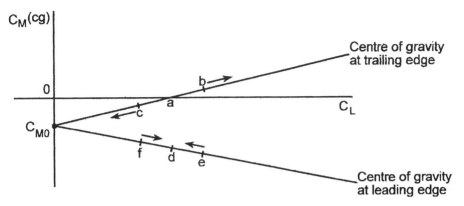

Figure 4.8 Graphs of $C_M(\text{cg})$ against C_L with the centre of gravity at the leading edge and at the trailing edge

pitching moment which tends to pitch the nose back down again, reducing the angle of attack and hence C_L, until the original situation at 'd' is restored. If instead the disturbance had produced an initial reduction in α and C_L, the aircraft would have moved from 'd' to 'f', the pitching moment would have become less strongly nose down, and this change in pitching moment would allow the nose to pitch back up so that point 'd' was restored. The aerofoil is now stable in pitch, and this corresponds with a negative slope of the $C_M(\text{cg})$–C_L graph, or

$$\frac{\mathrm{d}C_M}{\mathrm{d}C_L} < 0.$$

Thus we can now state categorically the condition for the system to be stable, as follows:

> **An aircraft modelled as an aerofoil will be stable in pitch provided that the centre of gravity is placed in such a position that the slope of the graph of $C_M(\text{cg})$ against C_L is negative, i.e. downwards to the right.**

We now have the infuriating situation that, if we place the aircraft's centre of gravity too far back, the aircraft will be trimmable but unstable, and if we place it too far forwards it will be stable but untrimmable. The first situation is viable but unsatisfactory, and the second, although providing stability, is unworkable in practice because the aircraft cannot be trimmed. Perhaps we should investigate whether there is any in-between position for the centre of gravity which satisfies both requirements simultaneously. We will pursue this line of thought now, but sadly it will not solve the fundamental problem. It will, however, open our eyes to the solution to another problem which we posed

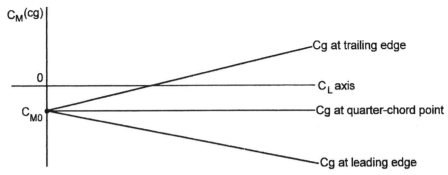

Figure 4.9   Graphs of $C_M(\text{cg})$ against C_L with the centre of gravity at various positions

earlier, and that is how to cope with the vagaries of the movement of centre of pressure, which give us so much bother.

AERODYNAMIC CENTRE

The two graph lines of Figure 4.8 correspond to two extreme positions of the centre of gravity. If we were to plot the $C_M(\text{cg})$–C_L graphs for a number of intermediate positions of the centre of gravity along the aerofoil chord, we would get an array of straight lines fanning out from the fixed point C_{M_0} in the angle between the limiting lines we have already discussed. But the underlying problem would still pertain; all lines sloping upwards from C_{M_0} would (eventually) pass through the positive C_L-axis to give us a trim point, but they would all represent unstable situations; and all lines sloping downwards would give us stability but no possibility of trimming the aircraft.

There is one special line of this fan which looks interesting, even though it does not solve the trimability/stability conundrum, and that is the one which neither slopes upwards nor downwards but remains horizontal. Presumably there is one centre of gravity position somewhere between leading and trailing edge which would produce such a line, and to find it we can use our previous set of wind-tunnel test results again, and convert to a variety of different moment centres until we find the position that produces a horizontal graph. In fact, this exercise will reveal that the required graph line occurs when the centre of gravity position is at the *quarter-chord point*[3] (i.e. a quarter of the chord's length behind the leading edge), a discovery which is supported by thin aerofoil theory. The resulting graph line is shown together with the previous lines in Figure 4.9.

[3]This result relates only to subsonic aerofoils. For supersonic aerofoils the corresponding position is at mid-chord.

We observe straight away that, since the $C_M(cg)$–C_L line is now horizontal, an aircraft with its centre of gravity at the quarter-chord point will be neither stable nor unstable, but neutrally stable, since the pitching moment is not altered either nose upwards or downwards by any change that occurs in angle of attack. Furthermore, there is still no trim point, since the line does not cross the C_L-axis. But let us consider what happens this time on our wind-tunnel model, starting off with the aerofoil set at its zero-lift angle of attack, corresponding to the C_{M_0} point on the graph. If we progressively increase α and hence C_L, we move to the right along the line, and the pitching moment about the quarter-chord point remains stubbornly unchanged. The only way that this can be is that all the additional bits of lift that we are adding must act through the quarter-chord point itself, since if they acted anywhere else they would produce a change in moment about this point. Since we started from the case where $C_L = 0$, 'all the additional bits of lift' must be precisely synonymous with the total lift. This immediately means that, provided we take moments about the quarter-chord point of an aerofoil, we can completely ignore the itinerant nature of the lift force as displayed by the fore-and-aft movement of the centre of pressure, and can *always* treat the entire lift force as acting at the fixed quarter-chord point. Thus if the aircraft's centre of gravity is placed at this quarter-chord point, the line of action of the weight force exactly coincides with that of the lift force.

But hold on a minute! The graph never crosses the C_L-axis which means that there is no trim point; but now you are telling me that the lift and weight forces *do* coincide, which is the usual condition for trim! What is going on? I am confused.

What you have to remember is that we do not now have the lift force acting in its natural position, which is the centre of pressure. Instead, we have taken the liberty of shifting it sideways to a much more convenient point, in the manner that we discussed near the end of Chapter 3. The principle that we developed there is so important in the present context that it will bear stating again:

> **Axiom 3. Any force may be represented by an equal and parallel force acting at any other point on the object, together with a couple. The magnitude of the couple is the magnitude of the force times the distance it is moved sideways.**

So we have shifted the lift force from its migratory centre of pressure to the fixed quarter-chord point, and in compensation we have had to add the constant couple coefficient C_{M_0}. The direction of this couple would not be easy to ascertain simply by considering the lift force shift from centre of pressure to quarter-chord point, since within the range of C_L values considered the centre of pressure actually moves past the quarter-chord point as its magnitude changes; but fortunately we already know from previous considerations that the pitching moment couple (which is always the same as C_{M_0}) is nose-downwards for any cambered aerofoil.

This point, at which we can always consider the entire lift of the aerofoil to be acting, is called the *aerodynamic centre* of the aerofoil, and its use revolutionises the entire stability analysis of an aircraft's longitudinal pitching motion. In superficial literature on the subject you will meet the centre of pressure but will usually not be introduced to the aerodynamic centre, since to understand it one has to have a grasp of fairly sophisticated concepts (which we now have) of forces and couples acting on rigid bodies. One is extremely limited in how deeply one can discuss an aircraft's pitching behaviour if restricted to the language of centre of pressure – which is often why longitudinal stability is thought to be such a difficult topic to understand. But by replacing the wandering lift force by an equal force at a fixed location, together with a constant couple (which must never be overlooked), we reduce the problem to one involving only one variable: the magnitude of the lift force.

To illustrate the simplification that the concept of aerodynamic centre can provide, we recall from earlier in this chapter the difficulty we encountered when we tried to anticipate how the $C_M(cg)$–C_L graph line would behave in two circumstances: firstly, when the centre of gravity was at the trailing edge and the centre of pressure was still aft of the trailing edge; and secondly when the centre of gravity was at the leading edge. But now it is easy to see how the pitching moment changes, since the increases in lift force always act through the fixed aerodynamic centre which is between the leading and trailing edge, so that an increase in lift always means an increase in nose-up pitching moment about the trailing edge and an increase nose-downwards about the leading edge. In fact, some authors may persuade you that it is 'obvious' which way the graph will slope in each case, simply by considering changes in magnitude of C_L without regarding the centre of pressure's change in position, but this is less than honest if the aerodynamic centre has not already been introduced into the vocabulary.

THE STABLE, TRIMMABLE AIRCRAFT

We have some unfinished business to consider from earlier, since we have not yet resolved the incompatibility problem of stability and trimability. Looking back at Figure 4.9 we see that locating the aircraft's centre of gravity anywhere aft of the aerodynamic centre will result in a trimable but unstable aircraft. The one and only way to make the aircraft stable is by placing the centre of gravity ahead of the aerodynamic centre; the further ahead, the steeper the curve and the more stable the aeroplane. Whilst this provides stability, it means that the aircraft cannot be trimmed and can therefore not be regarded as an aircraft at all. Locating the centre of gravity at the aerodynamic centre might have looked promising, but it turns out not to resolve either of the problems. How are we to proceed?

We might tackle the problem from several possible angles. We could consider the aft centre of gravity graph with its existing trim point, and ask whether there is anything we could do to it to make it stable; or we could take a stable, forward centre of gravity graph and consider ways of making it trimmable. In either event, we note that the problem stems from the fact that the conventional cambered aerofoil we have chosen has a nose-down zero-lift pitching moment by its very nature, and so we could ask whether the basic design of the aerofoil section could somehow be modified so that it would produce a nose-up zero-lift pitching moment instead. Then the array of $C_M(\text{cg})$–C_L graph lines would radiate from a C_{M_0} point above the origin, and so those with negative slope would be trimmable as well as stable.

Let us look very briefly at this last possibility first. All we need to do in order to make the zero-lift pitching moment of the aerofoil positive is to turn the aerofoil section upside down. If we did this, the primary effect would be to shift the straight portion of its graph of C_L against α to the right, as shown in Figure 4.10. This is because, just as a given amount of positive camber balances out a certain amount of

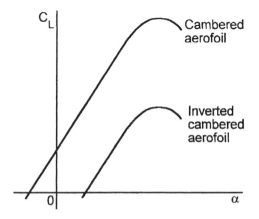

Figure 4.10   Lift curves of a cambered and an inverted cambered aerofoil

negative angle of attack to produce zero lift, so the same amount of negative camber will require an equivalent positive α to achieve the same end. However, the stalling characteristics of the inverted aerofoil are likely to be very inferior since it was never designed to be used this way up, and so it is to be expected that the maximum value of C_L available would be extremely limited.

The idea has some potential, but it does not look very attractive from the point of view of designing a competent aircraft. We will leave it on one side for now, but it so happens that we will meet something very like this idea a little later on, since hidden in the concept of negative camber there lurks the solution to our problem.

Another possibility that we can dismiss even more quickly is that of using the aft centre of gravity graph which has a trim point, and trying to do something about its stability. We have, however, already seen that stability depends purely and simply on the slope of the graph being negative, and this in turn depends only on the position of the centre of gravity and nothing else. Thus the only way to make the aft centre of gravity graph stable is to move the centre of gravity forward beyond the aerodynamic centre, and so we might as well start off by looking instead at the graph representing that situation.

Let us therefore take a closer look at the forward centre of gravity graph, which has a negative slope for stability but has no trim point. On paper, if we were to slide this line up the graph axes keeping the line parallel to itself, eventually the left hand end would move up past the origin, and from then on the line would intersect the positive C_L-axis, and we would have stability with trimability. Is it possible to achieve this on the aircraft itself?

The answer to this is yes, but not without allowing ourselves some licence with our initial aircraft modelling assumptions. A look at the graph shows us that we require to change the aircraft's value of C_{M_0} from its natural negative value to some suitable positive value. But we already know that a cambered aerofoil alone, as we have up to now modelled our aircraft, always has a negative value of C_{M_0}, and so we are going to have to add some additional feature in order to produce the required nose-up pitching moment.

Leaving aside for now the possibility of some solution along the lines of the inverted cambered aerofoil discussed above, there are two approaches that may be adopted to achieving the required nose-up pitching moment: an aft tailplane or a canard foreplane. If a tailplane behind the wing is used, the aerodynamic force on it must normally be downwards in order to achieve the required nose-up pitching moment about the centre of gravity, and this downwards force is equivalent to additional dead weight which will have to be compensated for by providing an equal amount of additional lift from the wings. This means

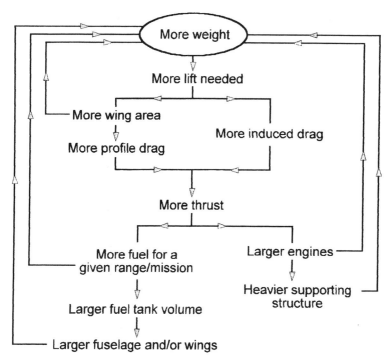

Figure 4.11 **The vicious circle of increasing weight in aircraft design**

that larger wings are needed, and thus there will be more weight. In order to keep the tailplane's undesirable down-force small, it is best to place the tailplane on a long moment arm behind the wing, and whether this consists of fuselage or a dedicated boom or booms, it will itself add structural weight (in addition to the weight of the tailplane itself) which must be compensated for by even more wing lift and hence even more weight. These are not insubstantial considerations when designing an aircraft, since the merit of the design is extremely sensitive to weight increases, as is shown in Figure 4.11, and extra weight has a cumulative effect on the economics of the design considerably greater than the mere additional weight itself might suggest. The tailplane is consequently not a feature that the designer will adopt enthusiastically without very convincing reasons, and so before settling on that option let us consider the alternative.

If the required trimming moment is instead achieved by means of canard surfaces ahead of the wings, the major disadvantage of the tailplane, that of the aerodynamic down-load, is immediately converted into an advantage. (True, we still have the additional weight of the surfaces themselves and of the supporting structure, but that is a price that it seems we are going to have to pay, regardless of our approach.) To provide a nose-up pitching moment, a trimming surface in front of the centre of gravity must normally exert an up-load, and so the use of canards would not only obviate the need for additional lift from the wings, but would actually mean that the canard, whilst providing trim, would also shoulder some of the lifting task of the wing. Consequently much that was disadvantageous in Figure 4.11 is thrown into reverse, and it should be possible to design a substantially lighter (and that would normally mean better) aircraft using canards.

But, I hear you cry, that cannot be, for if it were we would have tail-first aeroplanes filling the skies today, rather than the ubiquitous tail-at-the-back types that are the norm. Where's the catch?

Contrary to common belief, it is not because canards make an aircraft unstable and an aft tailplane makes it stable that aft tailplanes are usually used – stability depends only on the centre of gravity position. But although there are significant aerodynamic reasons for thinking twice about using canards, such as the substantial interference that they produce in the airflow over the wing[4], almost certainly the main reason for the ubiquitous choice of tailplane is that it looks right, and that that is the way nature does things and we have always done it. Furthermore, it gives the *impression* of being necessary for stability, just as arrows and darts always fly with their tail feathers at the rear.

A lot more must and will be said about canards later in the book, since they are very much a feature of today's aircraft design philosophy, and they are undoubtedly an intriguing idea with substantial advantages for certain purposes. For the purpose of the present discussion, however, let us decide upon the customary aft tailplane for providing a down-load and consequently the nose-up pitching moment that we need.

Now that we have met our fundamental aircraft design criteria of stability and trimability by means of a main lifting wing together with a smaller down-loaded tailplane, let us look a little more closely at the detailed implications. There is no use in designing an aircraft capable of flying at one trim state only, since it must be able to achieve a substantial range of trimmed C_L values for use at different speeds and heights and for manoeuvring situations when the lift force has to be temporarily changed. The way that this is achieved is by providing a means of varying the applied nose-up pitching moment by altering the tailplane down-load through the pilot's use of his controls. Usually

---

[4]Another serious disadvantage of canards is discussed on page 222, in the third paragraph of the sub-section on canards.

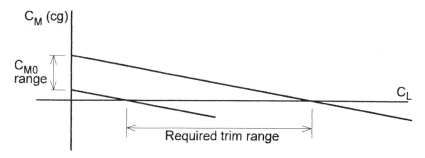

Figure 4.12 $C_M(cg)$–C_L graph of a stable and trimmable aeroplane

this is achieved by means of elevators, which are hinged aerodynamic control surfaces attached at the rear of the tailplane, which effectively vary the camber of the tailplane, and these are operated by the pilot pulling or pushing on his primary flying control, either a control column or a steering-wheel-like yoke. Figure 4.12 shows the effect of this on the $C_M(cg)$–C_L graph for a moderately stable aeroplane. Note that C_L is the lift coefficient of the entire aircraft, so that it now includes a small contribution (usually negative) from the tailplane.

There is a tricky point that arises here which often causes confusion and misunderstanding. You may have spotted the word 'normally' a little earlier when saying that a tailplane produces a down-load and a canard an up-load. Despite the superficial appearance to the contrary, it is actually possible (at large angles of attack on aircraft with limited stability) for the tail-load to be *upwards*. This is because of the rather confusing juxtaposition of, and interrelationship between, the forces and moments, and the only way that I have been able to think of explaining it clearly to you is to step out of character and resort to a little bit of mathematics. But it only involves simple algebra and a straight line graph based on nothing more than Newton's First Law for rotation. If the maths bothers you, then just *accept* that the tail-load can at large aircraft angles of attack be upwards because the wing's nose-up pitching moment has become so large, and skip the next three paragraphs.

Figure 4.13 shows the aerodynamic forces and moments on wing

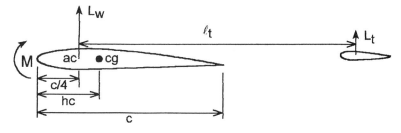

Figure 4.13 Force system on wing and tailplane

and tailplane, using fairly conventional notation which requires a little explanation. Forces and moments are all shown in the conventional positive directions, so that a down-load or a nose-down pitching moment will have a negative value in the mathematics. The overall lift is portrayed as the wing lift force acting at the aerodynamic centre together with the tail lift and the overall pitching moment defined about the centre of gravity. The aerodynamic centre is fixed at the quarter-chord point, and c stands for the chord length; h is the fraction of the chord aft of the leading edge at which the centre of gravity is located, so that hc is its actual distance aft of the leading edge. L_t is the tail lift (positive upwards) and ℓ_t the distance of the tailplane lift behind the aerodynamic centre.

The aircraft being trimmed, let us now take moments about the centre of gravity, so as to eliminate the effect of weight. We will take clockwise as positive. This gives:

$$L_w(h - \tfrac{1}{4})c - L_t[\ell_t - (h - \tfrac{1}{4})c] + M = 0$$

or

$$L_w(h - \tfrac{1}{4})c - L_t\ell_t + L_t(h - \tfrac{1}{4})c + M = 0$$

We can combine the similar-looking first and third terms in this equation, and thus get it into a form containing total lift rather than wing lift (since $L = L_w + L_t$), which is more useful. Hence we have:

$$L(h - \tfrac{1}{4})c - L_t\ell_t + M = 0$$

To convert all the terms into coefficient form, we will divide through by $\tfrac{1}{2}\rho V^2 c$, the c being included because it is necessary for the moment term M. We thus have:

$$C_L(h - \tfrac{1}{4}) - C_{L_t}\frac{\ell_t}{c} + C_M = 0$$

Now let us divide everything by ℓ_t/c and rearrange the equation in a form which matches the standard equation of a straight line graph, $y = mx + c$ (n.b. a different c), so that we can plot and examine the graph. The standard equation is printed underneath, term by term, for ease of comparison.

$$C_{L_t} = \left(\frac{h - \tfrac{1}{4}}{\ell_t/c}\right)C_L + \left(\frac{C_M}{\ell_t/c}\right)$$
$$y = \quad m \quad x + \quad c$$

If (and only if) h is greater than a quarter, or in other words the centre of gravity is behind the aerodynamic centre[5], the top and bottom of

---

[5]But for stability it must be ahead of the neutral point, introduced on page 96.

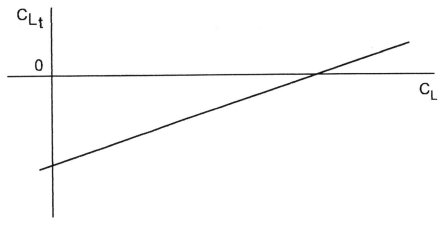

Figure 4.14   Graph of C_{L_t} against C_L

the fraction inside the first brackets in this equation are both positive, which means that the slope (this first bracketed term) is positive. For the intercept on the vertical axis (the second bracketed term), we substitute $C_L = 0$, so that C_{L_t} equals the second bracketed term, and we know that the pitching moment M (and hence the bracketed term containing C_M) is negative for a conventional aerofoil. We are now in a position to sketch the graph of C_{L_t} against C_L, as in Figure 4.14.

As we have come to expect, at low values of C_L the line is below the horizontal axis so that the tail force is indeed negative, or downwards. But above a certain value of overall lift it is clear that, since the slope of this graph is positive, it is quite possible for the line to cross the horizontal axis and for the tail-load actually to be upward.

In passing, it will be instructive to take a brief glimpse at a very neat trick that aircraft aerodynamic designers often employ in order to simplify their thinking about the rather tricky forces and moments on an aerofoil. It can be shown that the lift force on an aerofoil may be thought of as consisting of two parallel components, each due to one of the two different features of the aerofoil which give it lift. The first component is that due to the angle of attack alone (as if the aerofoil were symmetrical), and it acts at the aerodynamic centre, which is to a good approximation at the quarter-chord point. The second is the lift provided by the aerofoil's camber alone (as if the angle of attack were set to zero), and to a fairly good approximation (although not as good as the other) this component can be shown to act at the half-chord point. This is illustrated in Figure 4.15(a), in which L_α means the lift due to angle of attack and L_C refers to that due to camber, and clearly

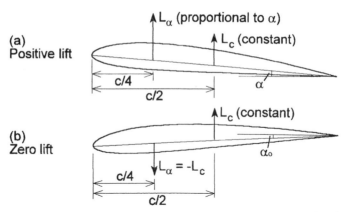

Figure 4.15   **Representation of lift as separate components due to angle of attack and camber**

$L = L_\alpha + L_c$. (This is yet another different use of c, but it will only be used in this and the next paragraph.)

The clever part of splitting the lift force in this way is that L_c, the lift due to camber, only depends on the camber and not on the angle of attack, and thus L_c is constant. Only L_α, the lift due to angle of attack, varies. Furthermore, the *locations* of both L_α and L_c remain fixed at quarter and half chord respectively at all times, so that by this approach there is only one variable force magnitude to deal with, and no balancing moment to be treated as a separate entity. If the angle of attack is set to the zero-lift angle (nose slightly down for a positive cambered aerofoil), then since L_c is constant upwards, L_α must be equal to it in magnitude but downwards, as shown in Figure 4.15(b). Between them the two forces do indeed produce a couple with a nose-down zero-lift pitching moment, but the representation is in terms of forces only, and so is easier to handle.

Let us now revert to our previous discussion. In Figures 4.16 (a) and (b) (sequel to Figure 4.12) we look at what happens if the centre of gravity has not been placed far enough forward, so that in graph (a) the aircraft is less stable than is desirable and in graph (b) it is actually unstable. If an aircraft is loaded in such a way that it has only a very small margin of stability as in Figure 4.16(a), very much less elevator and control column force and movement will be required than before to achieve the same range of C_L values. This has the effect of making the aircraft very sensitive to the controls, or 'twitchy' for the pilot to fly. Many pilots have experienced just this phenomenon when the back seats of a four-seater tourer are occupied by large adults who

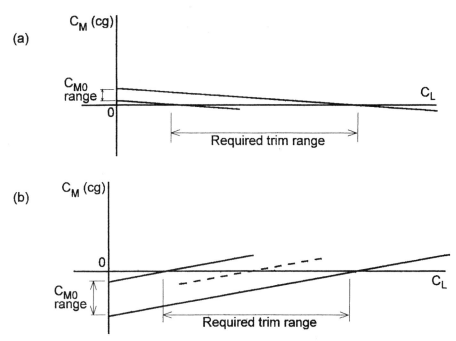

Figure 4.16 $C_M(cg)$–C_L graphs of (a) marginally stable and (b) unstable aircraft

have put some baggage behind their seats. It is verging on being a dangerous and uncontrollable situation, since if the centre of gravity were to move aft a little bit more so that the neutral stability position were reached and the slope of the graph lines became zero, then the entire C_L range would be allowed for without any control movement at all, and the aircraft would not know how to behave. (This is not illustrated, since the graph would look just like its axes alone.) If with the graph line horizontal the control column is pulled back a very small amount to achieve a nose-up pitching moment, the line moves up to a position above and parallel to the C_L-axis, and consequently there is no trim point but an unrestrained nose-up pitching moment, which will force the aircraft nose to pitch up incessantly until the pilot pushes the stick forward again – and almost inevitably he will over-shoot the neutral position, resulting now in a nose-down pitching moment. The pilot will have to 'balance' his control at exactly the cor-rect neutral position all the time, regardless of C_L value. But in order to alter his angle of attack to trim the C_L value according to whether he is flying at high C_L low speed, at low C_L high speed, or in high C_L manoeuvres, he must temporarily pull or push the control column to achieve the trim state, and then immediately return it to the precarious neutral position. Clearly this is a very unsatisfactory state of affairs.

Let us take this one stage further, and consider what happens if the centre of gravity is located even further back than the point which gives neutral stability, so that the aircraft is unstable, as in Figure 4.16(b). In the first instance let us suppose that the aircraft is trimmed at a mid-range C_L value, as indicated by the point where the intermediate dashed graph line intersects with the C_L-axis. The pilot will have his work cut out in applying compensating pitching moments to prevent a departure in pitch resulting from the natural instability of the aircraft. But he also has an additional problem. Let us suppose that the pilot wishes to pull out of a gentle dive. He requires extra α and C_L, and as usual this is achieved by pulling back on the control column, thus applying a nose-up attitude change to increase the lift coefficient. But after that the situation is reversed. In order to continue flying at the higher C_L value, the dashed graph line in Figure 4.16(b) has to be moved downwards and not upwards, and this means that when the pilot has achieved this situation he will have to hold more nose-*down* pitching moment, which must be achieved by a *forwards* displacement of the control column. But in order to raise the angle of attack to attain this C_L value in the first place, the aircraft must be pitched nose-up, which means first of all pulling *back* on the control! In fact sustained maximum C_L will correspond to a fully forward control position and minimum C_L to fully backwards, an exact reversal of the normal state of affairs, although conventional control movements are needed to get into these situations in the first place. In practice, the pilot will be so preoccupied with the constant rapid adjustments to compensate for the instability that the overall change in trim will follow automatically, but it would present a very serious problem if large rapid changes in C_L were required. Fortunately for the Wright brothers, the state of the art of flying had not by their day progressed to the need for a large C_L range, since their speed and altitude was not far off constant and turns and manoeuvres were relatively gentle. But it helps us to understand why their unstable philosophy did not endure for very long.

Let us turn our attention briefly to what happens if an aircraft is made very stable indeed by means of placing the centre of gravity excessively far forward, as illustrated in Figure 4.17. The same 'required trim range' is bracketed on the C_L-axis as in the previous graphs, but this time because of the steepness of the graph it is necessary for the tailplane to apply a considerably larger nose-up pitching moment than previously, even to achieve the lowest required C_L value. To achieve higher C_L values than this demands even greater

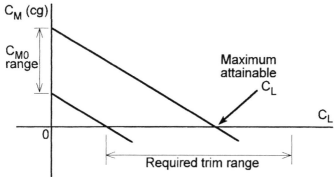

Figure 4.17 $C_M(cg)$–C_L graph of an excessively stable aircraft

nose-up pitching moments, so that clearly the down-load on the tailplane may be excessive, adding an unacceptable additional lift requirement to the wing. It is likely, as illustrated in the figure, that sufficient pitching moment authority will not be available from the tailplane to cope with the entire C_L range hoped for, so that an upper limit of C_L is reached prematurely.

This presents us with the rather intriguing possibility of designing a totally unstallable aircraft. Either by providing the aircraft with insufficient tailplane authority to enable it to reach the wing's maximum lift coefficient, or by simply placing the centre of gravity far enough forward, we can ensure that it is totally impossible for it ever to reach the stalling angle of attack! We can even modify an existing aircraft to render it unstallable, simply by placing sufficient ballast in the nose.

Intriguing, yes, but not in fact very practical. The most serious effect of limiting the maximum lift coefficient available is that it makes the minimum flying speed higher, so that one hazard, the stall, is replaced by another, an excessively high landing and take-off speed. Furthermore, it would be fairly inane, after going to the bother of providing a wing with a certain lifting capacity, not to make good use of as much of that capacity as possible, especially in view of the design penalty imposed by the wing's weight and the high induced drag of the tailplane.

It is surprising what a great amount of insight can be gained by studying just a simple straight line graph, even without putting any numbers to it. Before we leave the $C_M(cg)$–C_L graph, we will use it once more (in Figure 4.18) to illustrate another approach to trimming an aircraft that has been given an initial nose-up zero-lift pitching moment by a fixed aerodynamic surface at the rear. Rather than the $C_M(cg)$–C_L graph line moving up and down parallel to itself this time, the line always passes through a fixed C_{M_0} point but it is given a range

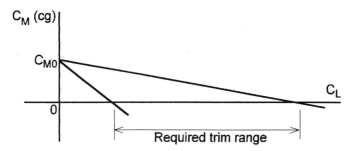

Figure 4.18   The use of variable stability as a means of trimming an aircraft

of different slopes, so that it passes through the C_L-axis at different points. This is achieved by moving the aircraft's centre of gravity fore and aft during flight, which is normally done by pumping fuel from one tank (typically in the wings) to another (often in the tail fin) or vice versa. The chief advantage of this method is that *trim drag* (the induced drag due to the down-load on the tailplane plus the additional wing drag due to its extra lifting demands) can be kept to a minimum. The applied pitching moment only needs to be sufficient to raise the steeper, high-stability and low-C_L-limit graph line in Figure 4.18 to the required C_{M_0} point, and beyond that trimming is achieved by shifting the centre of gravity backwards.

This is a slow and elaborate means of trimming an aircraft, and therefore it is not commonly used except in special circumstances. One such situation is the use of relaxed static stability which we shall look at presently, and another is the Concorde supersonic transport aircraft. Although in our discussion we have tacitly assumed that we were talking about subsonic aerofoils, in fact exactly the same general principles carry over to supersonic aircraft, except that the aerodynamic centre of a supersonic aerofoil is not at the quarter-chord point but is often at about the half-chord point instead. Thus when an aircraft such as Concorde accelerates from subsonic to supersonic speed, it is necessary to shift the centre of gravity a long way aft so that it doesn't become excessively stable in the supersonic regime, with the penalties discussed alongside Figure 4.17 (page 95). The same system of fuel-pumping is also used in Concorde for the more routine and moderate trimming requirements during normal flight. One disadvantage that the $C_M(cg)$–C_L graph reveals is that the aircraft has a considerably reduced level of stability at high C_L values, when more would be desirable.

NEUTRAL POINT
When we began the present discussion we established that we could model the complete aircraft (less tailplane at that stage) by means of

just an aerofoil-shaped wing, and as our investigation developed we came across the very useful device of the aerodynamic centre, by means of which our work was greatly simplified. Furthermore, we related the stability or otherwise of the aircraft to the fore-and-aft position of the centre of gravity in relation to the aerodynamic centre. If the centre of gravity were to be at the aerodynamic centre itself, the aircraft would be neutrally stable. However, once we had introduced the additional feature of a tailplane, you may have noticed that our thinking became a little muddled, since we were still thinking of the aerodynamic centre of the aerofoil as the stability-determining position even though we were no longer envisaging the aircraft as consisting solely of an aerofoil.

We must now rectify this discrepancy by introducing an additional and very important aircraft design concept, the aircraft's *neutral point*. In the parlance of the children's verbal reasoning test or parlour game, we may state simply that

> **the neutral point is to an aircraft as the aerodynamic centre is to an aerofoil.**

This implies simply that, as soon as we had added the tailplane to our aircraft, it ceased to be the aerodynamic centre of the aerofoil that determined the critical centre of gravity position between stability and instability, but it became another point which is called the neutral point. We may therefore more precisely state the condition for an aircraft to be stable or otherwise as follows:

> **An aircraft will be longitudinally stable if the centre of gravity is ahead of the neutral point, and vice versa.**

Both the neutral point's precise position and that of the centre of gravity are very important to those responsible for loading an aircraft with passengers, cargo and fuel before flight, in order to ensure an adequate margin of stability in flight. The neutral point's location is fixed at design and is specified, and the centre of gravity position must be determined according to the load distribution.

We learned earlier that, based on theory and borne out by wind-tunnel tests, the aerodynamic centre of a subsonic cambered aerofoil is at the quarter-chord point. In order to visualise how the neutral point behaves it is useful now to regard the modified aircraft – wing with tailplane (still ignoring aerodynamic forces on the fuselage and other parts) – as if it were a sort of hybrid single aerofoil consisting of two parts as shown in Figure 4.19. Now even though the lift on the front part is upwards and that on the rear part normally downwards, regarding the pair as a single aerofoil means that the whole system

Figure 4.19   Modified aircraft model

may be thought of as having one aerodynamic total reaction, which is its overall lift (disregarding components in the flow direction as heretofore). We can thus repeat all the arguments that we have applied to an aerofoil in earlier parts of this chapter. The centre of pressure is as nomadic as before, and set at zero lift in a wind-tunnel it would be at infinity behind the aircraft. However, the zero-lift pitching moment is no longer nose-down but nose-up, because of our deliberate addition of the tailplane to achieve this very purpose as illustrated in Figure 4.12.

If we investigate as before where the centre of gravity should be placed in order for the $C_M(\text{cg})$–C_L graph to be horizontal, i.e. for neutral stability, we would expect to discover that it was somewhere around the 'quarter-chord' point of the new pseudo-aerofoil, i.e. further back than the wing's aerodynamic centre, but probably not as far back as quarter of the 'pseudo-chord' (from wing leading edge to tailplane trailing edge) since most of the aerodynamic force is still concentrated in the wing region. This point is the aircraft's neutral point, and just as with an aerodynamic centre, the overall lift force and all changes to it can be thought of as acting at this point, provided the (now positive) zero-lift pitching moment is not left out.

This provides us with a very clear and easy way of thinking about an aircraft's stability. If in flight the aircraft's nose pitches up the total lift increases, and the increase acts at the neutral point. Provided the centre of gravity (regarded as the pivot) is ahead of the neutral point, the result is an increased nose-down pitching moment which will tend to restore the aircraft's original attitude, and so the aircraft is stable. The greater the distance is between the centre of gravity and the neutral point, the more stable is the aircraft, and so this distance is given the name *static margin*.

We have now met two different parameters which both tell us how stable (or otherwise) an aircraft is: the slope of the $C_M(\text{cg})$–C_L graph and the static margin. As so often occurs in aerodynamics, the fairly involved mathematics underlying the analysis happens to reveal a very simple and convenient direct relationship between these two quantities:

The static margin, when expressed as a fraction of the mean chord length, is equal in magnitude to the slope of the $C_M(\text{cg})$–C_L graph.

Note that the sign of the slope for a stable aircraft is negative, whereas the static margin is regarded as positive. Hence the words 'in magnitude' are necessary here. This useful relationship means that we can talk about the static margin, a more convenient and obviously meaningful phrase than 'the slope of the $C_M(\text{cg})$–C_L graph', with impunity, knowing that it effectively means exactly the same thing.

Before leaving this topic, there is one ghost that should be firmly laid to rest, and that is the myth that the *purpose* of a tailplane is to make an aircraft stable. It is true that a tailplane has a significant stabilising effect, as is clear from the fact that the neutral point of the wing–tailplane combination is further aft than the wing's aerodynamic centre, so that a positive static margin is increased by the existence of a tailplane. However, the centre of gravity can be placed at will, and ultimately the static margin can be given any desired positive or negative value simply by the choice of the centre of gravity position. So, although a tailplane has a stabilising effect, its purpose is *not* to make the aircraft stable, and it is not needed for stability, but rather to provide a positive zero-lift pitching moment and the means for adjusting the longitudinal trim, and also for a purpose related to dynamic stability that we will meet in the next chapter. Thus the American name 'horizontal stabiliser' for the tailplane is misleading. An aircraft can as easily be unstable with a tailplane as it can be stable without one – but stability without trim is a useless commodity.

Likewise, an aircraft provided with canard surfaces for longitudinal trim is less stable on account of the canards than it would be without them, because they shift the neutral point ahead of the wing's aerodynamic centre, thus reducing a positive static margin. But again, simply by moving the centre of gravity forward ahead of the neutral point a canard aircraft can be rendered totally stable, and that, with a little re-rigging to adjust the angle of attack, is all the Wrights would have had to do to make their *Flyer* stable! Some of today's light canard aircraft are demonstrating not only excellent stability but extremely safe handling characteristics in other ways as well.

TAILLESS AIRCRAFT

When we were initially considering the modification of the aerofoil-only model of an aircraft by the addition of an aerodynamic trimming surface, we saw that a major disadvantage of the aft tailplane is that it carries with it a significant drag penalty for a number of reasons. When searching for increased efficiency, aircraft designers are always looking out for any possible ways of reducing overall aircraft drag, and so it is not surprising that many forays have been made into the possibility of designing a tailless aircraft. For example, the idea of a flying wing for a transport aircraft has always held a strong appeal. It would be large enough to accommodate passengers, cargo, fuel, engines and flight deck all within the aerofoil envelope of the wing, so that all the dead weight and aerodynamically useless clutter of fuselage, engine nacelles and particularly a tailplane could be done away with.

The pursuit of the tailless aircraft was particularly active in the late 1940s and early 1950s when the great aeronautical challenge of the day was to 'break the sound barrier'. Not least of the problems to be overcome was the fact that the drag of an aircraft increases to a high peak at around the speed of sound. At these speeds propellers were beyond their useful operating range and could not produce sufficient thrust, and jet engines were at that time insufficiently well developed. At first the only way to explore flight at speeds approaching and above the speed of sound was to rely on the assistance of gravity in a steep dive, and so clearly any potential means of reducing drag significantly were earnestly explored.

We can best discuss whether such a concept is feasible by referring again to Figure 4.19. If you visualise the chord lines of the two aerofoils being drawn in, it is clear that the basic trim requirement is met as a result of the relative inclinations of the chord lines – the front surface chord is inclined upwards relative to that of the rear surface, and the two together present a 'dished' appearance. This is such an important characteristic that it is often referred to by the term *longitudinal dihedral*. Just as a forward centre of gravity position is necessary for stability, so longitudinal dihedral is essential for trim; but you should be aware of explanations which get this the wrong way round, or which even present longitudinal dihedral as the complete solution to providing longitudinal stability.

We now wish to investigate whether this concept of longitudinal dihedral can be built into a single flying surface, so that we can dispense with a separate tail surface. If it were possible to join the two aerofoils of Figure 4.19 together in some aerodynamically satisfactory manner, we might arrive at something rather like the inverted cambered aerofoil that we briefly introduced earlier on, which would appear to provide some in-built longitudinal dihedral. It would appear that perhaps we could design an aerofoil with a large forward portion having a positive camber and a small aft portion having a negative camber. But the main snag with this is that the down-load on the aft region must be kept as small as possible in order not to sacrifice lift, which means that the overall chord length of the new-style aerofoil will need to be very large in order to produce sufficient moment. If the wing area is to be kept within sensible bounds, this implies that the wing span must be very small, and the result is a very low aspect ratio, with a corresponding unacceptably high induced drag[6] and poor roll stability and control characteristics.

With the problem of low aspect ratio wings in mind, there is another way we could look at Figure 4.19. Rather than regard the wing as straight and of uniform cross-section as we have done throughout this chapter up to now, let us imagine the wing to be swept back and tapered. In this scenario the drawing of what was the wing now represents just the root of the wing, and the drawing of the tailplane becomes the wing-tip. The intermediate sections of the wing from root to tip (not shown) are progressively twisted more and more nose-down. We say that *washout* is applied. We now have the rudiments of our requirements in a single wing without a tailplane, and depend on the sweep-back alone to provide the necessary pitching moment arm.

This would appear to be a very attractive proposition if a highly swept wing is already being proposed for its high speed advantage. This is because a powerful solution to wing-tip stalling, the chief aerodynamic problem of swept-back wings, is also to provide the wing with washout[7], and so we would be killing two birds with one stone. However, a very substantial amount of sweepback together with a very high aspect ratio would be necessary in order to get the wing-tips far enough back to perform satisfactorily as longitudinal trimming devices. A glance at the planform drawing of any of today's swept-wing high aspect ratio transport aircraft will show that the wing-tips are only about half (or less) as far aft of the roots as they would need to be if they were to substitute for the tailplane.

This method of achieving longitudinal trim is, however, used on a number of tailless microlight aircraft and hang-gliders. It was also used on the de Havilland DH108 experimental tailless aircraft which was built in the late 1940s for research at around the speed of sound, but the pitching moment arm of the wing-tips was insufficient to render this a successful concept.

The desirability of swept-back wings together with their structural inefficiency led to the concept of the delta winged aircraft. By filling in the space between swept wing and aft fuselage, it was possible to incorporate transverse stiffeners to support the wing-tip regions, so

---

[6]Induced drag and its relationship with aspect ratio is discussed in Chapter 12 of *Flightwise – Principles of Aircraft Flight.*
[7]This is discussed in the section 'Solutions to Tip-Stalling Problem' in Chapter 13 of *Flightwise – Principles of Aircraft Flight.* The remainder of this paragraph presupposes an understanding of much of the material covered in that chapter.

that large sweepback angles became possible, and wings would extend much further aft. Moreover, there was now a full wing span available at the very back of the aircraft, and so the concept depicted in Figure 4.19 became possible in a single wing. The delta wing thus brings to fruition the idea that we mooted earlier of the inverted cambered aerofoil, and has proved to be successful in terms of longitudinal stability and trim without excessive trim drag. However, being of relatively low aspect ratio, delta wings are not ideal for aircraft from which highly economic subsonic or transonic cruise performance is a requirement.

But the idea of the delta wing brings our discussion around full-circle to the typical paper dart with which we started this chapter. It *is* necessary for trimming purposes to provide a down-load at the trailing edge, and unfortunately this militates against the use of downward-inclined trailing edge flaps for providing additional lift coefficient for low speed flight. Whether you bend the trailing edges upwards or downwards, you can't win 'em all!

RELAXED STATIC STABILITY

One of the buzz-words of present-day aircraft design philosophy is relaxed static stability, which invariably refers to longitudinal stability. The concept emerges directly from the fact that a stable aircraft with a down-loaded aft tailplane has an inherent trim drag and thus a performance penalty, and consequently there is a potential for enhancing performance simply by making an aircraft less stable, i.e. relaxing its static stability.

When used in today's combat aircraft, there is also an additional advantage to be gained from relaxing the static stability, and this is that changes in aircraft C_L can be made more rapidly. Although this is really a function of control, which will be dealt with later on, it is worth laying to rest here the false notion that relaxing an aircraft's static stability makes it more manoeuvrable, since manoeuvrability depends directly and only on the maximum lift that is available. It is the *rate* at which changes can be made from one lifting state to another that is improved by relaxing the stability, and this is termed *agility*, rather than manoeuvrability. It is the task of natural stability to fight against any change in pitch which is imminent, and the airframe cannot discriminate between the demands of a turbulent gust of air and those of the pilot. Thus if the aircraft is less stable it will offer the pilot less resistance to his pitching control inputs, resulting in greater agility.

The possibility of using relaxed static stability is made tenable by virtue of the capability of modern computer technology, which can be harnessed to operate the trimming surfaces very rapidly (e.g. many times per second) in response to every departure from the trimmed state of an unstable aircraft. Thus a computer can render an unstable aircraft effectively stable so far as the pilot is concerned, freeing him or her for other tasks. We have seen how the trimming direction of the controls switches into the reverse of normal if an aircraft is unstable, which illustrates the extremely complex task that the computer at the controls has to cope with. For example, to perform a pull-up from level flight the trimming surface must first of all apply a nose-up pitching moment, immediately followed by a greater nose-down correction once the required higher C_L value is achieved. Whilst all this is going on, the same computer and control surface must be coping with the constant up-and-down adjustments that will be demanded by gusts trying to create unstable departures from the trimmed state, even whilst this trimmed state is being altered. A very demanding task, but within the capacity of today's computer technology.

Relaxing the stability of an aircraft is a very major psychological departure from traditional aircraft design philosophy, in that the very flyability of the aircraft depends on the constantly reliable operation of a complex system outwith the pilot's control. At today's speeds (unlike in the day of the Wright brothers) the pilot would be unable to control most unstable aircraft at all as his reactions would be far slower than those of the computer. Furthermore, there is no way that the aircraft could be quickly switched back into 'stable' mode in the event of a system failure, since the neutral point is fixed in the aircraft's design and the centre of gravity certainly could not be moved far enough forward quickly enough, by any conceivable means. In a relaxed aircraft, therefore, the system is in full charge, and must be totally relied upon for the aircraft's very survival.

Relaxed static stability is not only used in combat aircraft, but has been incorporated into some of today's civil transport aircraft. In this case, the relaxation is merely carried out to reduce the static margin, rather than to render the aircraft actually unstable. For example, before flight the Airbus A320 is loaded in such a way that it has a conventional and adequate degree of natural stability, since the pilot will be expected to be able to control the aircraft fully. Once in the cruise, however, a large amount of fuel may be pumped from wing tanks to an empty tank in the tail fin, substantially reducing the aircraft's static margin. As seen in Figure 4.16(a) this means that a very much reduced trimming tail-load is required, with a commensurate reduction in aircraft drag and hence thrust and fuel consumption. The controls still operate in the conventional sense, although to the pilot they will be very sensitive, but during the cruise control inputs are small, and for the automatic pilot (which is normally employed during the cruise) this increase in sensitivity is no problem at all. When preparing for approach and landing, any remaining fuel in the fin will be pumped forwards again to restore the conventional stability margin.

CHAPTER 5
Longitudinal Dynamic Stability

INTRODUCTION

We have come to accept that longitudinal static stability is regarded as an almost essential feature of an aircraft if a pilot is to have a tolerable task in flying it. But if an aircraft is to be successful the designer cannot rest content with making it merely controllable; it must be endowed with such characteristics that make it comfortable and easy to manage and, above all, it must handle safely without being subject to strange quirks in its motion that could be dangerous or might give anxiety to pilot or passengers. We have seen that if the level of static stability is only marginal then the controls become very twitchy and bothersome to handle, but we must now look beyond this basic need of static stability to investigate how the aircraft will behave immediately after an initial trim change, or a temporary pitch disturbance due to turbulence in the air. We must look at its dynamic or oscillatory tendencies.

Our concern in *Flightwise* is to establish the underlying reasons for aeroplanes possessing the shape and proportions that they are endowed with. Hence we should be failing in our task if we were merely to consider and describe the nature of the typical oscillations that an aircraft undergoes. Instead, we shall undertake a fairly rigorous and systematic investigation of how the characteristics of these oscillatory motions are dependent on such features as the size and configuration of the aircraft, the relative size, position and aerodynamic characteristics of the tailplane and the size of the aircraft's static margin. To obtain answers to these questions we shall back up our common sense with confirmation and guidance from the results of mathematical analysis, but in keeping with *Flightwise* tradition we shall consider the mathematical method merely as a 'black box' with an input, a process and an output. The input consists of the theoretical foundations that the black box's inner workings are built upon together with the raw data that are required to feed the process. The process itself includes some advanced mathematics which we shall leave to others, but it also includes some mathematical cunning which will enable us to formulate a very precise and useful method of describing an aircraft by means of a set of special numbers, which are called *aerodynamic derivatives*. Finally, the output that may be obtained by feeding in the raw data and 'turning the handle' will show us which oscillations occur, at what frequency and how heavily damped, and how these characteristics are related to the physical features of the aircraft.

We shall continue in this chapter to treat the aircraft as a body which is symmetrical about the plane of the longitudinal and normal axes. Furthermore, during all of the movements and oscillations that we shall be dealing with, this plane of symmetry will never move outside its initial plane. This is very convenient, since it means that any sideways motions and all rolling and yawing rotations can be completely left out of our deliberations since they are unaffected by and have no effect on the longitudinal motion. Thus we shall be able to adopt a gentle introduction to the equations of motion, by completely omitting half of the total set of six. We shall be making use of some of the conventions and concepts that were introduced in Chapter 2.

BUILDING THE MODEL
Newton's Second Law and Moment of Inertia

As usual in all things mechanical, our starting point is Newton's Second Law $F = ma$ which we will be applying in the forward (x) and downward (z) directions, producing two equations of linear motion. In addition to these two linear motions, there is also a rotational motion about the y-axis. Following the principle introduced and discussed in Chapter 2 in the section on Moments and Rotational Forces, we shall need to use the rotational equivalent of Newton's Second Law to describe this motion. In that section we restricted ourselves to consideration of Newton's First Law since the rotational equivalent of his Second Law introduces a new concept that we did not require there.

For the rotational equivalent of Newton's Second Law we must identify the rotational equivalents for each quantity appearing in $F = ma$. We already know that the equivalent of a force F is a moment M, and the equivalent of a linear acceleration a is an angular acceleration that we will denote by α. But the equation $F = ma$ also requires that we find a rotational quantity equivalent to the rather elusive mass m, the inertia term. This is new to us, and so we must deviate briefly to investigate and come up with the answer.

Let us consider a heavy wheel that is stationary but free to rotate around its axis. We will apply a moment (or torque, the name usually given to a moment when it is applied by twisting a shaft rather than by applying a direct force at a certain distance from the axis) of known magnitude M, and measure the angular acceleration α that it produces. Now let us write down the formula for the rotational equivalent of Newton's Second Law, using known equivalents where possible and introducing a new symbol I for the equivalent of mass m. The formula will be $M = I\alpha$ or $I = M/\alpha$, from which we can calculate the value of this new rotational inertia quantity I. It is called the body's *moment of inertia*, and as with mass for linear motion it is the property that resists change in rotational speed.

What does the moment of inertia of a rotating object depend on? It is certainly a function of the heaviness (mass) of the wheel, but there is something else. If one were tasked with designing a flywheel out of a given amount of metal that could be cast into any shape, in such a way that the flywheel would have the maximum possible moment of inertia (an ideal property in a flywheel), instinct might dictate, and experiment would soon verify, that it was best to position most of the metal as far away from the axis as possible. Thus most of the metal should be in the form of a hoop, with just enough of the material left over to form a flange or spokes to support the hoop from the hub. In fact, the contribution to *I* of every little bit of mass d*m* making up a wheel[1] is (d*m*)r^2, where *r* is the distance of the little mass element from the axis. Thus moment of inertia, whilst dependent on mass, is even more strongly dependent on the distance at which the mass is placed from the axis.

Unlike mass, the moment of inertia of a body is not a constant, but depends upon which axis rotation is being considered about. Consider, for example, a dumb-bell consisting of a pair of heavy spherical masses at opposite ends of a thin rod. Now if it has a spindle passing through the length of the rod and the centres of both spheres about which it can rotate, its moment of inertia will be a very low value, since the mass is all concentrated very close to the axis of rotation. If on the other hand the dumb-bell were mounted on an axis perpendicular to its rod and halfway between the spheres, then the large masses of the spheres would be located at a considerably greater distance from the axis than before, and since the moment of inertia is proportional to the *square* of this distance, its value will be very much larger than previously, and it will be very much harder to start and to stop the dumb-bell spinning.

Now to business. The set of equations based on Newton's Second Law, which describes an aircraft's longitudinal motion and will provide all our answers, is:

$$X = ma_x$$
$$Z = ma_z$$
$$M = I_y\dot{q}$$

They constitute a pair of force equations in the *x*-direction and *z*-direction, in which the linear accelerations of the centre of gravity are denoted by a_x and a_z respectively, and the aircraft's total mass is *m*. There is also one moment equation about the *y*-axis in which the

---

[1] d*m* means 'a little bit of *m*' in calculus notation, as introduced in the section 'Rates of Change' in Chapter 6 of *Flightwise – Principles of Aircraft Flight*.

subscript y is used with the moment of inertia term I_y to indicate about which axis rotation is occurring. The symbols X, Z and M are used for the forces and moment in accordance with the conventions introduced at the end of Chapter 2. Lastly, q was also introduced there as the pitch rate, or the rate of change $\dot{\theta}$ of the pitch angle, and so $\dot{q}$ is the rotational pitching acceleration (which might alternatively have been written as $\ddot{\theta}$).

Now these three fairly innocuous-looking equations will undergo some extensive processing inside our 'black box'. This consists firstly of putting their quantities into a form which reflects the characteristics of an aeroplane, so that the measurements of a particular aeroplane may be fed in as raw data, and secondly of making use of some special properties of a set of simultaneous equations, combined with some tricks of calculus. Out of the 'black box' we shall then be able to get answers for the particular aircraft data we have fed in, telling us what sorts of oscillations occur, what their frequencies are and how heavily they are damped. We will leave the more complex mathematics to the boffins and take on trust the answers that they give us. However, before handing the equations over to our mathematical friends let us have a look at the initial processing that is done to the individual equations, since this will open up to us a powerful and systematic language for describing the aeroplane: the language of aerodynamic derivatives.

Each equation represents a relationship of direct proportion between two quantities. On the left of each is a *cause*, either a force or a moment, and the second factor on the right is its *effect*, an acceleration or a rotational acceleration. Let us look at the right-hand sides first of all. In each case the first factor is the constant of proportionality, either the mass of the aircraft or its moment of inertia about the lateral axis, and these constants can be independently determined (by weighing, measurement and manipulation) for the aircraft in question. The second factor on the right is an acceleration, either of or about the centre of gravity. Now although a_x and a_z are indeed pure linear accelerations, their values actually depend on the nature both of the rotational and the forward motion of the aircraft. This is a consequence of the fact that we are allowing the aircraft axis system to rotate with the aircraft rather than staying aligned with the free stream direction. We need not concern ourselves with the details here, but will take it that the right-hand sides have now been manipulated into a suitable form for our purposes.

Aerodynamic derivatives

It is the left-hand sides of the equations where the clever bit comes in. When we ask ourselves what the actual force and moment values depend upon, we know that they can be produced only by aerodynamic means (including thrust) and by the force of gravity. The gravity force must be incorporated into the equations, but this is straightforward, and it is the aerodynamic element that we wish to look at now. Were we attempting to produce the set of equations to enable us to examine the response of the aircraft to its controls, we should need to expand the equations at this stage, but our concern here is simply to study the aircraft's stability, so we may ignore the controls. We shall therefore make the assumption that all the control surfaces are fixed in position[2].

Let us look first of all at the top equation and consider the force X which is the resultant force in the direction of flight. In undisturbed flight thrust equals drag and so the resultant forward force X is zero. Our interest, though, is in the situation following a disturbance to normal flight, and so it is the small changes to the steady-state force which concern us, and which will produce an acceleration. It will be safe to assume that the thrust force remains unchanged, since no power control adjustment is to be made by the pilot, and the change to flight conditions (air speed and density) will be so small that their effect on the performance of the thrust-producing system is negligible. Consequently we are simply looking at ways in which the drag force changes as a result of the disturbance.

There are a number of factors, of varying degrees of importance, which would cause the drag of the aircraft to change during the motion following a disturbance. For example, a change in the aircraft's forward speed has a direct effect on the drag as seen from the basic equation Drag $= C_D \frac{1}{2}\rho U^2 S$. But in addition the value of C_D may itself be altered. It consists of a profile drag element, which will alter if the wing's shape presented to the airflow alters due to a temporary change in upwash or downwash as the z-direction speed changes, and also an induced drag element, which is related to the change in angle of attack resulting from the same upwash or downwash. The tailplane is another contributor to the overall drag of the aircraft. As the aircraft pitches the tailplane will move fairly rapidly upward and downward because of its distance behind the centre of gravity. The resulting downward or upward airflow on the tailplane will have a considerable effect on its own induced drag.

---

[2]There are in fact two different ways in which an aircraft's stability can be analysed, and these are referred to as 'stick-fixed' stability and 'stick-free' stability. In the latter the control surfaces are still not actively involved by providing an input, but are allowed to deflect freely according to the varying aerodynamic forces on them. In this book we are concerned with stick-fixed stability, which is effectively the same as assuming that the aircraft does not have any control surfaces. This is the usual, and simpler, approach.

Similar considerations also apply to the Y force and to the M moment, and altogether this obviously presents us with a fairly complex scenario to analyse. We need a systematic approach, both to make the analysis feasible and also to make sure that we do not overlook any possibly important contributory causes. In order to see clearly where we are going, let us start by constructing a table of rows and columns. Down the side we will list the three forces and moments, and across the top we will write all the possible kinematic quantities of the motion which might in any way contribute to changes in the forces or moment. Clearly the linear and rotational speeds may contribute as we have already seen, and possibly also their rates of change, the accelerations. The table will look like this:

	u	w	q	$\dot{u}$	$\dot{w}$	$\dot{q}$
X						
Z						
M						

We thus have 18 possible cause/effect relationships to consider, corresponding to the 18 cells of the table. So we would need somehow to investigate (either analytically or experimentally) each of these 18 relationships, and having done so we could draw 18 graphs, one for each of the relationships, from X against u to M against $\dot{q}$. There will be one common feature of all these graphs, and that is that they will all pass through the origin, since if there is no disturbance there will be no change in the force or moment. But beyond this fact, there is nothing else in common that shouts out at us – there will just be a collection of randomly curved lines, and so to incorporate anything useful from these relationships into the equations of motion might look like a forlorn hope.

Although it will inevitably involve restricting the scope of our investigation to a certain extent, we can make good progress if we assume that the disturbances that we are considering are *small*. Then we could take a metaphorical magnifying glass to each of our 18 graphs, and 'zoom in' on the region close to the origin, ignoring the rest of the graph. By doing this with a sufficiently high magnification, we shall find that each graph will show an approximation to a straight line, and a straight line graph through the origin tells us that the two quantities are directly proportional to each other. This is what our mathematician friends call the process of *linearisation*, and it is an extremely powerful device that often makes progress possible in otherwise hope-

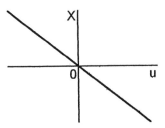

Figure 5.1 Representative linearised graph of force or moment against kinematic quantity

less circumstances. But we have to remember that the answers that we get will only be approximate, and that in practice the approximations will get worse the larger the disturbances become. This is not usually too important, but it might for example hide a reversal in the stability characteristics such as happens to the pencil standing upright on the right of Figure 2.1.

Now that we have a set of direct-proportion relationships, we can very easily write down an expression for the way in which X (or Z or M) changes on account of each of the kinematic quantities. Let us take the first by way of example. A representative graph, ostensibly of X against u, is drawn in Figure 5.1. The line is straight because we are looking at a magnification of a region close to the origin. Each of the 18 graphs is something like this, but one feature that is most important is whether the graph slope is positive (up to the right) or negative like Figure 5.1. This can usually be determined by carefully thinking about the situation. In the $X-u$ case, for example, a positive value of u means that the forward speed of the aircraft is increased; this in turn means that the airflow speed coming at it is increased, and consequently (usually) there is more drag. More drag means an increase in force in the *negative* x-direction, i.e. a negative change in X. Thus the slope of the $X-u$ graph will normally be negative, as it is drawn in Figure 5.1.

A proportional relationship only requires one parameter to specify the relationship completely, and that is the slope of the graph, which is the constant of proportionality. Thus the graph's slope tells us all that there is to know about the relationship in question, and so this number is crucial. The slopes of the graphs will depend not only on the characteristics of the aircraft, but also upon the flight condition pertaining.

Now the slope of the graph in Figure 5.1 may be expressed in calculus notation as $\dfrac{dX}{du}$, although you won't need to bother about that in just a few moments. For those of you who are well versed in calculus, you may have spotted that strictly we ought to use a special notation here, replacing the ordinary ds with what are called 'curly' ds (not to be confused with δs), so that the slope is written as $\dfrac{\partial X}{\partial u}$. The reason for these curly ds is that we are actually dealing with *partial derivatives*, which is simply a fancy way of saying that X doesn't just depend on u but on a number of other quantities as well. But we know that, and it doesn't make any difference to what we propose to do with the slope.

Anyway, these slope values are so crucial to everything that is to follow, that aerodynamicists give them the special name of *aerodynamic derivatives*. They don't even bother to use either the curly or the straight ds in this context, but introduce a new, simpler notation which does the job much more clearly. Instead of $\dfrac{\partial X}{\partial u}$ or $\dfrac{dX}{du}$ they simply write X_u, which in words means 'the rate of change of X with respect to u', but is usually verbalised just as the two letters spoken in sequence, '$X-u$'. Repeating this same approach for each of the other 17 aerodynamic derivatives represented by our earlier table, we will now fill out the table with all the proper names.

	u	w	q	$\dot{u}$	$\dot{w}$	$\dot{q}$
X	X_u	X_w	X_q	$X_{\dot{u}}$	$X_{\dot{w}}$	$X_{\dot{q}}$
Z	Z_u	Z_w	Z_q	$Z_{\dot{u}}$	$Z_{\dot{w}}$	$Z_{\dot{q}}$
M	M_u	M_w	M_q	$M_{\dot{u}}$	$M_{\dot{w}}$	$M_{\dot{q}}$

We now have to think about how these numbers, the aerodynamic derivatives, can be used to express the changes in our forces X and Z and moment M, and to do so let us again look at Figure 5.1 by way of illustration. If the small perturbation velocity is u for a certain disturbance, then, since the graph passes through the origin, to find the corresponding small change in X (let us call it dX) it is simply necessary to multiply u by the slope of the graph. Thus

$$dX = uX_u$$

There are a total of 18 possible contributors to the overall increase in X. Strictly speaking, all the other 17 might have a small corrupting influence on the answer that we have found for the first one. But fortunately we get a very good approximation by assuming that each of the influencing kinematic quantities does its stuff independently of all of the others, just as if only one of them happened at a time, rather than all at once. As a result, all the little dX contributions from each relationship add together like well-behaved vectors in a straight line, and the overall value of the aerodynamic contributions to X for the left-hand side of the first equation becomes

$$X = uX_u + wX_w + qX_q + \dot{u}X_{\dot{u}} + \dot{w}X_{\dot{w}} + \dot{q}X_{\dot{q}}$$

We must remember that, for completeness, to this must be added the appropriate component of the gravity force, but we shall not concern ourselves with that. We may now apply exactly the same principles to the left-hand sides of the other two equations, which thus become

$$Z = uZ_u + wZ_w + qZ_q + \dot{u}Z_{\dot{u}} + \dot{w}Z_{\dot{w}} + \dot{q}Z_{\dot{q}}$$
$$M = uM_u + wM_w + qM_q + \dot{u}M_{\dot{u}} + \dot{w}M_{\dot{w}} + \dot{q}M_{\dot{q}}$$

We are thus able to express all the forces and moments in terms of just the kinematic quantities and a set of numbers which are the unique property of the given aircraft at a particular flight condition. We introduced all 18 aerodynamic derivatives for the purpose of systematically ensuring that we did not leave anything important out, but fortunately we shall very soon be able to drop a large number of these as having a negligible effect. Furthermore, for each type of dynamic motion it turns out that just one or two of the derivatives are the major influences.

Not only do these ideas enable the mathematical model to be applied in any specific aircraft situation, but even more importantly for our own purposes it introduces us to the very powerful language of aerodynamic derivatives, by which we will be able to conduct detailed specific discussions about the individual aspects of the situations to be considered. When we come to look at the lateral and directional stability of an aircraft in Chapters 6 and 7, we shall use the same approach to introduce an additional set of aerodynamic derivatives relevant to our purposes there.

SHORT PERIOD PITCHING OSCILLATION

After a lot of hard mathematical work involving no further inputs than those that we have already considered, our black box spews out information revealing two almost separate and independent motions of the aircraft following a disturbance. These are referred to as the short period pitching oscillation and the phugoid, and they are collectively referred to as the longitudinal dynamic stability modes of the aircraft. Fortunately for us, to a fairly good approximation, in most conventional aircraft these modes can be treated completely separately from each other, since they are very distinct in both nature and frequency. Therefore we shall look at the short period pitching oscillation on its own for now, and leave the phugoid to the next section.

At last we come back to reality, and visualise an actual aircraft which is statically stable in pitch flying straight and level at a steady speed. A disturbance occurs due to a temporary turbulent gust in the airflow, or due to a brief pull back on the control column by the pilot wishing to simulate the motion, and then the gust passes or the pitch control is returned to its undisturbed position. As a result let us suppose that the aircraft's nose has been pitched up, which means that the pitch angle θ is no longer zero but has a positive value. Due to the natural stability θ immediately returns towards zero and may overshoot, resulting in a nodding, nose-up-and-down rotation about the centre of gravity, as shown in Figure 5.2. This is called the short period pitching

Figure 5.2   Short period pitching oscillation (aircraft flying right to left)

oscillation, and we shall sometimes abbreviate it to SPPO. The aircraft's mass is large and the temporary changes in the lift and drag forces during this motion are small and brief, so it is safe to assume (so far as this motion is concerned) that the centre of gravity continues along its straight path undeflected and with no change in speed, and that the oscillation is purely about the centre of gravity.

The time taken for one complete cycle, or period, of the short period pitching oscillation is typically of about 1 or 2 or 3 seconds, depending largely (but not only) on the size of the aircraft as we shall see, and a large transport aircraft such as a Boeing 747 may have a SPPO period of as long as 15 seconds. As we saw in Chapter 2, the frequency in hertz (cycles per second) is simply the reciprocal of the period (and vice versa), so SPPO frequencies usually come out as a fraction of one hertz. Sometimes frequencies are expressed not in hertz but in radians per second, since this is the unit that the mathematics naturally produces, and in that case the answer must be divided by 2π (about 6) to convert it to hertz.

In general, a relatively high frequency is desirable, as otherwise the pilot might be tempted to try to correct the natural oscillation by use of his pitch control, thinking that the aircraft's attitude is inappropriate. If such a correction were to be applied just at the time when the natural stability would be restoring the attitude anyway, the combined correction might be too great, and so the aircraft would pitch even further in the opposite direction. If the pilot were to apply repeated corrections which were in phase with the aircraft's natural frequency, the oscillations might grow larger and larger in amplitude rather than damping out, and the result would be what is known as a *pilot-induced oscillation*. However, larger and more sophisticated aircraft are usually equipped with *stability augmentation* as part of the flight control system, in which case the natural dynamic stability modes are automatically sensed and instantly compensated for by small control inputs. In such an aircraft, the dynamic motions that we are considering here will probably never be observed during normal flight. But even in such cases the principles still apply, since during test flights the stability augmentation systems may be turned off and the modes explored, to ensure safe handling in the event of a flight control system failure.

Frequency Formula

The frequency of the short period pitching oscillation emerges from our 'black box' (to the accuracy of the approximations that we have made) in the form of the somewhat inelegant formula

$$\omega = \frac{1}{2\pi} \sqrt{\frac{(M_q Z_w/m) - M_w U}{}} \text{ hertz}$$

Although (given the appropriate data for an aircraft) we could use this formula to work out the actual numerical value for the frequency, we are more interested in being able to understand how this frequency depends on the physical characteristics of the aircraft, and how it would be affected by changes in these features. For this purpose we may simplify the formula a little, by omitting the square root sign and the factor $\dfrac{1}{2\pi}$ which simply converts the answer from radians per second to hertz. In place of the equals sign, we will adopt a standard aerodynamicist's trick of using the symbol '~', pronounced 'twiddles' (as a verb) and simply meaning 'varies directly (i.e. not inversely) in some way with'. The formula now becomes

$$\omega \sim \frac{(M_q Z_w/m) - M_w U}{}$$

We will examine the separate contributors one at a time.

Effect of Moment of Inertia

We can see straight away that the factor I_y on the bottom of the fraction means that the larger the aircraft's moment of inertia in pitch, the lower the frequency. Since the y-axis approximately coincides with the wings of an aircraft, the mass of the wings themselves (even though they are very often heavily loaded by fuel and engines) contributes very little to I_y because the distance from the axis is small. A long heavy fuselage, however, sticks out a large distance in front of and behind the centre of gravity, and so its contribution to I_y is very substantial. This is a major reason why large transport aircraft have very low short period pitching oscillation frequencies, and it is also something that has to be taken into account by designers when they are 'stretching' a version of an airliner. The McDonnell Douglas MD-80 shown in Figure 5.3 is probably the most extreme example of such stretching, being more than 13 metres longer than the DC9 from which it originated, in order to accommodate an increase in seating capacity from 90 to 172. Although this additional length is created by inserting fuselage 'plugs', one ahead of and one behind the wing, the effect is to add extra mass at the extreme front and rear of the fuse-

Figure 5.3   McDonnell Douglas MD-80, probably the ultimate in stretching

lage, where the distance from the lateral axis is virtually as great as it could possibly be. When you bear in mind that the moment of inertia of a mass is proportional to the square of the distance from the axis, it is clear that the increase in I_y is very substantial indeed. Furthermore, the effect is made greater still if there are tail mounted engines, as in the case of the MD-80.

In passing, we might also note here that the first term on top of the formula's fraction is itself a fraction with divisor m. Thus, in addition to the moment of inertia, the aircraft's mass itself has an effect (although less significant since not applying to the whole formula). This is another reason why, on the whole, large aircraft have lower SPPO frequencies than do small ones.

Angle-of-Attack dependent Derivatives, Z_w and M_w

We must now look at the three aerodynamic derivatives on the top of the fraction, to determine what they actually mean and to see how they influence the short period pitching oscillation. Two of these (Z_w and M_w) have the subscript w which refers to the centre of gravity's speed in the downwards z-direction. On the face of it this does not sound particularly meaningful, until we look at a diagram to illustrate what it really implies (Figure 5.4). Although the aircraft has pitched nose-up, its centre of gravity is still travelling in the direction of the undisturbed flight path, along the velocity vector U. But whereas before the disturbance there was no W velocity in the z-direction

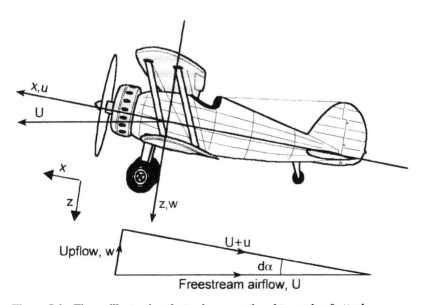

Figure 5.4   **Figure illustrating that *w* is proportional to angle of attack**

(because the x-axis was aligned with the flight path), now there is a component of the aircraft's velocity, w, in that direction, since the axes have rotated with the aircraft. (The other component is in the x-direction and is only very slightly changed from U, the change being so small that we are disregarding it for the purposes of examining the short period pitching oscillation.) As a result, the airflow meeting the aircraft's wings (shown in the vector triangle below the aircraft) is modified by upward airflow (relative to the aircraft) of magnitude w. The result of this is that the airflow meets the wing at an increased angle of attack, the increase being labelled $d\alpha$ in the figure. Now since the vector triangle is thin and approximately isosceles, it follows that the increase in angle of attack $d\alpha$, measured in radians[3], is approximately equal to w/U, so that $d\alpha$ is proportional to w. This leads us to the very important conclusion (which we shall meet frequently from here onwards) that a small perturbation velocity w should always be thought of as an increase in the wing's angle of attack. If this interpretation is used every time that the apparently innocuous term w is met, it will give a clear insight as to what is going on.

We are now in a position to examine the meaning of the aerodynamic derivatives Z_w and M_w. Since Z is the force in the z direction (i.e. the negative of lift) and w represents angle of attack, it follows that Z_w, which means $\dfrac{dZ}{dw}$, is almost synonymous with $\dfrac{dC_L}{d\alpha}$, which is the so-called lift curve slope, the slope of the graph of C_L against α for the aircraft. The only significant point of difference is that a positive w (as shown in Figure 5.4) creates an upward increase in lift, and since positive Z is downwards Z_w is always negative. But it is the magnitude, and not the sign, that is important at this juncture.

Thus we see that one of the contributory elements affecting the frequency of the short period pitching oscillation is the magnitude of the wing's lift curve slope. In Chapter 14 of *Flightwise – Principles of Aircraft Flight* it was shown that for a high aspect ratio wing the value of the lift curve slope is a maximum, but that it is substantially reduced on an aircraft having either a low aspect ratio or steeply swept-back wings. Thus one effect of designing an aircraft with short, swept wings is to make its short period pitching oscillation slower than it would be with long unswept wings. For example, the Panavia Tornado shown in Figure 5.5 would have a slower pitching oscillation with wings swept back than when extended forward. This is an unde-

---

[3]The definition of an angle measured in radians is given and explained in *Flightwise – Principles of Aircraft Flight* chapter 12, in the section headed 'Induced Drag'. It is also briefly defined on page 333 of this book.

Figure 5.5   Panavia Tornado IDS

sirable trend. The wings are frequently swept back for low-level pene-
tration of enemy defences, and it would be better in these circumstances for the dynamic stability to be crisp and quickly responsive to
the highly disturbed air which abounds at low altitude.

Let us now turn to M_w. Just as Z_w is synonymous with the lift curve
slope $\dfrac{dC_L}{d\alpha}$, so it follows that M_w will likewise correspond with $\dfrac{dC_M}{d\alpha}$.
Furthermore, since α is directly related linearly to C_L in the lift curve,
we may think of M_w as being synonymous with $\dfrac{dC_M}{dC_L}$, the slope of the
$C_M(\text{cg})$–C_L graph that was at the heart of our work in Chapter 4 on
longitudinal static stability. Thus M_w is directly proportional to the static margin of the aircraft, and as we have already seen this depends
only on the position of the centre of gravity. For the aircraft to be statically stable M_w must be negative, since the slope of the $C_M(\text{cg})$–C_L
graph has to be negative.

The second term on the top of the fraction in our 'twiddles' formula for SPPO frequency has a minus sign in front of it, and U must be positive. Thus for a stable aircraft ($M_w < 0$) the term $-M_wU$ is positive, and increasing the static margin therefore makes a direct contribution to raising the frequency of the oscillation, and vice versa. This bears out our intuition, which tells us that, as we make an aircraft less and less stable, its behaviour will become 'mushy' and the frequency will become unacceptably low. It relates directly to the poor response to the pitch trim control that we looked at in the previous chapter, alongside Figure 4.16(a). Thus static stability is not only desirable in its own right, but it also plays a significant part in ensuring satisfactory dynamic behaviour in pitch.

Damping Derivatives and M_q

We now come to consider the derivative M_q. This belongs to a special class of aerodynamic derivatives that we shall meet frequently on our *Flightwise* journey, known as the *damping derivatives*. The idea is very simple. If ever anything 'happens', an aerodynamic resistance is always automatically set up to oppose the happening, just as friction always opposes motion. As a straightforward example, if you start moving *forwards*, air resistance due to your forward motion (drag) results automatically from the forward motion, and pushes *backwards* on you, opposing your motion. Damping derivatives identify the direct aerodynamic resistance to motion, whether linear or rotational, and since the motion and the resistance must always[4] be in opposite directions, all damping derivatives are (by their nature) negative and cannot normally be otherwise.

One crucial thing to be aware of when dealing with any damping derivative is that the resistive force or moment only opposes motion *while the motion lasts*. Once it has stopped, the source of the opposition to it has been removed, so the force or moment disappears. Damping derivatives of themselves are therefore never actually stabilising, since they can never cause a *return* towards the starting situation. They can merely stem a departure, or slow down a return caused by something else.

M_q is called the pitch damping derivative, and refers to the resistive moment M resulting from a pitching rotation at a speed q. As the aircraft pitches nose-up, three aspects of its motion might possibly be significant in producing this resistive moment: the motion of the fuselage, that of the wing and that of the tailplane. The fore and aft portions of the fuselage, of whatever shape, are bodies moving upward and downward through the air, and as such they will generate profile drag in the downward and upward directions respectively. (We are here surrepti-

---

[4]But see Footnote 1 of Chapter 7 for an exception.

tiously introducing a new concept, that entire airflows and their effects may be resolved into component directions, just like vector quantities, and that each component of the airflow may be treated independently of the component at right angles to it, so far as its force effect is concerned. This is obviously a very useful trick when appropriate, but it must be treated with caution.) Since these fuselage portions are at a distance from the centre of gravity, their drag forces produce a damping moment. Whilst a long fuselage will tend to offer more pitch damping than a short one, the fuselage does not in fact make a significant contribution to M, and can usually be ignored.

Since the wing is located close to the centre of gravity, its rotational motion merely serves to provide a rate of change of angle of attack. Although this rate of change is significant to one of the aerodynamic derivatives which crops up when we come to consider the damping of the SPPO, it is not relevant here and can be ignored.

We have left the major M_q contributor to last, and that is the effect of the tailplane's downward motion through the air due to its considerable distance behind the centre of rotation. As a result of this motion, the airflow has an upward component relative to the tailplane

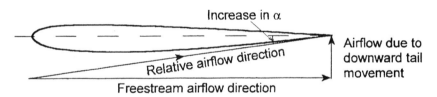

Figure 5.6   The increase in angle of attack on a downward-moving tailplane

as shown in Figure 5.6, and consequently there is an 'increase' in the tailplane's angle of attack (during its downward motion) and hence in its lift force, which exerts a nose-down pitching moment about the centre of gravity, opposing the nose-up rotation. (The word 'increase' was placed in inverted commas because the undisturbed tailplane force is, as we know, usually downwards, and so an increase would in fact initially be a decrease of a negative value. The purist's way of putting this would be that there is an 'upward increment' to the lift of the tailplane.)[5]

[5]For simplicity of illustration in Figure 5.6 it is assumed that the trimming angle of attack of the tailplane in undisturbed flight is zero, so that the negative camber is providing all the down-load. The dashed line in this instance therefore represents both the chord and the free stream direction.

This sounds all very technical and convoluted. But it is much easier to see what is going on if you think of the tailplane as a paddle or a hand-held fan that is being waved up and down in the air. It is clear that the larger the area of the fan or paddle blade, and the longer its handle, the more aerodynamic resistance, or damping, there will be to its up and down motion. Exactly the same applies to the tailplane of the aircraft, but by far the more significant of the two factors is the distance of the tailplane behind the centre of gravity. This is because the increase in the tailplane's angle of attack depends upon the tail length (in conjunction with the pitch rate) and so does the moment arm, so that the pitch damping derivative actually depends on the *square* of the tail length.

Both of the aerodynamic derivatives in the term $M_q Z_w/m$ on the top line of our formula for the SPPO frequency are negative, and so the whole term is positive. Thus the larger the numerical value of M_q, which effectively means the bigger the tailplane and/or the longer its moment arm, the greater the frequency of the short period pitching oscillation. Conversely, too small a tailplane, or too short a tail boom, will result in too little pitch damping and a very slow and sluggish response to pitch disturbances. Incidentally, because of the mass of the tail and tail boom, the same features which provide adequate pitch damping also contribute directly to the moment of inertia I_y, which *reduces* the SPPO frequency as we have seen. However, the aerodynamic pitch damping is a far more important consideration in most instances.

Tailless aircraft

Towards the end of Chapter 4 we discussed the possibility of making a tailless aircraft which was longitudinally both trimmable and statically stable, and we came to the conclusion that the chief difficulty was in placing the down-loaded part of the wings sufficiently far behind the centre of gravity to provide an adequate moment arm, so as to obviate an excessive down-load. But in practice, when tailless aircraft (other than deltas) have been experimented with, the underlying problem has proved to be not so much that of trim but rather of pitch damping. If the paddle effect of a large tailplane at a substantial distance from the centre of gravity is unavailable, there is no alternative means of providing the necessary M_q derivative. Thus even when statically stable, flying wings have always been found to have too low an SPPO frequency for adequate handling, and this more than anything else has stifled attempts to develop such aircraft beyond the experimental stage.

If the pitch trimming ability of an aircraft is limited, Figure 4.16(a) demonstrates that it must also have a restricted static margin, which

Figure 5.7   The Northrop B-2 'Stealth' bomber

means that the handling is inevitably poor. Add to this the problem of inadequate M_q and M_w (i.e. static margin) values producing a slow SPPO mode which would encourage pilot-induced oscillations and might lead to large variations in angle of attack, the consequent risk of stalling, and the difficulty of recovering safely from a stall without a conventional tailplane, and it would seem that the tailless aircraft was a lost cause. However, with the advent of sophisticated computer-aided control technology, some interest has recently been reawakened in the idea of the flying wing for use as a transport aircraft, and indeed the concept has achieved reality and maturity in the case of the Northrop B-2 'Stealth' bomber, shown in Figure 5.7.

SPPO Damping
We will now look at the factors which influence how quickly the short period pitching oscillation dies away. This is quantified by a non-dimensional number called the *damping ratio* and designated ζ (the Greek lower-case letter zeta, pronounced 'zeeter') which has a value between 0 and 1 for decaying oscillatory motion. A value of $\zeta = 0$ corresponds with an undamped oscillation as shown by the 'dynamically neutral' curve in Figure 2.3, and a value of $\zeta = 1$ represents the situation where the oscillation first becomes damped to such a degree that it doesn't overshoot the zero position. Values greater than or equal to 1 therefore match the 'dead-beat' damped curve in Figure 2.3. If ζ

becomes negative, we have divergent or dynamically unstable oscillations.

A general rule of thumb is that the amplitude of the oscillations
should reduce by at least about a half in each successive cycle, but the
value of the damping ratio is not a direct measure of this amplitude
reduction. In practice a value of about $\zeta = 0.1$ approximately equates
to the half-amplitude guideline, so that 0.1 is a good gauge of the minimum acceptable damping ratio. However, as earlier with the frequency, we are here more concerned with trends and influences than
with actual numerical values.

Just as we earlier used what we called a 'twiddles' formula for frequency, so now we represent the salient features of the formula for
the SPPO damping ratio in a similar way as:

$$\zeta \sim \frac{-Z_w\left(\dfrac{I_y}{m}\right) - M_q - M_{\dot{w}}U}{\omega I_y}$$

It is not appropriate for us to look at this formula in too much detail,
since we would thereby lose sight of the wood for the trees. In passing
we note that the first two terms on top represent positive contributions to damping since the derivatives are negative quantities. We
note the appearance of Z_w and M_q on the top line and I_y on the bottom
line, arranged differently but reminiscent of the formula for ω, which
aproximately cancels the ω on the bottom line. Thus we see that, on
the whole, the SPPO damping ratio is affected by much the same considerations as before, with the pitch damping derivative M_q taking a
prominent position, as might be expected.

There is, however, one notable new arrival on the scene, the aerodynamic derivative $M_{\dot{w}}$ in the last term of the top line, and it behoves
us to look at this a little more carefully. When we introduced the concept of aerodynamic derivatives earlier in the chapter we set out in a
table the full set of 18 possible derivatives that might be important, in
order to ensure that nothing slipped through the net. However, we
may take it on good authority from the experts that, in practice, and
with the exception of $M_{\dot{w}}$, the nine to the right of the table (those
depending on the accelerations rather than the velocities) are found to
be insignificant and can thus be omitted.

When aircraft designers started to use the methods which we are
outlining, they first of all included only the nine aerodynamic derivatives appearing on the left of the table, assuming that the accelerations
would have no significant effect. In most instances this proved to be a
valid assumption, and good results were achieved. But in the area of

the short period pitching oscillation the answers produced were turning out to be consistently inaccurate, and something seemed to be happening that was not taken into account by any of the derivatives being used. Eventually they discovered that the solution lay in the inclusion of the one additional derivative $M_{\dot{w}}$, and thereby proper accuracy was achieved.

To understand the significance of $M_{\dot{w}}$ we should bear in mind that $\dot{w}$ means the rate of change of the wing's angle of attack, and we must consider the downwash that an aircraft wing produces behind it, as explained in Chapter 12 of *Flightwise – Principles of Aircraft Flight*. In steady undisturbed flight this downwash has the effect of producing a downwards component to the airflow over the tailplane, and so the angle at which the tailplane is attached to the aircraft in design must be greater than would otherwise be required, by an amount equal to the local downwash angle. During pitching oscillations, as we have already seen, there arises a small perturbation velocity w which directly implies an increase in the wing's angle of attack, and hence of the downwash, resulting in a downward increment in the lift produced by the tailplane. We would expect this to be taken account of in determining the aerodynamic derivative M_w which we have already considered, and indeed it is to a certain extent.

But there is an additional consideration which also turns out to be important, and that is that the airflow takes a certain amount of time to flow from the wings to the tailplane, and so the tailplane is always experiencing the downwash that the wings produced a short time earlier. During this brief period, the tailplane's angle of attack has altered a little due to the rotational motion of the tailplane about the centre of gravity. Although not very long, this time is significant in relation to the periodic time of the oscillation. It means that the tailplane angle of attack must be worked out, not according to the prevailing downwash conditions at any moment, but according to the conditions that existed when the air now flowing over the tailplane actually left the wing. In mathematical jargon, there is a phase lag between the aircraft's rotation and the pitching moment, and the derivative $M_{\dot{w}}$ is known as the *downwash lag derivative*.

As with M_q, the value of $M_{\dot{w}}$ depends directly on the size and the moment arm of the tailplane, (the further back the tail is placed, the longer the airflow takes to reach it from the wing and the faster the tailplane moves up or down), and so the behaviour of $M_{\dot{w}}$ is closely related to the pitch damping action of M_q. But in addition, $M_{\dot{w}}$ depends on the rate at which the wing's downwash increases as its angle of attack is increased. The lower the aspect ratio, the greater the downwash behind the wing for any given angle of attack, and so $M_{\dot{w}}$ depends inversely on the aspect ratio of the wing. But at the same time its value is positive (not negative like M_q) so that the term $-M_{\dot{w}}U$ on the top of the ζ formula actually reduces the value of ζ because of the minus sign in front of it. This means that the larger the value of $M_{\dot{w}}$, the less damped is the pitching oscillation. The most obvious conclusion that we can draw from this is that low aspect ratio wings result in a less well damped short period pitching oscillation mode than do high aspect ratio wings.

SPPO Summary

By way of a summary after a considerable number of tricky logical discussions, we will redraw the relevant cells of the aerodynamic derivative table that we had earlier. The other major factor influencing the SPPO frequency is the moment of inertia I_y, which does not appear below since it is not an aerodynamic derivative.

	w	q	$\dot{w}$
Z	$Z_w \sim \dfrac{\mathrm{d}C_L}{\mathrm{d}\alpha}$ = Lift curve slope $\omega \sim$ Lift curve slope		
M	$M_w \sim \dfrac{\mathrm{d}C_M}{\mathrm{d}C_L}$ = Static margin $\omega \sim$ Static margin	M_q is pitch damping derivative Paddle action of tailplane Depends on tailplane area and square of tail length Inadequate in tailless aircraft $M_q \sim \omega$ and ζ	$M_{\dot{w}}$ is downwash lag derivative Varies with M_q factors Increases as aspect ratio decreases Subtractive effect on ζ (no affect on ω within approximations adopted)

PHUGOID

When we were considering the nature of the short period pitching oscillation, we made the assumption that the change in the Z force was so small and brief that the path of the centre of gravity was undeflected from the undisturbed flight path. However, although the Z force change does not have an appreciable effect so far as the SPPO is concerned (because it all happens so quickly), it does have a small but significant effect overall on the motion of the aircraft. If, for example, the net effect of the oscillating Z force is upward, then when the SPPO has died away the aircraft will be left flying with its centre of gravity following an upward-deflected path. Alternatively, such a situation could be arrived at by dint of the pilot pulling back steadily on

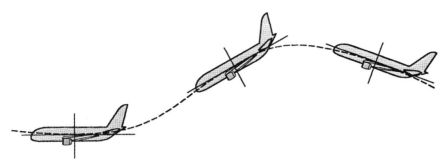

Figure 5.8   Phugoid (aircraft flying right to left, figure greatly compressed horizontally)

the stick for a second or two, and then centring it again to the correct trim position for the original steady speed level flight path.

Whichever way the situation is arrived at, the outcome is that the aircraft is flying along a climbing flight path[6], although no additional power is being applied to provide the needed extra potential energy, and no adjustment has been made in the pitch trim setting, which is still correctly adjusted for level flight at the flight speed just before the disturbance. The result is a motion called the *phugoid* stability mode, and it is illustrated in Figure 5.8.

Since no additional power is supplied by the engines, as the aircraft initially climbs it sheds kinetic energy (i.e. speed energy) in exchange for potential energy (i.e. height energy), and thus slows down, in the manner of a roller-coaster free-wheeling on an up-incline, as discussed in Chapter 4 of *Flightwise – Principles of Aircraft Flight*, in the section headed 'Flow Around Objects and Bernoulli's Principle'. The lift force depends (*inter alia*) on the speed of flight, and before the disturbance it was exactly balancing the aircraft's weight. But now with loss of speed the lift becomes insufficient for this purpose and the weight wins. By Newton's Second Law, this net downwards force approximately at right-angles to the flight path produces an acceleration in the form of a downward deflection of the path of the centre of gravity, so that the aircraft gradually stops climbing, levels out and then begins to descend. Like the roller-coaster, its speed will now begin to increase again as potential energy is converted back into kinetic energy, and the lift force will recover. But when the aircraft reaches its original height (at its original speed) it is still descending, and so the speed will continue to increase, the lift will become greater than the

---

[6]The net Z force could equally well be downwards, so that the result would be a descending flight path. The discussion that follows may easily be inverted for this situation.

weight and the aircraft will begin to level out and then pull up into another climb.

The phugoid, like the short period pitching oscillation, is thus a periodic motion which can be described by its frequency and its damping ratio. But before we go on to look at the values of these, let us make sure that we are completely clear about the difference in character between the two motions. It may prove useful to have your finger in the page of Figure 5.2 which illustrates the SPPO mode, so that you can compare it with the phugoid illustration in Figure 5.8. In both cases the aircraft is shown with its body axes fixed against the aircraft silhouette, and the centre of gravity is moving along a dashed line which represents the flight path.

But there the similarity ends. In the SPPO case we made the assumption that the forward speed of the aircraft, and hence the drag, was constant, which is why none of the aerodynamic derivatives containing X or u appeared in our formulae. The pitch angle oscillated about the norm, with the result that the wing's and tailplane's angles of attack and hence lift forces varied markedly, giving rise to the Z and M derivatives in our formulae. But now, in the case of the phugoid, we have a completely different scenario. The aircraft is found scarcely to oscillate at all about its flight path – it had finished doing that once the SPPO had died away – and so Figure 5.8 shows that, at each position, the aircraft's x-axis is tangential to the flight path at that point. (Note that the diagram has had to be greatly compressed horizontally to fit on the page. If it were drawn to a true horizontal scale, the flight path curve would become virtually indistinguishable from the x-axis in the vicinity of the aircraft.) So it is not now the pitch angle which varies; not the angles of attack of wing and tailplane; hence not the coefficient of lift nor the pitching moment. Instead we now have an oscillation of forward speed and height, of which it is the speed term that appears in our equations.

The name 'phugoid' was ascribed to this motion by the prominent and brilliant aeronautical engineer F. W. Lanchester, who is renowned for not having had much of a way with words. He was searching for a classical-sounding name based on the idea of flying (up in the air), but he appears to have scanned his Latin dictionary a little too hastily. The source word that he chose was *fugare*, which is indeed the Latin verb for 'to fly', but with the meaning of fleeing or running away, rather than airborne flight. The same source word also gives us the English words 'fugitive' and 'centrifugal force'. Not only did he choose the wrong word, but in his idiosyncratic style he substituted a 'ph' for the initial 'f'. However, the name finishes appropriately (one out of three!) with the suffix '-oid', which derives from Greek, and means 'form' or 'shape'.

Phugoid Frequency and Damping

You may have spotted the words 'scarcely' and 'virtually' creeping into the phugoid description two paragraphs back. In our attempt to make matters simple and digestible we have in fact exceeded the bounds of acceptable approximation whilst describing the phugoid. If we were to write out the formula for its frequency based on the mathematical model using approximations corresponding to those that were deemed suitable for the short period pitching oscillation mode, we should come up with a rather messy expression involving more than a dozen different parameters that the period depends upon, including inertia terms and aerodynamic derivatives. But this does not invalidate the above description of the phugoid as being a simple roller-coaster energy-exchanging motion, since its dynamics are strongly dominated by this aspect. The effect of each of the dozen or so parameters in the formula may be merely thought of as modifying to some degree the basic roller-coaster motion.

Having said that, it will still be useful to take a brief look at the set of aerodynamic derivatives which appear in the formula, and we do so here in the same tabular format as before.

	u	w	q
X	Important	Minor	–
Z	Important	Minor	–
M	Usually negligible	Minor	–

You will observe that there are no derivatives based on pitch rate q, because the pitch *rate* is negligible, even though the pitch *angle* varies sufficiently for w (which corresponds with angle of attack) to vary a little so that X_w, Z_w and M_w each have a minor effect. X_u is more important, since it reflects the way in which the varying drag assists or opposes gravity to alter the forward speed. It is in effect a damping derivative, since the resulting force directly opposes the change in speed which produces it. Finally, Z_u shows the way in which the normal force varies aerodynamically with speed, and this will have the effect of modifying the shape of the flight path, as we have seen.

The frequency of the phugoid mode is very much lower than that of the short period pitching oscillation mode, and so it is more convenient and usual to refer rather to the periodic time. Typically a full cycle takes in the region of 40 to 60 seconds, and it depends much more on the aircraft mass and speed of flight than on its aerodynamic shape. Consequently there is little that the designer can (or need) do to adjust it, since there are always other much more important aerodynamic considerations to be taken into account.

If the approximate formula for the phugoid frequency is messy, the corresponding formula for the damping ratio is far more so, and certainly need not concern us here. In general it is found that the phugoid mode of an aircraft is only very lightly damped, which is not surprising since, as we have already seen, the aerodynamic considerations are secondary to the dynamics of the kinetic and potential energy transfer. In some instances (particularly at high speed) some aircraft experience an undamped, or even a marginally divergent phugoid mode. Fortunately, however, this is not usually a matter of great concern, since the periodic time is so long that the pilot (or autopilot) always has ample time to make small manual corrections to compensate. Indeed he or she will usually do so automatically, and may be unaware of the presence of the phugoid at all. But the phugoid can be troublesome for a novice pilot, for whom the task of maintaining constant speed at a steady height represents a considerable difficulty until much flying experience has been gained. He or she must learn to judge when a rising altimeter reading together with a falling indicated air speed (or vice versa) is simply a phugoid effect that will correct itself if left alone, or whether the throttle or pitch controls need adjustment for the required trimmed flight conditions.

CHAPTER 6
Lateral and Directional Static Stability

INTRODUCTION

By restricting our observations and discussion to those motions in which the aircraft's plane of symmetry never moves outside its starting position we have so far painted only one half of the aircraft stability picture. Because of the symmetrical nature of all of these motions, we were conveniently enabled to put to one side any situation where this was not the case. In this chapter and the next, as we turn our attention to the other half of the scene, we shall find that we have to twist our minds round some rather more tricky phenomena, involving rotations about two axes at once, as well as movement of the centre of gravity away from the undisturbed flight path.

When dealing with longitudinal stability, it turned out that there was a fairly natural division between the static and the dynamic stability analyses. Consequently we approached these two topics from completely different standpoints, and did not need to introduce the combined equations of motion until the latter topic. But it does not turn out to be so simple to disentangle the different aspects of lateral and directional stability, since at every turn we find that, when considering a particular aerodynamic effect, there are one or two secondary effects which simultaneously come into play.

Only when considering the static stability of the aircraft can we maintain a distinction between lateral and directional motions, and even here we shall have to make some sweeping assumptions by way of simplification. By lateral motion we refer to rolling rotation about the aircraft's longitudinal (x) axis, and by directional motion we mean rotation (called yawing) about the normal (z) axis. When we move on in Chapter 7 to consider dynamic stability, we shall find that because of the substantial interaction (technically referred to as cross-coupling) that occurs between the two we must drop the distinction between lateral and directional motions and refer to them together, although when we reach that point we will follow common practice and refer to such motions simply as lateral dynamic stability modes.

DIRECTIONAL STATIC STABILITY

The directional static stability of an aircraft is most easily understood when thought of by its colloquial name of 'weathercock stability'. An aircraft that is directionally stable could be used as a weathercock if it were mounted on a vertical pivot through the centre of gravity and raised into the wind. The idea of a weathercock is that it always points into the wind, so that it indicates where the wind is coming from rather than the direction in which it is going, and the pivoted aircraft must likewise point into the wind. If there is a small disturbance (or a change in the wind direction) something must happen naturally which will provide an aerodynamic restoring moment to realign the fuselage with the wind direction.

As we did with longitudinal motion (except when considering the phugoid), we may assume for our present purpose that a yawing disturbance creates such a small and short-lived side-force on the fuselage that the aircraft's centre of gravity does not deviate from the original path, and thus that the motion is purely rotational. In Chapter 2 we stated that the angle of rotation about the z axis (the third of the triple $[x, y, z]$) is designated by the letter ψ, the third of the triple of Greek letters $[\phi, \theta, \psi]$, and also that positive was clockwise when looking downward from the centre of gravity. In fact this provides a strong argument in favour of the convention of defining the positive z-direction as downward. Had it been defined as upward and had we followed our usual 'clockwise is positive' convention when looking outward along the positive axis of rotation, we should have come across a very confusing situation in which instinct and rule would have been at odds with each other.

In order that we may consider what design features contribute to or tend to undermine an aircraft's directional static stability, it is first of all necessary to examine what effect a small disturbance in yaw has on the airflow around the aircraft. To do so, let us look at Figure 6.1, in which the aircraft's nose (and x-axis) has yawed clockwise through a positive angle ψ. The aircraft's centre of gravity is still travelling in its original direction which is straight up the page, and its forward speed is still U, but there is now a crabwise component to the motion. If we break down the velocity vector u into two perpendicular components along the aircraft's x-axis and y-axis directions, we see (in the right-hand diagram) that the size of the component parallel to the x-axis is very little changed from U, and we will therefore ignore this change. (For the sake of those versed in trigonometry, it is actually $U \cos \psi$, and for a small angle ψ, $\cos \psi$ is approximately equal to 1.) However, the other component shows that the aircraft now has a small sideways velocity (whose magnitude is $v = U \sin \psi$) along the y-axis direction, but in the negative-y sense.

This very important sideways velocity component is frequently given the name of sideslip, but this is a most unfortunate misnomer since the word sideslip is also (and more properly) used for a sideways motion of the centre of gravity, which does not occur here. As we shall discover in the next chapter, confusion between the two uses of this

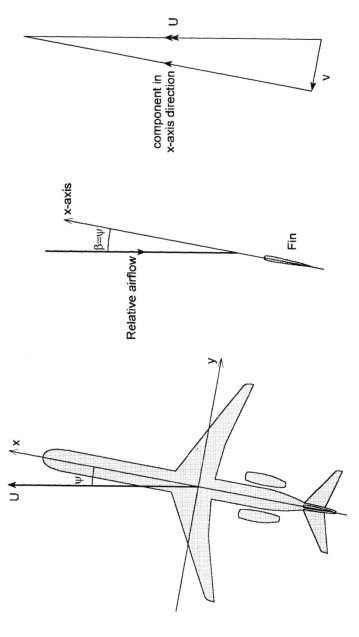

Figure 6.1   Side-flow angle resulting from yaw

word makes it impossible to understand the dynamic stability modes properly, and so it is most important at this stage to be ultra-precise in our terminology. We will therefore refer to the velocity being discussed here as the y-axis component of the aircraft's forward velocity, and reserve the word sideslip for later, when the path of the centre of gravity *is* deflected.

As a result of the yawed attitude of the aircraft in Figure 6.1 and the resulting y-direction component of the velocity, it is clear from the central diagram of Figure 6.1 that the relative airflow, the reverse of U, meets the fuselage and fin at a sideways angle equal to ψ. This is the angle of attack of the fin, and is usually referred to (again misleadingly) as the sideslip angle. It is sometimes given the symbol β, since it is analogous to α, the angle of attack in the pitching plane. It is the aerodynamic side force due to this side-flow angle that must be harnessed to produce the necessary restoring moment to straighten up the aircraft and provide directional stability.

Before looking at the ways in which this is achieved, let us confront the question which you will no doubt have been asking in the previous paragraph: why have we introduced a new symbol β, when we already had a perfectly good symbol ψ, and it is clear that β and ψ are no different from each other? Yes, it is true that in the present situation these angles are exactly the same as each other, but this will not be the case when we have also to consider a genuine sideslip. If we had not made the assumption that the centre of gravity were continuing to move along its undisturbed flight path, but if instead some force had acted sideways for long enough to deflect the centre of gravity significantly from this path, then the side-flow angle β would be contributed to not only by the yaw angle ψ but also by the overall sideways motion of the centre of gravity, which is rightly called sideslip. The side-flow due to a positive yaw angle ψ comes from the left, as seen in Figure 6.1, whereas the side-flow that would arise from a positive sideslip, i.e. the centre of gravity moving to the right, would come from the right, and so the two contributions to β would not be additive but mutually opposed. We need not worry about this in the present discussion, but we will come across it again later in this chapter and in the next.

What aerodynamic effects will the side-flow have on the aircraft in Figure 6.1 that will apply a yawing moment? First of all, the wings are no longer performing symmetrically, and so they would each be expected to produce slightly different lift and drag forces from those which they develop during symmetrical motion. But although the side-flow effect on the wings will turn out to be of the utmost significance in our later deliberations, fortunately the change produced in their drag, and hence yawing moment, is so small in comparison with other considerations that we can usually ignore it when discussing directional stability[1]. The two major features that we must look at are the fuselage and the as yet unmentioned tail fin.

A fuselage, at least on an aircraft of the type depicted in Figure 6.1, may be regarded as a long thin object moving through the air in approximately the direction of its longitudinal axis. Aerodynamicists call such an object a *slender body*, and other examples are a sporting javelin, a ballistic missile's body and a simple pole (such as a broom handle or a bamboo cane) thrown by hand through the air. Without allowing ourselves to be diverted into the complex aerodynamics of the flow around such slender bodies, which involves a combination of axial flow, circular cylinder flow with boundary layer separation, and shed vortices, let us take it on trust that the resultant yawing moment produced by these phenomena is usually destabilising. This is because the theory shows that the centre of pressure of the resultant side-force is ahead of the mid-point of the slender body. Now of course we could arrange (by appropriate mass distribution) for the centre of gravity to be ahead of the centre of pressure. (In Figure 6.1, the side-force is to the right, and if it acts behind the centre of gravity the resulting moment will be anticlockwise, tending to undo the yawing disturbance.) But this is not usually convenient because longitudinal stability and trim considerations have prior claim on the location of the centre of gravity, and in any case such an approach would not be capable of producing a sufficient restoring moment for the aircraft's stability requirements. Incidentally, the centre of gravity of an Olympic-standard throwing javelin has to be between 35% and 42% of the total length back from the front tip, which might make it marginally stable, or at least less unstable than if the centre of gravity were at the midpoint. If you want to throw a bamboo cane like a javelin, I suggest you throw it thick-end-first!

Thus whilst the influence of the wings is usually negligible, the fuselage generally has a directionally destabilising effect, and so an additional stabilising moment is needed. This is normally taken care of by means of a vertical tail fin, placed as far behind the centre of gravity as possible. The fin is usually given a symmetrical, uncambered aerofoil section set with its chord lying in the plane of symmetry so that in unyawed flight it produces no lift force.[2] Thus the angle β is the angle of

---

[1]An exception is an aircraft with highly swept, high aspect ratio wings, especially if it is tailless. We shall meet this later.

[2]Remember that lift is not defined as 'upward' but normal to the airflow. Thus here lift means the side-force on the fin. Note also that if there is some asymmetry in the airflow around the aircraft, due for example to the slipstream of a single propeller at the front of the fuselage, then the fin may be set at a small angle of attack to compensate for this.

attack of the fin due to the side-flow, and this is equivalent to the angle of attack α of the wings; hence the choice of the adjacent Greek letter. (There is no equivalent angle of attack in rolling motion.)

In the previous chapter we found that the small perturbation velocity w in the z-direction could be thought of as a direct analogue of the wing's angle of attack, and hence w is directly related to the aircraft's coefficient of lift. By exactly similar reasoning from the velocity diagram in Figure 6.1, the small perturbation velocity v in the y-direction may be regarded as directly representing the side-flow angle β. We do not have a 'coefficient of total side-force' in the same way as we have an overall aircraft coefficient of lift, but if (as is usually the case) the yawing moment of the fuselage (and other aircraft parts) can be neglected in comparison with that produced by the fin, then we may conclude that, at least approximately, the sideways lift coefficient of the fin force producing this moment is directly related to v.

When we look at lateral dynamic stability in the next chapter, we shall be introducing and using the equations of motion in an almost identical way to that met in the previous chapter, and will thus encounter a very interesting new set of aerodynamic derivatives. As a foretaste, it is appropriate to introduce one of these derivatives here, and that is the rate of change of yawing moment (N) with side-flow velocity v, or $\dfrac{\partial N}{\partial v}$ which as before we will write and refer to simply as

N_v. It is directly analogous with the pitching stability derivative M_w which you will recall corresponds with the aircraft's static margin and hence gives a measure of the aircraft's degree of static stability. M_w had to be negative for static stability in pitch, so what is the corresponding rule for N_v and yawing stability? To answer this, look again at Figure 6.1 in which a positive yaw angle is depicted, and as we have seen, the aircraft's y-direction velocity v is negative. If the yawing moment produced is to tend to restore the aircraft to its original orientation, it must be anticlockwise, which is negative. Thus for a stable situation, both N and v must be negative (or both must be positive), so that N_v itself must be positive. (Do not try to remember facts such as this as 'rules', but rather make sure that you can quickly and correctly work them out for yourself when required, as we have just done. I could not remember whether N_v was positive or negative until I worked it out with you just now.) Thus a tail fin provides a positive N_v, whereas a long fuselage gives a negative contribution to the aircraft's N_v value.

Let us look at some of the practical factors and constraints that must be considered when designing an aircraft's tail fin. The yawing moment that a fin can produce is not only needed for simple directional static stability; it is also required for dynamic stability and (together with a rudder) for control purposes, as we shall see later on. So although the fin's 'design case' (the flight situation which envisages the greatest possible yawing moment being needed) does not necessarily emerge from considerations of static stability, the general principles in designing the fin are the same.

It is critically important that, when most needed and thus producing the largest side-force, the fin should not stall, since this would result in the aircraft suddenly departing into a state of instability when already disturbed through a large yaw angle, a highly dangerous scenario in which the aircraft could turn tail and perhaps break up. Being placed above and at the rear of the fuselage, a fin is presented with seriously disturbed on-coming airflow when the aircraft is flying at a large angle of attack. The slender-body flow around the fuselage will contain vortices and perhaps turbulence in its wake, and there may also be vortices from leading edge root extensions on the wings, and such effects can make it even more difficult to ensure that the fin is not susceptible to stalling. These difficulties are compounded by the fact that, in steady level flight, a large aircraft angle of attack implies a low air speed, which in turn means that for a given side-flow angle the fin's side force will be much less than at a higher speed, especially in view of the fact that lift forces depend on the *square* of the speed. Furthermore, in the interests of low drag, the fin's aerofoil section is usually very thin, which means that a sharp leading edge with accompanying leading edge stall (as discussed in Chapters 9 and 13 of *Flightwise – Principles of Aircraft Flight*) are likely to be the order of the day.

Since the tail fin's moment depends on its distance behind the centre of gravity, the length of the fuselage is a major factor, and a very short aircraft may require an excessively large fin, with its related drag and weight penalties, together with the hidden penalty of the greater weight of the sturdier tail structure to withstand the large loads. A very striking example of where a short fuselage has necessitated the use of an excessively large tail fin is seen in the Panavia Tornado interdictor-strike aircraft shown in the bottom silhouette of Figure 5.5. The area of the tail fin is about half that of the side elevation area of the entire fuselage, and approximately equal to the area of one wing! When the initial specification of the aircraft was raised, it was regarded as so important that the aircraft should be 'small' that a totally arbitrary maximum fuselage length was specified. Not only did this necessitate an excessively large fin size, but also the Rolls-Royce RB199 engine had to undergo a major redesign in order that it would be short enough to fit in the arbitrarily short fuselage! However, as can be seen from Figure 5.5, the substantial sweepback of the fin (needed for high speed flight performance) is very beneficial in that it forces the centre of pressure substantially further aft than would be possible without sweepback.

In a number of recent combat aircraft designs with very broad bodies on account of two jet engines being mounted pannier-style astride the fuselage, twin fins have been adopted. By this means relatively small fins can be used even on short fuselages, but wide spacing is essential to avoid excessive mutual interference. Just as in the case of the wings of a biplane aircraft, the region of low pressure of one fin is the same region as that of higher pressure of the other, and so each fin tends to downgrade the performance of the other. This design approach has been used on a number of Russian combat aircraft as well as the McDonnell Douglas F-15 Eagle and the Grumman F-14 Tomcat. In recent times, whilst some aircraft designers have abandoned the use of twin fins after early prototype testing (such as on the Eurofighter 2000), others have adopted the ploy at a similar stage, having initially used a single fin, thus demonstrating that the balance of advantage over disadvantage is by no means clear-cut.

When transport aircraft get stretched, the slender body destabilising effect becomes worse, and so it is often necessary as part of the redesign to increase the fin area, even though the stretching itself increases the tail moment arm. Often a triangular fillet is added to the base of the leading edge of the fin as a post-design 'fix' to avoid resizing the whole fin, and this achieves additional lift at high side-flow angles by shedding a vortex over the fin surface, which produces lift as discussed in the section 'Leading Edge Vortices – The Plus Side' in Chapter 13 of *Flightwise – Principles of Aircraft Flight*. A good example of the use of this so-called 'leading edge root extension' (abbreviated LERX)[3] may be seen on the fin of the short, stocky-fuselaged Boeing 737 airliner, on the -300 model onwards, these models being substantially stretched from the earlier -100 and -200 versions which do not have a tail fin LERX.

Perhaps the most extreme example of this device is to be seen in the Nimrod maritime reconnaissance aircraft which was based on the Comet airliner. This aircraft was found to have somewhat too small a fin when modified for the new rôle, in particular because of the 'slender body' destabilising effect of the large bomb-bay pannier doors beneath the fuselage. A large highly swept root extension was added to the front of the tail fin to provide more side force at high side-flow angles. However, when during the Falklands campaign the Nimrods were equipped with in-flight refuelling probes protruding forward of

---

[3]The term LERX is more commonly applied to wings rather than fins, but there is nothing contradictory or inappropriate in using it for both situations.

Figure 6.2   British Aerospace Nimrod MR2P showing tail fin augmentation devices

the nose, once again their directional stability became inadequate and required enhancing. Since the swept root extension had already been used, the solution adopted was to add small vertical fins to the tips of the horizontal tailplane, as seen in Figure 6.2. As if to get every last ounce of fin effect possible, this was also augmented by the addition of a very small triangular keel on the bottom of the tail boom. A larger surface in this position, although desirable aerodynamically, is impracticable because of the closeness of the tail to the ground during landing and take-off.

Another way of enhancing the effect of the fin is to use a T-tail, as on the McDonnell Douglas MD-80 shown in Figure 5.3. The tip-shielding effect of the high tailplane means that the fin behaves more as if it were two-dimensional, and the tip losses are largely eliminated. This not only enhances the stall angle a little, but also improves the response to side-flow, since the slope of the fin's lift curve is increased.

LATERAL STATIC STABILITY

As we move on to the third and last aspect of an aircraft's static stability, its lateral or rolling stability, we shall find that we are dealing with an entirely different kind of motion compared with pitching and yawing which have certain similarities to each other. To illustrate this, think what would happen if, as before, we were to assume that a disturbance in roll had occurred, but that it was so brief that we could ignore any temporary overall deviating force on the centre of gravity. It would be as if the aircraft were sliding along a rigid rod passing through the middle of its fuselage along its x-axis. Let us suppose that, after the disturbance had passed, the aircraft and its plane of symmetry are banked over at an angle ϕ (the first of the triple $[\phi, \theta, \psi]$) from its undisturbed state, as shown in Figure 6.3, and no longer rolling[4]. The aircraft's lift-force magnitude is unaffected by what has happened since the aircraft's speed and angle of attack to the airflow are unaltered, and the lift still acts perpendicular to the plane of the wings, the x–z plane, and in the aircraft's plane of symmetry.

Thus, although the aircraft is now banked, both of the forces are still acting through the centre of gravity, so neither of them can produce any moment (restoring or otherwise) about the centre of gravity. When we were examining longitudinal and directional stability, we found that the airflow over the aircraft was in a new direction following a disturbance, and that it could hence be tapped to provide the required restoring moment. But in the present case the airflow is still meeting the aircraft parallel to the x-axis as it was before the disturbance. Therefore there is no point trying to think which parts of the aircraft might respond aerodynamically to the disturbance, since there is nothing to respond to. It would seem, therefore, that an aircraft disturbed to a banked position would possess neutral lateral stability.

In the previous paragraph the words 'bank' and 'banked' were used, but the word 'roll' did not appear at all. Throughout our discussions of lateral motions of an aircraft it will be absolutely essential that you keep very clearly in your mind the distinction between the words bank and roll. It is largely on account of confusion between these distinct concepts that some highly misleading and thoroughly erroneous explanations have been presented to generations of aspiring aviators by well-intentioned mentors and authors, some of which explanations we will pick up on later. Putting it very simply, roll is speed and bank is position. In other words, an aircraft may be banked (displaced from level flight) at a particular angle ϕ which is not varying at all with time, as in the situation in Figure 6.3. Alternatively, it may be rolling, in which case its bank angle is constantly increasing or decreasing, and its roll rate is the rate of change of bank angle. Rolling is rotation about the x-axis, the first of the $[x, y, z]$ triple, and so the roll rate is given the symbol p, the first of the $[p, q, r]$ triple. In Figure 6.3, $p = 0$.

Although the banked aircraft of Figure 6.3 has neutral stability in roll now that it has reached its banked position, in order to get into that state from the wings-level position it must have rolled, and during that rolling motion things were very different, as shown in Figure 6.4.

---

[4]ϕ, and a little later p, are both in fact negative in this example, since the aircraft is shown pointing towards us. However, this need not concern us in the present context.

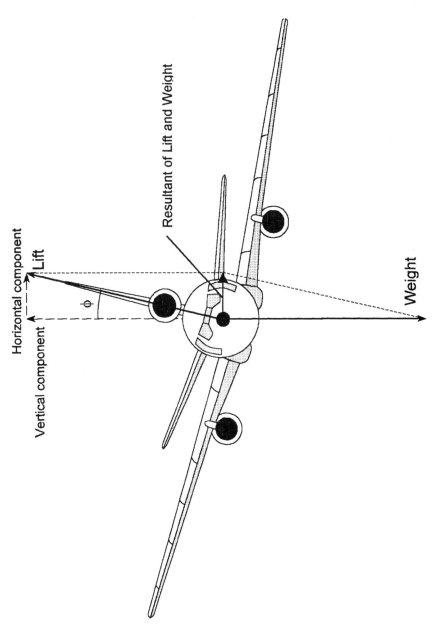

Figure 6.3   Forces on a banked aircraft which is not rolling

The down-going wing is descending through the air, and so relatively the air is flowing up to meet it, thus producing an increased wing angle of attack, greater lift coefficient and thus more wing lift, as shown in the right hand velocity triangle in Figure 6.4. (The two velocity triangles have been rotated through 90° about the picture's vertical in order that they can be drawn in the plane of the paper.) Conversely, the relative airflow meeting the up-going wing is more downwards than usual, as shown by the left-hand velocity triangle, so that its angle of attack, lift coefficient and lift are all reduced. Although the total lift may be little changed from usual, its distribution *is* now changed, and there will be a moment produced around the centre of gravity in the direction opposing the roll.

At a first glance, we might be tempted to think that this provides the required restoring moment for static stability, and this has frequently been presented as an explanation of lateral static stability by ill-informed but well-intentioned authors. However, a second look will show that this is definitely not the case. The moment is not restorative at all, because it never tries to rotate the aircraft *back* to its starting position – it simply opposes roll while rolling is taking place, and as soon as rolling stops the moment completely disappears. Furthermore, if (by some as yet unexplained method) the aircraft does begin to roll back towards its starting position, the moment due to the asymmetric lift that we have been looking at again comes into effect, but *resists* the restoration rather than assisting it.

When considering longitudinal dynamic stability, one of the aerodynamic derivatives that cropped up was M_q, which was shown to be one of a class called the damping aerodynamic derivatives. Damping derivatives are those in which the force or moment has the same direction as the related kinematic quantity, but is always of the opposite sign and always opposes the motion whilst that motion persists. We have in the present situation another example of a damping aerodynamic derivative: the motion is roll, with roll rate p, and the resistive moment is the rolling moment L (the first of the triple $[L, M, N]$), so the aerodynamic derivative is $\dfrac{\partial L}{\partial p}$ or simply L_p, the roll damping derivative. As with nearly all damping derivatives, its sign cannot be other than negative. We will look more closely at this derivative and its characteristics a little later on in the context of lateral dynamic stability. Strictly speaking L_p has nothing at all to do with lateral static stability, but it has been introduced here in order to dispel a myth and to clear the decks before we can examine the real issues of lateral static stability.

Here we are, already three pages into the section on lateral static

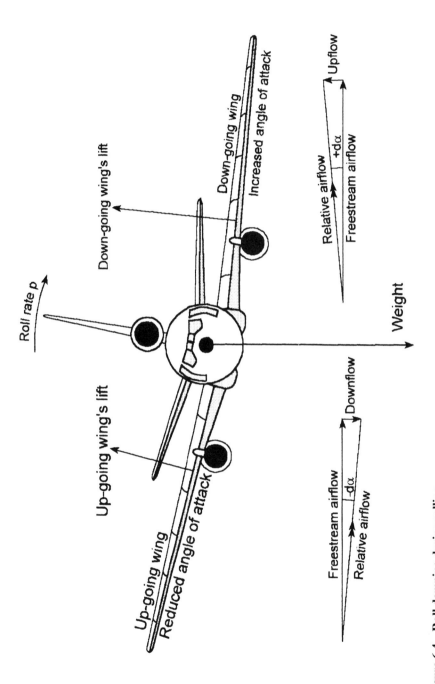

Figure 6.4   Roll damping during rolling

stability, and we have so far met nothing but negative or dismissive comments! We have seen that on the basis of our previous assumptions of the centre of gravity continuing undeflected there can be no restoring rolling moment. We have also seen that rolling itself is no agent for producing a restoring moment, since the moment disappears once the rolling stops. Is the quest futile, or is there a trick that we have missed?

The answer comes through abandoning the cherished assumption that in longitudinal and directional static stability the centre of gravity is undeflected from its path. Looking back at Figure 6.3, we see that the two forces of lift and weight are no longer directly opposite each other, so although they do not produce any moment about the centre of gravity, they do exert a resultant force (shown with a double-headed arrow) on the centre of gravity. Horizontally, this force consists of the dotted arrow labelled 'horizontal component of lift', and vertically it consists of the very small downward resultant arising from the fact that the weight is now slightly greater than the vertical component of lift, the latter being slightly less than the actual lift on account of the small bank angle ϕ. Together these components provide a resultant force on the centre of gravity that is roughly perpendicular to the plane of symmetry and is in the direction of the down-banked wing. The force being through the centre of gravity, the aircraft consequently sideslips without rotation down the slope of its wings.

Once again we have reverted to rather technical language to explain a very simple-to-understand phenomenon which is familiar to us all. If you drive a car straight along one side of a fairly steeply cambered road, the friction of the tyres ensures that the centre of gravity is undeflected. However, if the road surface were covered in a sheet of ice and you did not take any special action to compensate, gravity (or strictly a small component of it) would pull your car down the slope of the camber. You would thus have a small sideslip velocity to be added vectorially to your much larger forward velocity, and so would proceed forward along a path which is at a small angle to the undisturbed path, and the air would flow towards you in the opposite direction along this same line.

Returning to the aircraft, let us suppose that it is flying forwards (up the page in Figure 6.5) and that it is sideslipping (not rotating) to the right at a speed v. The relative airflow comes from ahead and the right, as shown in Figure 6.5. The resulting side-flow angle of attack is again given the symbol β, and from the velocity triangle of the freestream airflow velocity vector U and the sideslip-induced airflow velocity vector v we see that, as with α and w in Chapter 5 (Figure 5.4), β is near enough directly proportional to v, and qualitatively they may be thought of as being synonymous.

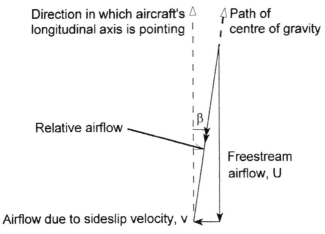

Figure 6.5   **Relationship between side-flow angle and sideslip velocity**

When we considered Figure 6.1 earlier in this chapter, we saw that an aircraft having yawed to an angle ψ experiences a side-flow angle β which, in the absence of any perturbation of the path of the centre of gravity, is equal in magnitude to ψ. In the present context there is again a side-flow angle β produced, but it is due to a completely different cause. Here β is caused by a sideways non-rotating motion of the entire aircraft with its nose still pointing in the undisturbed direction. But in the earlier discussion β was the consequence of the nose pointing in a different direction from the flight path, although the centre of gravity was still travelling unperturbed along the original flight path. So a side-flow angle can be, and is, produced by both of these causes, and the two can indeed happen simultaneously, but it helps our analysis enormously if we can keep the separate contributions distinguished in our minds. One of the great advantages of the process of linearisation that we discussed in Chapter 5 is that, provided it produces an acceptable approximation to reality, we can work out similar things due to different causes separately and just add the answers together. Technically this is sometimes called 'the principle of linear superposition'.

You may have noticed that we have indulged in a bit of sloppy thinking when discussing Figure 6.3, in saying that a side-flow velocity is caused by a side force, because of course a force produces an acceleration and not a velocity. The side-flow velocity is therefore not a constant value depending on the force, but rather an amount that increases from zero while the force persists, until matched by an equal resistive aerodynamic side force. However, it is the side-flow velocity at any instant that dictates the magnitude of the forces that we are about to look at, and once again we can take refuge in the approximation of linearisation provided magnitudes do not get too large.

At last in side-flow due to sideslip we have identified a feature which results, albeit indirectly, from the fact that the aircraft is banked even if it is not rolling. It now remains for us to investigate how this side-flow, and the resulting asymmetric airflow and sideways angle of attack, may be harnessed to produce a moment which will restore the aircraft to the wings-level position. (Note that we do not say to the starting position, since in this case, unlike longitudinal and directional static stability, the nature of the restorative agent depends on gravity, and will disappear once the aircraft is level and the lift and weight are once more in line with each other. We are here talking about straight flight, but in Chapter 9 we shall reconsider this statement in the context of turning flight.) In conventional shorthand terms, we require a rolling moment L about the x-axis, and the kinematic agent which we are going to use to produce it is v, the velocity of the aircraft's centre of gravity in the direction of the y-axis. The aerodynamic derivative relating these is $\dfrac{\partial L}{\partial v}$, abbreviated as usual to L_v. Putting yourself in the pilot's seat, a sideslip to your right (i.e. positive) implies that the right wing is low and needs to invoke an anticlockwise (i.e. negative) rolling moment. Consequently L_v must be negative to provide lateral static stability. Let us turn now to look at what features of an aircraft may enable this restorative rolling moment to be achieved.

Dihedral

The oldest and most firmly established method of producing a restorative rolling moment on an aircraft is to set both wings at a small angle, called the *dihedral angle*, above the line of the lateral axis, an idea which was probably inspired in the first instance by the falling and fluttering of leaves from trees. The effectiveness of the principle may very readily, if crudely, be demonstrated by dropping from arm's length above and in front of you a smooth sheet of paper in almost any manner you choose, and observing its descent to the ground. Inevitably there will be some residual curl in the paper, and as it falls and sideslips through the air you will see that the leading edge of the paper will tend to catch the air and be pitched up into a scooping motion. The paper will then slip away backwards and repeat the behaviour, and gentle undulations like those of a falling leaf will ensue until the paper comes to rest.

The reason why dihedral works is both obvious at a superficial level but tricky to explain rigorously. It involves thinking about a three-dimensional situation, but in a book we must content ourselves with a drawing on a plain two-dimensional page. Figure 6.6 is a simplified representation of an aircraft having a pair of wings with a large dihedral angle, since exaggeration is useful for visualisation. The upper surfaces of the lower blocks with the heavy outlines are the planes in which lie the lines through the wings' trailing edges. These planes embody the free stream airflow direction lines. The intersection of these two planes is parallel to the aircraft's longitudinal axis, the flight path. Above them, as if transparent, is another pair of planes through all the section trailing edges and inclined upwards to the first planes at an angle α, the angle of attack of the wing cross-sections to the undisturbed free stream airflow. These then are the planes containing all the aerofoil chord lines. (We are assuming that the wing is of uniform chord length throughout and neither swept nor twisted.) The aircraft's horizontal forward motion is out of the page, down to the left, and it is sideslipping (due to reasons already discussed – clearly the x-y plane cannot be horizontal here) in the positive y-direction.

If there were no sideslip, all the aerofoil sections would be performing in the manner of the two partly hidden aerofoils shown, at an angle of attack of α. But as shown in the velocity vector diagram, as a result of the sideslip the actual airflow relative to the aircraft meets the wings at an angle to the free stream airflow. Consequently the airflow that would have passed over the two partly concealed aerofoil sections will instead pass over the other sections alongside and inclined to them.

Looking first of all at the starboard wing (the positive-y side, but on the left in the figure) it will be seen that the trailing edge of the new diagonal aerofoil section that the airflow is following is further inboard than before, and because of the dihedral it is therefore lower down, although the leading edge is at the same level as before. (The chord length is actually increased a little, ameliorating the effect, but this is much less significant.) Consequently, the aerofoil has been effectively tipped nose-up, and the angle of attack is increased, as clearly shown in the figure. If we now move across to the other wing, we find that the effect of the dihedral is to raise the trailing edge relative to its starting level, and consequently the nose of the aerofoil section is effectively tipped downwards and the angle of attack is reduced. (The two partly hidden aerofoils have angles of attack which are identical with each other.) Thus the leading wing in the sideslipping direction has, overall, more angle of attack and hence more lift than the other wing, and a restoring rolling moment is produced.

An alternative conceptual way to understand what is going on is to imagine that you are walking around a parked aircraft with dihedral. You start in front of one wing, and it happens that your eyes are just the same height as the chord line of the aerofoil section that you are

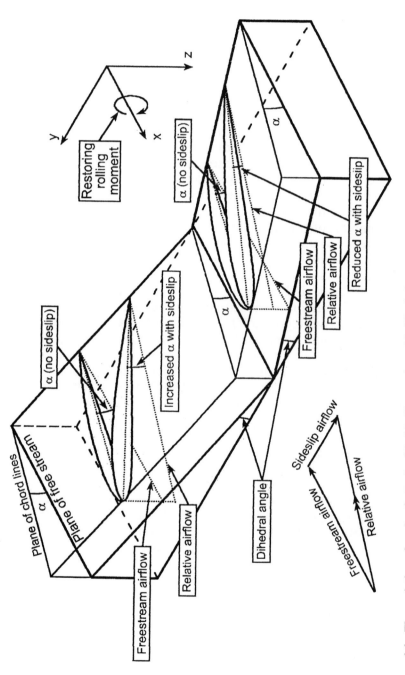

Figure 6.6   The variation of angle of attack with sideslip on wing with dihedral

looking at. As you walk towards the wing tip, you keep your eyes on this same cross-section, and gradually because of the dihedral you will find that you are seeing more and more of the lower surface of the wing at that cross-sectional position. Thus if the airflow had been flowing from your eyes along your line of sight, the angle of attack would have gradually increased the further round you moved.

As well as in aircraft wings and falling leaves, dihedral is also to be found in simple 'kite-shaped' toy kites. I remember once watching a programme on television in which two teams of young university undergraduates competed against each other in a whole package of outdoor self-sufficiency and initiative activities such as cooking, bridging and shelter-building. For one of their tasks, each team was provided with a good quality standard child's kite, together with string and material to make a tail. The task was simply to fly the kite (for a certain amount of time); the wind conditions were perfect, and there was plenty of flat unobstructed open space. Despite the favourable circumstances, I remember feeling almost ill as I helplessly watched the various members of these teams attempt in vain to launch their kites into the air. They tied the string to the frame and the tail to the bottom, but each time they tried to launch the kite it simply rolled over and plunged into the ground! They tried with two people, one launching and one pulling; they tried running into wind; they tried throwing it high; they checked to see that it was in good condition; they even tried pulling it whilst running downwind! I was so frustrated, as the solution was there in their hands and I couldn't tell them. But I seem to recall that eventually one of the two teams managed to solve the puzzle and fly the kite successfully.

What were they doing wrong? They had simply tied the string to the wrong, although perhaps the most obvious, place, the intersection of the wooden cross-poles supporting the kite's corners. This meant that when the wind blew on the kite from the string side, the kite was restrained by the poles at the corners and edges, and the middle filled out with air pressure. Consequently the left and right faces of the kite were inclined *downwards* relative to the plane of the kite frame, and so they did not have dihedral but exactly the opposite, which is called *anhedral*[5]. The kite was thus totally unstable in roll, and as it sideslipped it was bound to plunge into the ground, however they tried to launch it. The secret was simply to tie the string on to a loop provided on the opposite face of the fabric, rather than on to the crossed poles, thereby letting the poles hold the edges of the kite out behind and away from the windward side. This time as the kite was

---

[5]My trick for remembering which is which out of dihedral and anhedral may be useful to you. Anhedral begins with an A, and the wing shape resembles a flattened A.

launched in the wind it naturally took up the desired dihedral form, and flew with no problem.

A little later it will be helpful to have a look at some examples of the use of dihedral and anhedral in actual aircraft. We shall, however, obtain more value from the exercise once we have considered other methods of achieving roll stability as well, because we shall then be able to look at all the relevant features simultaneously and form a more rounded impression of any particular design.

Sweepback

Dihedral is not the only means of obtaining roll stability in an aircraft, but it is the most common and important one. In fact a number of features of aircraft contribute (in most cases positively[6]) to its L_v derivative and hence to its rolling stability, so much so that it is sometimes an excess of stability that is a problem. Although the word dihedral specifically means the one device of inclining the wings upwards, the term 'dihedral effect' is often used to describe the roll-stabilising effect of any device that achieves the same end. Without exception, all such devices depend for their functioning on the aircraft sideslipping and on the resulting sideways component of airflow.

Although not provided primarily for this purpose, swept-back wings provide a most significant contribution to the so-called dihedral effect. Once again we shall use a very stylised diagram to demonstrate the various features of sweepback which have a bearing on the creation of a rolling moment due to sideslip. Figure 6.7 shows in plan view a pair of highly swept, constant chord wings attached at a centreline which represents the aircraft's fuselage. Whereas it may have been quite difficult to conceptualise how dihedral achieved its effect, when it comes to explaining sweepback we are spoilt for choice since there are a number of contributory explanations. The figure is thus rather cluttered with words and arrows, since it is serving more than one purpose, and you may appreciate guidance to find your way through it.

The aircraft is flying up the page and sideslipping to the right, and the resulting relative airflow is shown in the velocity triangle at the top of the diagram. The relative airflow vector is copied at the same scale just in front of each of the two wings, and in each case is split into two components, one normal to the wing and one parallel to it. Only that component of the airflow which is normal to the wing can have any effect in producing lift, since the component which is parallel to the wing only flows *along* it towards the tip, without flowing over any aerofoil section at all. If you compare the two velocity diagrams in

---

[6]Although a stabilising L_v is negative, we still tend (rather sloppily) to refer to a stabilising value as making a positive contribution to roll stability.

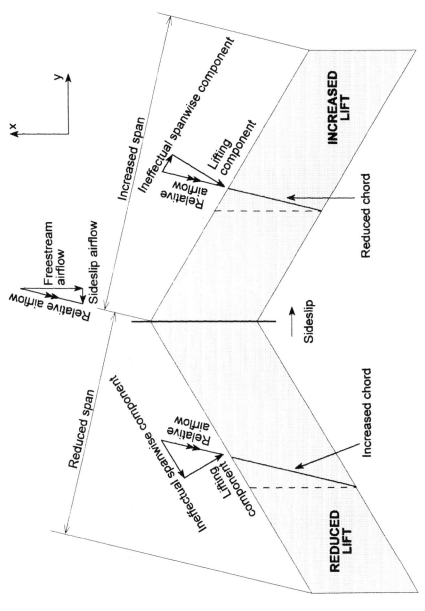

Figure 6.7 The effects of sweepback on rolling moment due to sideslip

front of the wings, you will observe that the relative airflows (with double arrows) are equal and parallel, but that, due to the sweepback, the lifting component on the right-hand wing is greater than that on the other wing. Since the lift of a wing depends on the square of the airspeed causing the lift, the right wing gets considerably more lift than that on the left, and so an anticlockwise rolling moment (as seen by the pilot looking forward) is obtained as required.

The figure also shows that the effective span of the right-hand wing is greater than that on the left due to the sideslip, and also that the chord length over which the relative airflow passes is greater on the left than on the right. This has two effects. First of all, the effective aspect ratio (normally defined as span divided by chord) is substantially greater on the right wing than on the left, on account both of the effective span and the effective chord changes. This means that the tip losses are more significant on the left wing, which once again means that the right wing obtains more lift. Secondly, although not specifically shown, the effective aerofoil section is also modified by the change in effective chord length. The absolute measurement of maximum camber of the aerofoil sections on left and right remains unaltered[7], but since the right wing's effective chord length is less than that of the left wing, the right wing's effective camber (the ratio of maximum camber to effective chord) is increased and so the right wing has a greater C_L than that of the left. Thus not only is the additional lift produced by an increase in air speed, but also by an increase in coefficient of lift, and the rolling moment is further enhanced.

You may meet explanations of the dihedral effect of sweepback which concentrate on the difference in effective span of the two wings, but which fail to make the link between that and aspect ratio and the resulting difference in tip losses. The hidden implication is that a greater span means a greater area (which of course it doesn't), and hence a greater total wing lift. However, another correct way of interpreting the modification of aspect ratios of the two wings is to say that the lift curve slopes (the slopes of the graphs of C_L against α) of the two wings are altered in the way discussed in Figure 14.2 of *Flightwise – Principles of Aircraft Flight*. But this is simply another way of expressing the change in wing lift due to the tip losses as discussed above.

Yet another approach to explaining the phenomenon is to point out that the effective thickness:chord ratio of the into-wind wing is greater than that of the downwind wing because of the change in effective chord length that we have discussed above. But what is often not

---

[7]A detailed explanation of aerofoil terminology, including camber, is given at the start of Chapter 9 of *Flightwise – Principles of Aircraft Flight*.

pointed out is that the thickness:chord ratio of an aerofoil *on its own* does not affect the lift coefficient. To understand this, remember that the lift curve slope of any aerofoil, whilst unstalled and well away from its stalling angle, is approximately a universal constant of about 1 in 10° of angle of attack.[8] It follows that any uncambered conventional aerofoil at an angle of attack of, say, 5° will have a C_L value of almost exactly $\frac{1}{2}$, regardless of the thickness:chord ratio. However, if the aerofoil is cambered, then a reduction in chord will, as we have seen above, bring with it an increase in its camber, and it is this that produces the extra C_L and thus wing lift.

We have so far met three contributory causes for the L_v effect of sweepback, but there is yet another, although this one is not uniquely related to sweepback[9]. Although shown only by a central line in Figure 6.7, there is inevitably a fuselage between the two wings. During symmetrical flight this has either no effect or a small symmetrical effect on each wing. But now, with a sideslip airflow, the fuselage offers a considerable shielding effect to the downwind wing, (the left in the figure). The details of the fuselage side-flow wake will vary from design to design, but it is certain that the wing downwind of the fuselage will be subject to some disturbance, be it in the form of turbulence, vortices or simply a modification of the relative airflow direction. Although it is possible that some of this effect may be favourable, as we shall see in the next section, it is very likely that the lift of the downwind wing will be degraded to some degree by the fuselage interference, whereas the upwind wing is facing a totally undisturbed airflow which will enhance the sweepback effect, providing a favourable rolling moment.

The dihedral effect of sweepback is found to depend directly on the overall lift coefficient of the aircraft, and therefore a swept-wing aircraft is most laterally stable at low speeds when the angle of attack is high[10]. This can create a particular problem for the pilot of a swept-wing aircraft when landing on a runway at which there is a crosswind[11]. During the approach he or she must point the nose of the aircraft at an angle to the centreline of the runway along which it is flying, in order to take account of the crosswind. But just before touching down the pilot must yaw the aircraft with the rudder so that its longitudinal axis is parallel to the runway, to prevent the undercarriage from receiving a large side-load on touching down. During this

---

[8]This is dealt with in the section 'Aerofoil Characteristics', including Figures 9.3 and 9.4, in Chapter 9 of *Flightwise – Principles of Aircraft Flight*.
[9]This feature is considered again later in this chapter, under the subheading 'Mid-Wing'.
[10]This is explained in Chapter 9, around Figure 9.2.
[11]Cross-wind landing will be explained more fully in Chapter 9, around Figure 9.4.

brief period the crosswind is producing a side-flow to the aircraft, and this will tend to pick up the upwind wing and roll the aircraft in the downwind direction. The pilot will have to be prepared for this and to compensate by using the ailerons.

We have seen that sweepback is a powerful agent for providing a stabilising rolling moment due to sideslip, for four reasons. It is such a powerful stabilising influence that sometimes the need for sweepback for other purposes threatens to provide an aircraft with too much lateral stability, and so L_v has to be reduced by other means. But as we proposed at the end of the previous section, let us proceed to cover the remaining L_v contributors before looking at particular examples.

Wing Height Relative to Fuselage

By comparison with the first two L_v agents, the third area that we must consider is rather more abstruse. Essentially we must look at the position at which the wings of the aircraft are attached to the fuselage, together with the aerodynamic nature of the fuselage itself. Once again the production of a stabilising rolling moment depends entirely on the presence of sideslip, and once again misinformation abounds.

In Chapter 5 of *Flightwise – Principles of Aircraft Flight* it was argued at length that, if we could assume that air was inviscid, the airflow round a circular cylinder placed normal to the free stream would follow the potential flow pattern shown in Figure 6.8. Now, *if* the air were inviscid (which it isn't) and *if* we could split the relative airflow

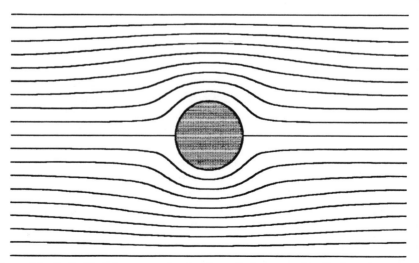

Figure 6.8   Inviscid airflow around a circular cylinder normal to the free stream

into two separate phenomena at right angles which did not interact with each other, one being the free stream flow and the other the sideslip flow (which we can't), *then* we could regard the cylinder figure as representing the fore-and-aft view of a typical pressurised aircraft fuselage, and by drawing in the wings we would be able to see where there was upflow on a wing producing extra angle of attack and lift, and where downflow.

Although such idealisation is not possible, the concepts involved are in fact very helpful. The boundary layer due to the large axial velocity has a long distance (from the nose) in which to grow, so over most of the fuselage it is turbulent and quite thick, and this ensures that the transverse flow remains attached until well round the fuselage. Furthermore, since the transverse flow is much slower than the longitudinal flow, the curves of the transverse streamlines apply a relatively small modification to the straight streamlines of the axial flow, and so the resulting helix-like flow is not nearly as tightly curved as Figure 6.8 would suggest. However, there *will* be some separation and a consequent sideways turbulent wake, and there may also be some shed vortices, and so although the potential flow model is a useful guide to behaviour, it does not tell the entire story. Furthermore, the fuselage will often be some other shape than a circular cylinder, it may not extend far in front of the wing, and there will be bits and pieces protruding from it, all of which means that each aircraft must be considered on its own merits, using the potential flow model as a guide.

Low Wing

With these thoughts as background, let us consider the effects on lateral stability of the two most common ways of designing the wing-fuselage intersection: the low-mounted wing and the high wing. The reasons for the designer's choice of one or the other (except insofar as the choice was dictated by considerations of lateral stability) are legion, but need not concern us here. In Figure 6.9 is shown a front view of a typical airliner with cylindrical fuselage and low-mounted wing. It is banked and consequently sideslipping towards the lower wing. Superimposed is the potential flow pattern of Figure 6.8, inclined with the wings to represent the sideways component of the resultant airflow caused by the sideslip. Bearing in mind the limitations of this model discussed in the preceding paragraphs, it will still be clear that the side-flow will cause the freestream flow to be deflected somewhat downwards in the root region of the lower wing, reducing the angle of attack and hence the lift in that region. Also, provided the potential flow model is reasonably valid on the wake side of the fuselage, there will be an upflow, an increase in angle of attack and hence additional lift on the root of the upper wing. Consequently the effect of mounting the wings low on a circular fuselage is actually destabilising in roll.

But this is not the end of the story for the low-wing configuration. We have already mentioned that the potential flow pattern may not be a reliable model for the sideslip flow, even over a circular cylindrical fuselage, and for other cross-sectional shapes of fuselage the model may well break down altogether, with considerable side-flow separation and form drag. In Figure 6.9 we implicitly assumed d'Alembert's paradox to apply since we were invoking the inviscid model, and thus did not consider any sideways drag on the fuselage. But if the fuselage does cause side-flow separation, sideways form drag will result, and we must consider what effect this may have on the rolling stability.

Unlike the wing lift-forces, the side-force on the fuselage acts perpendicularly to the plane of symmetry, and the direction of the rolling moment it produces will depend upon whether the sideways centre of pressure is above or below the aircraft's centre of gravity. A lot of the mass of an aircraft is in the wings, especially if they contain fuel tanks and carry engines, and so a low wing configuration hints at a low centre of gravity. The Second World War Spitfire and a number of other older aircraft with single or tandem dual seating rather than side-by-side seats tend to have high, thin fuselages, presenting a considerable side area, sometimes known as a keel surface, to the airflow, and if, as was often the case in such aircraft, the point of action of the side-force was above the centre of gravity, sideslipping would produce a restorative rolling moment, as needed for stability. Also, many aircraft have a large, high tail fin which is designed to produce a large force in sideslip. Although primarily intended for its yawing (N_v) contribution as considered earlier, a large high tail fin may in fact make a substantial contribution to a restorative L_v derivative. The conflict of interest in the tail fin's function will crop up again when we are considering dynamic lateral stability.

High Wing

We have seen that a low-mounted wing has mixed influences on rolling stability depending on a number of factors. But on the other hand, a high wing mounted at the top of the fuselage is nearly always stabilising in roll. Unfortunately the fact that this works well and 'looks obvious' for the wrong reasons has resulted in it being referred to as 'pendulum stability', but this is a seriously misleading term. Sometimes apologists for this term think that they are circumventing the problem by substituting the description 'high wing, low centre of gravity', which is certainly noncommittal in *how* it works, but still implies that stability is produced through the gravitational force in some way, rather than by an aerodynamic force.

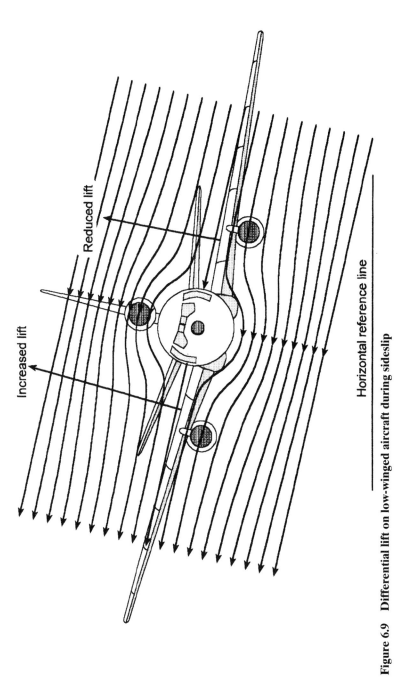

Figure 6.9   Differential lift on low-winged aircraft during sideslip

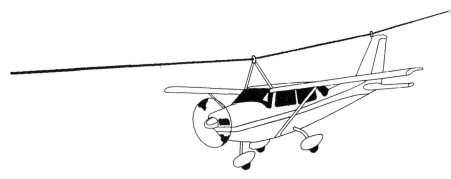

Figure 6.10   The so-called pendulum effect!

Consider a simple pendulum consisting of a mass on one end of a light rod with the other end pivoted to an overhead fixed point. If the pendulum is pulled to one side and released it will swing back towards the vertical and so it is statically stable. Rotation occurs about the fixed pivot, and so it is convenient to take moments about that pivot, and hence the rather complicated reaction force which acts through that point can be ignored. The only external force is the weight of the pendulum, acting vertically through the centre of gravity of the pendulum, and the restoring moment is the weight multiplied by the horizontal distance between the centre of gravity and the pivot.

If a high-winged aircraft in its rolling motion were to resemble a pendulum, it would be necessary for there to be a fixed point above the fuselage, about which the aircraft could swing under the action of gravity, and some form of sky-hook would be needed, or rather an overhead cable in the direction of flight along which the aircraft could slide, as shown in Figure 6.10. This false idea has probably been encouraged by observation of other aerial objects such as balloons, parachutes and airships (Figure 6.11), in which it seems even more

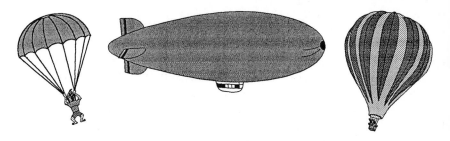

Figure 6.11   Misleading examples of so-called pendulum stability

obvious (until one questions a little more deeply) that the basket, the parachutist and the gondola swing like pendulums below the envelope or canopy. In the cases of the airship and the balloon, the principle by which rolling stability is obtained is quite different, and is in no way dependent on sideslip as in the case of the aircraft. If the gondola or basket is displaced slightly to one side of its central position, the restoring moment is provided by the couple of the upward buoyancy on the envelope and the downward weight acting through the centre of gravity, until the two forces line up with each other again. But on a fixed-wing aircraft the lift-force, unlike buoyancy, does not act vertically but in the plane of symmetry, and always through the centre of gravity.

In the case of the parachutist, the direction of the resultant aerodynamic force on the canopy is in fact very variable, and adequate rolling stability cannot be taken for granted by parachute designers. Essentially, however, it depends, as with aircraft, on the aerodynamic effects of sideslip, which will be resisted far more strongly by the drag of the canopy than that on the parachutist. Thus the canopy's sideways movement is severely restricted and more closely resembles a sky-hook, but in reality the situation is comparable to the sideways drag of a high keel surface on a low-wing aircraft as discussed earlier, and the restoring moment is produced by aerodynamic side-force above the centre of gravity.

So if the term 'pendulum stability' is a misnomer for the roll stabilising mechanism of high-winged aircraft, how is it properly explained? Gravity always acts through the centre of gravity, and therefore can never have a moment about that point, and so the righting agent has to be an aerodynamic force, and once again it depends entirely on sideslip. Just as we used the potential flow model around a low-winged aircraft fuselage to form an initial impression of what was occurring, so we can do it again in Figure 6.12. We see that there is now an upflow on the lower wing resulting in an increase in its angle of attack and lift, and (although less reliable now in view of the more angular shape of the fuselage) probably some downflow and reduction of lift on the higher wing. Consequently the high wing configuration is naturally stabilising in roll, just as the low wing is destabilising.

There are a great many large transport aircraft with high wing and cylindrical (pressurised) fuselages, but the configuration is far more familiar on smaller aircraft with unpressurised and much more angular fuselages, and in particular on light tourers and trainers such as the many models produced by Cessna. (The aircraft in Figure 6.10, apart from the cable attachments, and in Figure 6.12 is the Cessna Model 182 Skylane.) Not only will such fuselages create much more sideways form drag, but also there may be draggy attachments such as

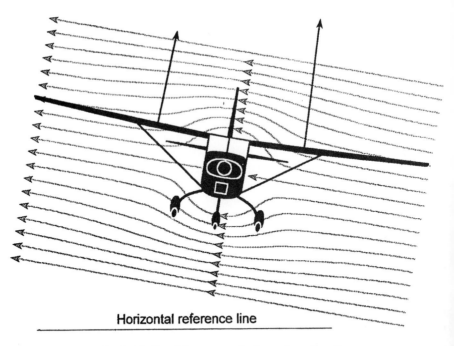

Horizontal reference line

Figure 6.12   Idealised sideslip airflow around a low-wing aircraft

non-retractable undercarriages which may have a significant destabilising effect because of their vertical distance below the centre of gravity. The wing itself will produce a certain amount of sideways drag force (largely due to the skin friction element), just as it will on a low wing, but in the high wing case this effect is stabilising because it acts above the centre of gravity, and is often presented as the primary cause of anchoring the top of the fuselage to provide the necessary sky-hook on which to hang the 'pendulum'. Hang-gliders and weight-shift microlight aircraft, in which the wing is set even higher relative to the centre of gravity, probably owe their roll stability almost entirely to the sideways drag of the wing and not at all to the potential flow pattern over the lower superstructure, and in this case perhaps the use of the term 'pendulum effect' is rather more apt than for conventional aircraft. They may be thought of as occupying the gap between aircraft and parachutes.

As an approximate rule of thumb, it is handy to note that the rolling stability produced by side-flow around a high wing is equivalent to dihedral of between 1° and 3°, and a low wing is equivalent to between 1° and 3° of anhedral. By way of comparison, 10° of sweepback produces about the same amount of dihedral effect as 1° of dihedral.

Mid-Wing

According to the explanations that we have been looking at, it would appear that an aircraft with its wing protruding from each side of the fuselage at mid-height of the fuselage would obtain no dihedral effect from the side-flow around the fuselage. This, however, is not quite true, because in sideslip the fuselage hides the downwind wing in its sideways wake, shielding that wing from receiving the clean airflow that it requires for lift, so that the unshielded wing produces a restorative rolling moment. With moderate to high aspect ratio wings this is not a very important feature, since only the root region of the shielded wing is adversely affected. But in the case of very low aspect ratio wings, this can be a major source of dihedral effect, since the entire span of the downwind wing may lie in the wake of the fuselage, degrading its lift very seriously.

Although we have so far entirely divorced the longitudinal motion from the lateral-directional motion in our thinking, there may in fact be some appreciable coupling between the two classes of stability in this mid-wing, low aspect ratio design. This is because the loss of lift in sideslip by the shielded wing is not compensated for by any additional lift on the upwind side, and so there will be a net loss of wing lift, affecting Z and M in the longitudinal equations. However, both the mid-wing configuration and such very low aspect ratios are very rare in aircraft design, so this is scarcely ever a problem.

Examples

Having now thoughtfully reviewed how wing dihedral, sweepback and the wing–fuselage interaction can influence the roll stability of an aircraft, we will close the chapter by looking at a number of examples illustrating the use of these principles. Such a survey must necessarily be extremely cursory, but if you would like to consider more examples may I recommend any book containing three-view silhouette drawings of a wide range of aircraft, such as *Jane's World Aircraft Recognition Handbook*, written by Derek Wood and published by Jane's Information Group. With your growing insight into the reasons for many of the features of an aircraft's shape, you will find yourself thumbing through such a source with increased fascination as you spot illustrations confirming the lessons learnt. Sometimes you will come across others which seem to belie the principles, which will provide you with a source of open-ended speculative questions to sharpen up your powers of logical reasoning, even if you aren't able ultimately to read the designer's mind completely.

A scan through a large selection of silhouettes will show that probably the most common general layout (so far as the features being considered here are concerned) is the low wing (swept or unswept), circular (or approximately so) fuselage arrangement with a moderate amount of dihedral. An example is the McDonnell Douglas MD-80 airliner in Figure 5.3, but the style is not limited to large airliners and will be seen across a range of types from combat aircraft to light personal tourers and trainers. You will also find that there is a very large number of aircraft with high (shoulder-mounted) wings, and in general these have less dihedral or none at all.

The use of dihedral, the cornerstone agent of rolling stability, may be clearly seen in the McDonnell Douglas DC-10 frontal views of Figures 6.3, 6.4 and 6.9. This aircraft has a moderate amount of dihedral, about 5°, compared with the maximum amount used on some aircraft which would appear to be around 8° to 9°. Often the tailplane will be given a different amount of dihedral from the wings, (it is greater in the DC10), and although this will provide a contribution to L_v its primary purpose is usually to get the tailplane into a region of air that is not going to be unduly influenced by the wing wake or by engine exhaust. For example, another very different McDonnell Douglas aircraft, the Phantom fighter (of which over 5000 were built), has very pronounced *anhedral* on the tailplane, in order to keep the roots above the jet engine efflux whilst also keeping most of the tailplane's lifting surface below the wake of the wing when it shock-stalls.

Sweepback is a very powerful L_v agent. In the early 1950s when Boeing were designing the 707 – the first long-range high subsonic speed jet airliner – there was serious concern about whether the pronounced sweepback being proposed (for the reasons discussed in the section 'Raising the Critical Mach Number in Chapter 11 of *Flightwise – Principles of Aircraft Flight*) would create so much lateral stability that it would unacceptably compromise the aircraft's roll control, especially in crosswind landings. In the event this did not turn out to be an insurmountable problem, and the aircraft has operated successfully with its very large leading edge sweepback angle of about 40°. With the confidence gained from this, the subsequent and much bigger Boeing 747 was given an even greater sweepback of about 42° at the leading edge, and despite this its wings are still set at a moderate dihedral angle, which is just as well, since it allows room for the under-slung engines beneath the low mounted wing, without having to resort to excessively long undercarriage legs. However, through the use of supercritical wings (also discussed in Chapter 11 of *Flightwise – Principles of Aircraft Flight*) the more modern airliners are able to save substantial amounts of structural weight by using very much less sweepback, but it is still a major contributor to roll stability.

In comparison with transport aircraft, most fighters with sweepback

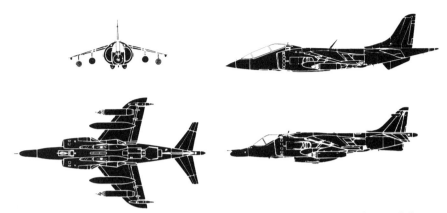

Figure 6.13   British Aerospace Harrier GR3 having high, swept wing and large anhedral angle

tend to have considerably less dihedral, or even none at all, because more agility in roll control may be had if the rolling stability is subdued. Many, indeed, have a moderate amount of anhedral, as seen in the case of the Tornado in Figure 5.5, and nowhere is this use of anhedral more marked than on the Harrier vertical take-off and landing aircraft, of which the GR3 version is shown in Figure 6.13. Without this anhedral of about 10°, excessive rolling stability would be provided through the combination of wing sweep and the wing's high position on the very fat fuselage, which is almost circular just ahead of the wings. The reason for this wing mounting arrangement is that the very large single Pegasus engine has to be mounted at the centre of gravity because its four pivoting vertical-lift nozzles must be evenly spread around the centre of gravity of the aircraft, like table legs, for equilibrium in the hover, and must be able to rotate into the normal flight position whilst producing high thrust levels. The wing must also be at the centre of gravity, and if it were below the engine it would be in the way of the jets from these adjustable nozzles.

Given this constraint on where to mount the wing, the marked anhedral is fortuitous for another reason. Since the undercarriage cannot be stowed in the wing roots because they are too high, it is housed in the fuselage. Furthermore, in order to keep the wheels out of the way of the hot jets from the nozzles, the designers have chosen to use a bicycle, rather than a tricycle, undercarriage, but for lateral support on the ground this necessitates the provision of a small wheel and strut at each wing-tip. These wing-tip outrigger legs can be seen retracted (folded back) in the plan view of Figure 6.13. If it were not for the anhedral, they would have had to be very much longer, and such a simple solution would not have been possible.

Some years ago when the idea of using forward-swept wings was attracting much interest[12], one cohort of Aircraft Design students at Cranfield University (then Institute of Technology) took as their group design project the interesting challenge of redesigning the Harrier jump jet with a forward-swept wing, and an interesting result emerged. The forward-swept wings would have produced a similar amount of positive (destabilising) L_v to the negative L_v produced by the existing swept-back wings, for exactly the same reason in reverse, and the overall rolling stability of the aircraft would have been seriously deficient. The solution proposed was the standard method of improving roll stability, and that was to give the wings dihedral. Consequently, instead of pointing downwards from the high shoulders of the fuselage, the wings now pointed substantially upwards, so that the wing-tips were a very considerable height above the ground, and the previous use of outrigger wheels was totally impracticable!

The Harrier shows the use of the high wing for achieving roll stability, and so does the Cessna Model 182 Skylane of Figures 6.10 and 6.12. Other aircraft amongst the many which exemplify this feature are the British Aerospace BAe 146 feederliner, unusual also for its four engines, its T-tail, its low noise emission and its good short-field performance; and the relatively recent Argentinean basic and advanced jet trainer, the FMA IA 63 Pampa, shown in Figure 6.14. Since Dornier assisted with its development, the Pampa is largely based on the Dassault-Breguet/Dornier Alpha Jet, which somewhat resembles the Harrier in appearance (although it is not a vertical take-off aircraft) except that the Pampa has a straight wing rather than the swept wing of the Alpha Jet. Figure 6.14 shows that the Pampa has no sweepback and about 1° of anhedral, and so it clearly obtains no roll stability from either dihedral or sweepback. It follows that its L_v is provided solely by the fuselage effect of the high wing, and this is great enough to require some degrading by means of a little bit of anhedral.

Although the high wing concept tends in one's mind to be associated more with small aircraft than with large, this is not in fact justified. Most of the world's largest transport aircraft use this ploy as the best way to keep the very long wings and under-slung engines off the ground, whilst having (i) a fuselage which is low enough for convenient loading of cargo and (ii) undercarriage legs which are sufficiently short to be endowed with the necessary strength. The most extreme example is the world's largest aircraft, the 84-metre long and 87-metre wingspan Ukrainian Antonov An-225 Cossack, which has a maximum take-off weight of 600 tonnes, and is designed specifically

---

[12]Forward-swept wing aircraft will be discussed at length in Chapter 14.

Figure 6.14   FMA IA 63 Pampa with high unswept wings and slight anhedral

for carrying big piggy-back loads such as a space shuttle. Such a load, whilst raising the sideways centre of pressure on the aircraft, would most significantly raise the combined centre of gravity perhaps to near the plane of the wings, and so its effect on roll stability would not be a foregone conclusion.

Figure 6.15 shows the Learjet 24D executive transport, which has low, almost totally unswept wings with no more than about 0.5° of dihedral. Scarcely any roll stability can come from the dihedral or from the sweepback, and the low wing on the cylindrical fuselage will offer a destabilising L_v contribution. Can this aircraft be stable in roll? How much contribution does the tail fin make by way of a high keel surface? What about the sweepback of the tailplane? Almost certainly the principal answer in this case is the presence of the T-tail above the tail fin. This will give the tail fin a much greater lift-curve slope than an unshielded fin, so that it will produce substantially more side-force for the same side-flow angle, and the relatively short fuselage will mean that the fin's moment arms about the x and z axes are not as dissimilar as on longer aircraft. Another low-winged aircraft (not illustrated here), displaying even less dihedral and sweepback

Figure 6.15   Learjet

than the Learjet, is the Yugoslavian-built basic trainer Soko G-2 Galeb, but this has neither a T-tail nor any wing or tailplane sweep-back or dihedral at all, and the wings are low-mounted. It would not appear to follow any of the rules!

Finally, let us look at the Lockheed F-104 Starfighter as shown in Figure 6.16. It was an early Mach 2 supersonic fighter which, although very different in style, was developed at about the same time as the English Electric Lightning, also a Mach 2 fighter, whose wings were swept at 60°. In Chapter 10 of *Flightwise – Principles of Aircraft Flight* we discussed (at Figure 10.9) the difficulty of flying this aircraft at low enough speed for landing, and now that we come back to consider it from the roll stability point of view it looks no less interesting, as it is in many other respects as well.

The wings are virtually unswept, having no more than about 5° of sweepback at the quarter-chord line (which is where sweep is usually measured[13]), and so very little if any roll stability is provided from sweepback, yet the designers have given the aircraft a hefty 10° of

[13]The appropriate position at which to measure sweep is fully discussed in Chapter 14 in the subsection 'Forward Swept Wing Aircraft'.

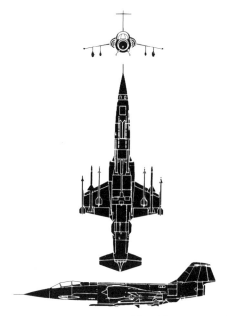

Figure 6.16 **Lockheed F-104 Starfighter, with mid, unswept wings and anhedral**

anhedral, the same amount as on the Harrier (where it was clearly justified). The explanation is two-fold. Firstly, there is a very high tail fin, whose height is almost as great as the length of each wing, and the tip of this is shielded by a T-tail, making the fin virtually two-dimensional in its performance and thus highly effective as a stabilising roll contributor, both on account of moment arm and magnitude of side-force produced. Secondly, the extremely low aspect ratio wings are mid-mounted on a fairly bulbous fuselage, so that in sideslip the trailing wing lift is very seriously degraded because of being immersed in the close wake of the fuselage. Although such means of obtaining lateral static stability are very uncommon, it is clear that together these two features are highly effective in producing a restoring rolling moment, as evidenced by the designer's need to shed so much stability by means of wing anhedral.

CHAPTER 7
Lateral/Directional Dynamic Stability

INTRODUCTION

It has probably nagged on your mind in a number of instances during the previous chapter that most of the phenomena that we have been considering cannot really be as clinically compartmentalised as you have so far been led to believe. Yawing and rolling motion are in fact inextricably intertwined, and it is now, as we come to consider the aircraft's complete dynamic motion following disturbances in roll and yaw, that we shall take the opportunity of looking carefully, although necessarily only superficially, at such interactions. We are touching the edge of a very complex subject.

In this the final chapter specifically dealing with aircraft stability, we shall be drawing on many of the concepts and ideas that we have met and discussed in some detail in the foregoing chapters. We shall be making extensive use of the shorthand notations introduced at the end of Chapter 2, with which you will by now be becoming familiar and comfortable. We shall also be introducing a further mathematical 'black box', based on Newton's Second Law equations, for the lateral/directional motions which is directly parallel in essence to the longitudinal 'black box', and so shall not need to repeat in detail the way in which the new set of aerodynamic derivatives is derived. We shall therefore be able to make more rapid progress. Although for brevity, and in accordance with common practice, we shall usually abbreviate the phrase 'lateral/directional' simply to 'lateral', you should bear in mind that we are not restricting ourselves to rolling and banking but are including yawing.

Having now reached the stage of jogging rather than walking, we shall find that we are having to get our minds working in a fairly agile manner around the complex motions and the unexpected interactions that are involved. We have come to the point at which static flat drawings on the page can no longer do justice to all the visual imagery that is essential to understanding, and we need dynamic, three-dimensional pictures. The one 'prop' that I have always found absolutely essential when teaching stability and control in the classroom is a sturdy model of any conventionally configured aircraft, about 1 or 2 feet in length, which I can grasp firmly by the fuselage between wings and tail and move about in the air to demonstrate the various motions to be considered. One additional item which proves very useful is a bamboo cane which can be held by the left hand in front of the aircraft pointing in the free stream flight direction, as a visual fixed reference whilst the aircraft axes are dancing their jactitations.

While preparing to write this chapter, I soon discovered that I could no longer manage to muster my thoughts properly without the aid of such an aircraft model in front of me, although a classroom-size one would be inappropriate in my study. Likewise, I am sure that you will find it extremely useful, indeed almost indispensable, to have at your elbow a small sturdy model of any *conventional* aircraft which you can repeatedly pick up and move around. Therefore I would urge you to go out to your nearest toy or model shop and buy one, as I have just done myself. I quickly came across a Matchbox toy BAe Hawk Trainer in RAF Red Arrows livery; it is about 4 inches long, virtually indestructible, it cost £2.99 at my local Woolworths store, and it is ideal for the job. I have also availed myself of a kebab skewer from the kitchen drawer to act as a flight path reference, but a knitting needle or a pot-plant cane would do equally well.

EQUATIONS OF MOTION AND AERODYNAMIC DERIVATIVES
The Lateral Equations
The three motions of an aircraft that we are now concerned with are the sideways linear motion in the y-axis direction and two rotations consisting of rolling about the x-axis and yawing about the z-axis. Based on Newton's Second Law, the equations of motion in their basic form are:

$$Y = ma_y$$
$$L = I_x\alpha_x$$
$$N = I_z\alpha_z$$

where the x and z subscripts to the Is and αs signify the axes about which they are taken. The treatment of the equations follows exactly the same pattern as that which we discussed for the longitudinal motions in Chapter 5, and as in the former case the force and moment terms on the left of the equations may be expanded to take account of aerodynamic and gravitational forces. Once again we are considering stick-fixed stability, so that no control forces need to be taken into account, and furthermore the engine thrust force is assumed to be parallel to the x-axis and therefore does not become involved at all.

The Inputs
First of all, let us look briefly at the two moment of inertia terms I_x and I_z. The fuselage makes very little contribution to the rolling moment of inertia I_x since its mass is concentrated close to the x-axis. In high aspect ratio aircraft, I_x is mainly due to the mass of the wings,

especially when these carry large fuel loads and wing-mounted engines as in most large transport aircraft, and its value can be very substantial. Rapid changes in roll rate are not usually a requirement of such aircraft, but they often are in aircraft with low aspect ratio wings and fuselage-mounted engines such as most modern fighters. Fortunately in these cases I_x is much lower, although the fin and tailplane may constitute a more substantial proportion of the whole. This contrast is clearly illustrated by the Starfighter (Figure 6.17) and the McDonnell Douglas DC-10 (Figure 6.3). The yawing moment of inertia I_z contains almost exactly the same contribution from the wings as did I_x since the wings extend outwards from both the x-axis and the z-axis. However, I_z is a very much greater quantity, since it additionally contains a major contribution from the fuselage, which extends fore and aft from the z-axis.

The aerodynamic elements of the forces and moments in the equations may be expanded by introduction of the relevant aerodynamic derivatives, a completely new set in this case, and these will form the backbone of our investigation of the relationship between the aircraft shape and its lateral motions. It is not necessary to introduce any acceleration terms in the way that we earlier had to introduce $\dot{w}$, and so our complete set of lateral derivatives is represented by the cells of the following table, in which the symbols are given their definitions to refresh your memory, together with some additional brief notes:

	Sideways velocity v	Roll rate p	Yaw rate r
Side force Y	Y_v Fin, keel area	–	–
Rolling moment L	L_v Dihedral effect	L_p Roll damping	L_r Differential lift
Yawing moment N	N_v Weathercock	N_p Differential drag	N_r Yaw damping

Before we go on to look at the specific lateral motions that arise, (the so-called 'dynamic stability modes'), it will be useful for us to spend a few minutes looking at the elements of this table of aerodynamic derivatives, so that we shall be familiar with them when they crop up later. The first thing that we notice is that the heading items in the top row (the rates) and those in the left-hand column (the force and moments) correspond with each other in order, and therefore the cells on the leading diagonal of the table, (Y_v, L_p and N_r) must all be damping derivatives, the concept of which was introduced in the section of Chapter 5 headed 'Damping Derivatives and M_q'. The symbol

Y_v refers to the sideways drag force which arises during sideways motion (as distinct from any rotation), and depends primarily on the sideways-projected area of fuselage and fin (the aircraft's keel surface) and on the cross-sectional shape of the fuselage – a cylindrical fuselage being less draggy than a slab-sided one. L_p is the roll damping derivative that we have already met in the context of roll stability, and is the one that we dismissed as *not* on its own being able to provide stability but merely to check a roll[1]. N_r is the yaw damping derivative, and refers to the resistive moment occurring when the aircraft yaws, again not a restoring moment. This derivative is due largely to fin and nose side-forces and to the difference in drag between the two wing-tips (because of the difference between their speeds), and the moment arms at which these forces act will depend on the fuselage length and the wingspan respectively. (I found my toy aeroplane useful here, placed under my eyes on my desk, so that I could see what happened when I rotated it about its normal axis.)

The pair of derivatives L_v and N_v in the above table are the ones which, as we saw in Chapter 6, are responsible for producing a restoring rolling moment (the dihedral effect) and a straightening-up yawing moment (the weathercock effect) respectively. Although they both depend on the sideslip velocity v, we recall that in the rolling case this sideslip is occasioned by a linear motion in the y-direction, whereas in the directional situation it is the result of the aircraft having rotated about the normal axis, so that although the centre of gravity is still moving only forwards along the undisturbed flight path, there is a component of this velocity along the now skewed y-axis. The value of L_v was affected by wing dihedral, by sweepback and by certain features of the wing–fuselage abutment. That of N_v was mainly influenced by the size of the tail fin and its distance aft of the centre of gravity.

Reference to your model aircraft will show you that Y_p, the side-force due to rolling, is likely to be influenced only by very small asymmetric forces on the fin, and that, for Y_r, a yaw rate r only gives rise to what is approximately a couple due to side-forces on nose and tail fin. In practice both of these derivatives are insignificant and can be ignored. It therefore remains for us to look at the remaining two derivatives in the table, N_p and L_r.

The yawing moment N_p is due to roll rate. As the aircraft rolls, the

---

[1]It is possible for L_p to be positive, if an aircraft is flying beyond or close to its stalling angle. In this case, the lift of the down-going wing may *reduce*, and consequently the rolling moment due to asymmetric lift may be such as to cause the aircraft to continue to roll. This phenomenon is called *autorotation*, which is a rolling motion, not to be confused with a spin, although it may precipitate the latter. But this need not concern us in the present discussion.

resulting relative airflow comes upwards towards the down-going wing and downwards towards the up-going wing. Consequently the angle of attack of the down-going wing is increased just as was the case when considering the roll damping derivative L_p, and thus not only does its lift increase but so also does its induced drag, being dependent on lift. Meanwhile, the drag of the up-going wing is likewise reduced. The combined effect is that there is a yawing moment towards the side of the down-going wing, as a result of which a rolling motion brings in its train a yawing motion to the same side. A positive roll rate (down on the right) produces a positive yawing moment (clockwise when looking downwards), and so N_p has a positive value, and the sign does not change if the down-going wing-tip stalls, since its drag will still continue to increase. The downward speed of the descending wing is clearly greater the further out towards the tip you look, and so the resulting angle of attack, and hence drag force, is greatest in the tip region; and *vice versa* it is least in the tip region of the up-going wing. The tip region is also where the moment arm is greatest, and so the resulting yawing moment is quite an appreciable phenomenon, especially on aircraft with high aspect ratio wings. N_p must therefore be taken into account when considering lateral dynamic stability.

The other derivative of the pair is L_r, the rolling moment due to yaw rate. Whilst the aircraft is yawing, let us say to the right, there is no change in angle of attack on the two wings, but the left wing experiences a greater air speed, and consequently a greater lift force, than the other. Thus a positive yaw rate produces a positive rolling moment, so that L_r is positive.

The Outputs

So we have an interesting set of interrelated force and moment cause-and-effect phenomena to consider when investigating the lateral dynamic behaviour of an aircraft. Let us look now at what information we get out of the equations of motion once they have been processed. At a first glance it looks rather daunting, because we get no fewer than four types of motion revealed, but fortunately we can rapidly dismiss two of these, and move on to the remaining two, which are far more interesting.

First of all, we get the innocuous result of a motion with zero frequency and no damping, which simply means a neutrally stable mode. This is called the *heading mode*, and so we must briefly deviate to define and explain the word 'heading'. The heading of an aircraft is the direction in which it is flying, although this is not quite as simple as it sounds. Usually, even though the movement does not affect its flight in any way, an aircraft is operating in a mass of air that is moving bodily over the ground beneath, and to a person on the ground this movement is the wind. If the pilot of the aircraft never looks down or wishes to land, then he is only concerned with and aware of his motion relative to this mass of air. The aircraft's speed relative to this air mass is its true air speed, and the direction of motion relative to it is its heading. Providing the aircraft is flying symmetrically (i.e. with its velocity vector lying in its plane of symmetry), the aircraft's nose will be pointing in this same direction, and so the heading can also be thought of as the direction in which the aircraft is pointing. This also corresponds with the direction shown on a compass fixed in the aircraft. A compass therefore gives an aircraft's heading.

To an observer on the ground, or to a navigator in the aircraft trying to calculate how to reach a certain airfield, things are different. To the velocity vector consisting of the aircraft's air speed in the direction of its heading must be added the velocity of the air mass across the ground, which is called *drift*. The resultant of these two velocities is the actual velocity of the aircraft relative to the ground, which is what interests the navigator, and is what the person on the ground observes. The direction of this resultant velocity over the ground is called the aircraft's *track*, and its magnitude is the ground speed. If the wind is strong and not in line with the aircraft's flight, the ground observer will see a distinct difference between the aircraft's heading (i.e. the direction in which the nose is pointing) and its track (i.e. the direction in which the aircraft is moving), but the pilot with no close visual contact with the ground will only be aware of the heading, as shown on the compass.

We have just said that the aircraft's heading is the direction in which its nose is pointing, but that is only true during symmetrical undisturbed flight. If, due to a disturbance, the aircraft has yawed, its nose is temporarily no longer pointing along the heading direction, which is still the direction of the velocity vector. If it is sideslipping following a roll, the velocity vector itself is temporarily changed, but the heading is still the prevailing undisturbed direction of flight, i.e. the direction in which the nose is continuing to point. The key feature in all these situations is that the heading is the prevailing direction of flight relative to the surrounding air mass.

The aforementioned heading mode is simply the mathematical confirmation of the fact that if an aircraft's heading is changed, by whatever means, there can be no consequent aerodynamic forces or moments which would try to bring it back to its original heading. For the heading to have changed implies that the aircraft has yawed (through an angle ϕ), and also that the path of the centre of gravity has been deflected through the same angle ϕ. In this situation there will be no resulting sideslip and therefore no N_v effect to restore the aircraft to the original direction.

Secondly, the mathematical 'black box' reveals a non-oscillatory motion which is quite heavily damped, and this is a phenomenon that we met in Figure 6.4. The motion is called the *roll subsidence mode*, and it refers simply to the fact that rolling is always opposed (damped) by the differential lift of the wings. The damping derivative L_p is responsible for this, but the rolling moment of inertia I_x opposes the reduction in roll rate. Usually the same physical feature, the aspect ratio, affects both of these quantities in the same sense, but there are exceptions. If a low aspect ratio aircraft such as the Starfighter (Figure 6.17) has a large mass load distributed spanwise on account of wing-mounted weapons and heavy podded fuel tanks mounted at the wing-tips, then I_x will overshadow L_p, and roll damping will be very limited, so that rolling motion will tend to continue further than is desirable. On the other hand, a very high aspect ratio sailplane with extremely light wings carrying no distributed load will tend to be very heavily damped in roll.

The other two motions revealed by the 'black box' are both very important, and embody the main dynamic stability features of an aircraft. They are a pair of distinct motions, which conveniently correspond in certain respects to the pair of longitudinal modes, the short period pitching motion and the phugoid, that we looked at in Chapter 5. Being so important, we shall not relegate them to brief paragraphs at the end of this section, but will devote a separate section to each.

DUTCH ROLL

The Dutch roll mode is a very complex oscillatory rolling and yawing motion which is influenced by a considerable number of aerodynamic and inertia factors in varying degree, but by making some approximations we shall be able to visualise the basic elements of the motion. The derivation of the name is ignored by nearly all writers, but it seems likely that it was originally inspired by the combined rolling and weaving (yawing) motion characteristic of ice-skaters that is also referred to as a Dutch roll.

The Dutch roll may be thought of as the lateral analogue of the short period pitching oscillation that we met when examining longitudinal dynamic stability. The periodic time is of a similar magnitude, usually a little greater than the SPPO period because of I_z being substantially greater than I_y, and is typically in the range of 2 or 3 seconds up to about 15 seconds. Although not such a reliable approximation as it was for the SPPO, we may take it that the motion is rapid enough for the aircraft's centre of gravity to continue moving in a straight line along the undisturbed flight path. Just as the SPPO is an oscillation in pitch whose characteristics are substantially determined by the stabilising effect of the tailplane, so the Dutch roll may be regarded as pre-

dominantly an oscillation in yaw, dependent on the directionally stabilising and damping influence of the tail fin. Thus if an aircraft is
briefly disturbed in yaw, either by a gust in the airflow or by a deliberate deflection of the rudder by the pilot, and then the disturbing influence disappears, the directional stability produced by the N_v of the fin
will cause it to straighten up, overshoot and yaw the other way, and
thus to oscillate backwards and forwards about the z-axis, whilst the
N_r damping effect of the fin will subdue the oscillations. (Remember
that, even though the aircraft is not considered to be sideslipping,
there is still a side-flow angle of attack at the fin at all times when the
aircraft is yawed, due to the component of the overall velocity in the
y-axis direction.)

In the case of the SPPO, that was the end of the story, since there
was no asymmetric motion involved. However, the Dutch roll is not so
simple, because of the coupling that occurs between rolling and yawing, and we must examine a little more closely what goes on. To save a
lot of repetition of words, when we use either the word 'clockwise' or
'anticlockwise', we will take it for granted that the additional phrase
'as viewed by the pilot when looking outwards along the (appropriate)
axis' is implied. You will find it particularly helpful – nay, almost indispensable – to have your model aircraft handy. I have my Hawk toy on
a plain sheet of paper on my desk, with a straight line drawn up the
centre of the paper, over which the aircraft's longitudinal axis is lying.

Let us examine slowly and methodically a complete cycle of the
Dutch roll oscillation, starting with the undisturbed aircraft flying
straight and level. The pilot applies a short sharp rudder deflection
which makes the aircraft's nose swing to the right. Whilst the aircraft
is yawing clockwise, the left wing is advancing faster than the right,
and so receives more lift, and consequently the aircraft rolls clockwise.
This is the effect of the L_r derivative, and the rolling moment reduces
towards zero as the maximum yaw angle is approached and the yaw
rate reduces to zero. Furthermore, during this same yawing motion
the yaw angle ψ is increasing, so that there is a progressively increasing sideways airflow coming from the left (even though the centre of
gravity is not deviating from its straight-ahead path). Due to the dihedral (L_v) effect, this produces an additional clockwise rolling moment
reinforcing that due to L_r but in this case the rolling moment increases
towards a maximum value as yawing stops and the maximum yaw
angle is reached.

When the aircraft has reached its maximum yaw angle, the directionally stabilising moment of the fin (N_v) is at its maximum and starts
to yaw the aircraft back the other way, but there is still a clockwise
rolling moment in effect due to L_v. However, as the aircraft is now
yawing anticlockwise, the rolling moment due to L_r immediately starts

to act in the opposite way from before and to apply an anticlockwise rolling moment, whilst the clockwise L_v rolling moment reduces. Eventually the anticlockwise rolling moment is dominant, and the aircraft begins to roll back anticlockwise. Once beyond the straight-ahead ($\psi = 0$) position, the previous rolling moment pattern occurs in reverse, with both L_r and L_v moments acting anticlockwise, the L_v effect increasing and the L_r effect reducing as the yaw angle ψ approaches its maximum negative value. Clockwise yawing is then resumed, and the rolling rotation once more changes direction, slightly later than the yawing rotation.

Thus the Dutch roll motion consists of a yawing oscillation with a superimposed rolling oscillation. Both motions are of the same frequency, but the rolling motion is lagging somewhat behind the yawing motion – mathematically we say that there is a phase lag. If you manipulate your model aircraft in the manner of the Dutch roll (which takes a little practice – remember that there is no pitching motion involved), and if you imagine yourself sitting in the pilot's seat, you will observe that the nose in front of you will swing across the horizon in approximately a straight line from side to side, whilst also rolling first one way and then the other. But the most tell-tale symptom of the Dutch roll is to be seen by looking out sideways at either wing-tip. Both wing-tips will be observed to be describing approximately circular paths, with the tip moving rearwards at the tops of the circles and forwards at the bottoms: in other words, the right wing-tip is seen to be rotating clockwise, and the left wing-tip anticlockwise.

If an aircraft were designed with no dihedral stability (i.e. $L_v = 0$), then only the derivative L_r would be contributing to the rolling element of the Dutch roll. The rolling motion thus produced would be more nearly in phase with the yawing motion, and due to the inherent roll and yaw damping derivatives the motion would be expected to die out and to be dynamically stable. It is the dihedral derivative L_v which tends to be destabilising, since it achieves its maximum disturbing rolling moment just when recovery ought to be commencing, and it is possible for the motion to be unstable (the oscillations becoming divergent) if there is too much dihedral effect built in. Furthermore, the larger the value of the dihedral derivative L_v, the lower will be the frequency of the oscillations, since L_v is always opposing recovery. Even if marginally stable, it may be imagined that the Dutch roll is a very uncomfortable and unnerving motion to be experienced by all in the aircraft, not least the pilot, since at the extremes of each oscillation there can be the feeling that the rolling motion might not recover. It is therefore important that the aircraft is provided with a stable Dutch roll mode, as rapidly convergent as is compatible with other requirements that we shall consider presently.

How can it be that dihedral, and likewise sweepback, which are normally stabilising in roll, actually produce a destabilising influence during the Dutch roll? The answer to this lies in the nature of the sideways airflow producing the rolling moment. If an aircraft sideslips following a roll with no yaw, (the situation that we looked at when considering lateral static stability in the previous chapter,) the side-flow meets the aircraft from the side of the lowered wing, and hence gives it more lift to bring it back up to level. But if the side-flow is due to a yaw in the direction of the lowered wing (as in the Dutch roll, where the wing is initially lowered because of the differential lift of the L_r derivative), then that side-flow approaches the aircraft from the side of the *raised* wing, and thus tends to roll the aircraft the wrong way. Thus it is critically important to keep clear in one's mind the distinction between the two different ways in which a sideways airflow may be generated.

At first glance, therefore, it would appear that the answer to ensuring that an aircraft has a stable Dutch roll mode would be simply to ensure that it has as little dihedral effect built in as possible. But things are not so straightforward, and we shall have to return to the question of curing an unstable Dutch roll mode at the end of the next section.

SPIRAL MODE

Just as the Dutch roll mode is the lateral stability analogue of the longitudinal short period pitching oscillation, so we find that the final lateral mode to be considered corresponds in certain respects with the longitudinal phugoid mode, although it differs from the phugoid in the important respect that it is never oscillatory. This mode is called the *spiral* mode, or the *spiral dive* mode, and as the names suggest, it can result in the aircraft flying in a large circular and spirally descending path.

But we are jumping ahead of ourselves. You will recall that the phugoid could occur as a result of some residual vertical deflection of the flight path after a short period pitching oscillation had subsided. In much the same way, the spiral mode can be triggered by a residual disturbance, this time a small bank angle, left over when a stable Dutch roll oscillation has died away. Alternatively, this initiating bank angle could be generated by the pilot for investigative purposes by briefly rolling the aircraft using the ailerons, and then centralising his controls. Consequently the starting point for examining the spiral mode is an aircraft flying straight and level with one wing low, but with no rolling or yawing oscillations happening. Let us take it for the purposes of our discussion that the aircraft is banked to the right so that ϕ is positive.

The situation here is thus identical with that which we considered in Chapter 6 when looking at the means of achieving lateral (in that case specifically rolling) static stability. No restoring moment immediately occurs, but the resultant of the two forces, lift and weight, produces a sideslip which causes a sideways airflow component, and this we saw[2] is capitalised on by various design features to produce a restorative rolling moment, represented by L_v. One such feature was the tail fin, since it is usually above the longitudinal axis of the aircraft and so produces a restorative contribution to L_v. But the fin is at a much greater distance *aft* of the centre of gravity than it is above it, and so the yawing effect (N_v) of the tail fin is much more significant than its L_v contribution. Indeed, that is primarily what the fin is there for.

Take hold of your model! As the banked aircraft starts to sideslip to the right, it will start to roll back (anticlockwise) towards the wings-level state due to the rolling moment of L_v. At the same time, its N_v will make it yaw clockwise, so that the nose will descend down the slope at which the aircraft is banked. Since it is now yawing, the additional effect of the derivative L_r (the rolling moment due to yaw rate) comes into play, by which the advancing (left) wing achieves more lift than the other due to its greater forward speed, producing an upsetting, clockwise rolling moment. A conflict thus arises between the restoring (stabilising) rolling moment of the aircraft's dihedral features and the destabilising rolling moment of the differential wing lift due to yawing. If the latter wins, then the aircraft will bank more steeply, the sideslip will increase, and all the foregoing motion features will be increased. A spiral dive will ensue. On the other hand, if the dihedral stability wins, the wings-level situation will eventually be restored, although the aircraft will now of course be flying on a new heading, having undergone an uncorrected yaw, and it will have lost some height. If the two rolling moments exactly cancel each other out, the aircraft will continue gently to sideslip and yaw at a steady rate, whilst flying in a circular, descending path at a constant bank angle, but no recovery will occur.

Let us look briefly at the crucial rôle of the fin in the foregoing discussion. The fin's primary purpose is that of providing directional stability, or in other words a restorative yawing moment when the aircraft has yawed from its flight path. But in the present scenario, we find that the fin is providing exactly the opposite service, and is producing a yawing moment *away from* the initial heading. We have here

---

[2]When referring back to Figures 6.3 and 6.4, bear in mind that the aircraft there is facing you, and so it is actually banked at a negative angle ϕ. In the present discussion we are starting from a positive ϕ, since this is more convenient when holding and manipulating a physical aircraft model in your hand.

an identical dichotomy to that which confronted us when considering the Dutch roll mode. There we asked how it could be that dihedral, ostensibly a stabilising feature, could turn out to be destabilising. On this occasion we must ask exactly the same question about the fin and, exactly as before, the answer lies in the nature of the sideways airflow. For the fin to be directionally stabilising, it must receive its sideways airflow as a result of the fuselage having yawed. A clockwise yaw (positive ψ) results in airflow from the front left, which creates an anti-clockwise (restorative) moment by virtue of the fin. On the other hand, a sideslip to the right produces an airflow from the front right, which yaws the aircraft clockwise, a destabilising motion since there was no initial yawing disturbance to recover from. Once again it is the difference between the two mechanisms of producing a sideways airflow that is central to the issue.

Having looked at the cause of the spiral dive, let us turn now to consider its nature. The mode is non-oscillatory, since even if the dihedral effect wins and the wings return to level, this happens so slowly that the roll and side-force damping derivatives L_p and Y_v ensure that there will be no overshoot. The essence of the whole motion is its slowness. Whether the rolling moment due to yawing or that due to sideslip wins, the rate at which the departure or recovery occurs is very small. We cannot here speak of frequencies or periodic times, since the motion is not periodic, but it is customary to refer instead to the time taken for the parameter in question (in this case the bank angle ϕ) to halve or to double, for which typical times are around a minute or even longer. It is desirable for the spiral mode to be stable, but because of the slowness of the response (whether convergent or divergent) it does not matter unduly if the mode is marginally unstable. The pilot (or autopilot) will have plenty of time to take compensating action with the controls, and will normally do so automatically and unconsciously in the routine process of controlling the aircraft, without even knowing whether the aircraft is spirally stable or unstable.

It is not difficult to ensure that an aircraft's spiral mode is stable. The designer must simply give it sufficient dihedral effect (by any of the available means) to ensure that L_v dominates L_r. To be more precise, the mathematical model renders the rather elegant condition for spiral stability as:

$$\frac{L_v}{L_r} > \frac{N_v}{N_r}$$

which means that the dominance of the dihedral effect over the rolling moment due to yaw must outweigh the dominance of the directional stability over the yaw damping.

However, a problem arises when the designer considers both the spiral and Dutch roll modes together, since too much dihedral effect is directly destabilising to the Dutch roll. It is far more important to ensure a stable Dutch roll than a stable spiral mode. That is why care has to be taken always to ensure that the aircraft does not possess too much dihedral stability, which, particularly in the case of highly swept winged aircraft, often necessitates the incorporation of some anhedral, as exemplified by the Harrier in Figure 6.13 and the F-104 Starfighter in Figure 6.16.

If it is not always possible to keep the amount of dihedral effect as low as would be desirable for Dutch roll stability, as for example in the case of a swept-wing jet transport with low wings (placed low for other reasons) which needs to have dihedral for the sake of keeping wing-tips and under-slung engines clear of the ground; in any case some dihedral effect is needed for the sake of ensuring static stability following a roll, and thus keeping the spiral mode in check. Therefore many such aircraft are equipped with a *yaw damper*, a system which augments the natural stabilising and damping effect of the tail fin by automatic deployment of the rudder in phase with the Dutch roll oscillation.

Although they may be thought to have a superficial similarity to one another, a spiral dive should not be confused with a spin. Both contain elements of roll and yaw, but a spin is the result of an asymmetric stall, which (in level flight) occurs at a very low flying speed and high angle of attack. A spiral dive, on the other hand, occurs at normal flying speed, and with no variation in overall lift coefficient. It is not a sudden or dramatic event, and is readily corrected by routine application of the roll controls.

CHAPTER 8
An Overview of Flight Control

INTRODUCTION

If you wanted to study the subject of dietetics and nutrition in order to enable you to become an expert caterer, you would not expect your guide book to start by telling you about all the tools and equipment that a well-found kitchen should have in it, before considering the underlying principles. Likewise, an instruction book in the art of playing cricket would not begin by describing the various types of delivery that may be bowled or strokes that may be played with the bat, before you had been given some insight into the aims and rules of the game. But if you turn to almost any reference you choose (whether in-depth or simplistic) on the subject of the control of aircraft in flight, you will be virtually certain to be regaled, right at the outset, with a 'naming of parts' of the control surfaces, together with three neatly classified sub-paragraphs explaining that an aircraft can be controlled in roll, pitch and yaw.

Frankly, I believe that such an introduction is at best totally unhelpful, and generally confusing and demotivating. Our guiding principle in *Flightwise* is to delve constantly into answers to the question 'why?', but before that is possible, we must step back further and ask ourselves 'why what?' In other words, in the present context of aircraft control, we must first of all decide what it is that we require to do to the aircraft, and then what physical principles are involved in achieving this. Answering these questions will lead us into investigating how the aims are achieved in practice and why the various contributing parts of the aircraft are designed in the ways that they are.

FORCES VERSUS MOMENTS

The basic requirements of controlling an aircraft are to make its flight path change from one straight line to another and/or to change its speed of flight. In the words of the jargon, we wish to alter the aircraft's velocity vector either in magnitude or in direction or both. For a transport or touring aircraft this will consist sometimes of altering the aircraft's direction of flight from one heading to another in level flight without a change in speed, and at other times of changing the angle of elevation of the flight path[1], when starting, ending or

---

[1] This is the angle between the path of the aircraft's centre of gravity and the horizontal, that is to say the angle at which the aircraft is climbing or descending; not to be confused with the pitch angle θ or the angle of attack α. This is amplified at the end of this chapter, where we redefine the angle of elevation of the flight path as the flight path angle.

modifying a climb or descent, or when leaving or touching down on the runway at the moment of taking off or landing. Other types, such as agricultural and combat aircraft, have different, more complex control requirements involving the combination of vertical and horizontal changes in speed and direction, rapidly changing from one manoeuvre to another, and sometimes sustaining a vertical or horizontal curved flight path for its own sake. Ultimately the art of aerobatic flying, either for pure sport or entertainment or as developed out of the needs of hand-to-hand combat flying, combines all of the possible motions of an aircraft in virtually as many ways as may be imagined.

When talking about modifying the velocity vector of an aircraft, we're simply concerned with the motion of the aircraft's centre of gravity, and consequently we may treat the aircraft as a *particle*, rather than a rigid body. This means that we essentially need to consider only the forces acting on the aircraft, and not the moments. The moment-producing contribution of a force, as we saw in Chapters 3, only has the effect of rotating the aircraft *about* its centre of gravity without deflecting the centre of gravity from its original path at all. Although this was the province of aircraft stability as we have been discussing, it is decisively not the ultimate aim of aircraft control. Indeed, the only rotation about the centre of gravity that we ultimately require in a manoeuvre is such as to align the aircraft's longitudinal axis with the new modified flight path, and this is completely taken care of by the aircraft's natural stability, which we have already looked at extensively.

I would not be at all surprised if you were confused by this insistence that control is not about rotating an aircraft, since the way that aircraft control is very often taught is by saying exactly the opposite. You are likely to have been told that to control an aircraft completely involves being able to rotate it about each of its three axes: rolling being achieved with the ailerons, pitching with the elevator and yawing with the rudder. But rotating the aircraft in any one or combination of these ways is quite definitely not the ultimate purpose of the controls. It is true that these three modes of rotation are used, and are produced by the various control surfaces referred to, but these rotations are a *means to an end*, and not the end in themselves.

In order to emphasise the absurdity of treating the rotations and the control surfaces which cause them as the ultimate agent for aircraft control, let us take a brief look at an important conundrum that was presented and discussed at some length in Chapter 2 of *Flightwise – Principles of Aircraft Flight*, under the subheading 'The Forces Acting on an Aircraft'. Indeed, the whole of that chapter, entitled 'Forces and Aeroplanes', contains a crucial background discussion of forces, Newton's laws and the handling of vector quantities, and it is recommended to you if you find that some of the concepts arising in the following pages do not rest comfortably in your mind.

The conundrum in question arose after meeting the fact that in straight, level and constant speed flight an aircraft's lift-force equals its weight and its thrust equals its drag. We asked the question: is there any phase in an aircraft's flight, (if so, which phase?) during which the wings are required to produce *more* lift than the weight of the aircraft? In other words, is it safe to design wings capable of just supporting the weight of an aircraft, plus a reasonable factor of safety, or should there be some greater design criterion? We then immediately demolished the instinctive response of most people to that question by showing that, in a steady climb, rather than lift being greater than weight, it is in fact *less* than weight, diminishing towards zero as the climb approaches the vertical; the same also being true during a steady descent.

The answer was shown to be that it is during flight along a curved path that more lift is required than weight, and that the amount of lift required is not just marginally higher than in straight flight but is very substantially greater. The reason for this is the need to provide the large *centripetal* force which is needed to constrain the aircraft to keep turning inwards towards the centre of the circle. This inward turning constitutes an acceleration towards the centre of the circle, a continual changing of the direction of the aircraft's velocity vector, even when its magnitude, the aircraft's speed, is remaining constant.

Consider a turning aircraft banked at 60° to the vertical and maintaining level flight as in Figure 8.1(a). The forces on the aircraft are its weight acting straight downwards and the lift-force produced by the wings which, because of the symmetry of the wings, will act in the plane of symmetry. We may resolve the lift-force into two perpendicular components, one vertical and the other horizontal, which are shown using dashed lines. (Note that the lift-force is *replaced* by its components – they do not act in addition to the lift.) For the aircraft not to start climbing or descending, the vertical component of the lift must exactly equal the weight (by Newton's First Law), whilst the horizontal component of the lift provides the required centripetal force to produce the acceleration towards the centre and so maintain the circular flight path. (The centre of the circle is somewhere off the paper to the right.)

It is clear that the lift, being the diagonal of the vector rectangle, must be greater than either of its components. By scale drawing of the vector diagram or by simple trigonometry it may easily be shown that, in Figure 8.1(a) with a 60° angle of bank, the lift is exactly twice the weight. The aircraft is said to be 'pulling 2g', or that the ratio of lift to weight, which is called the *load factor*, is 2. If more centripetal force is

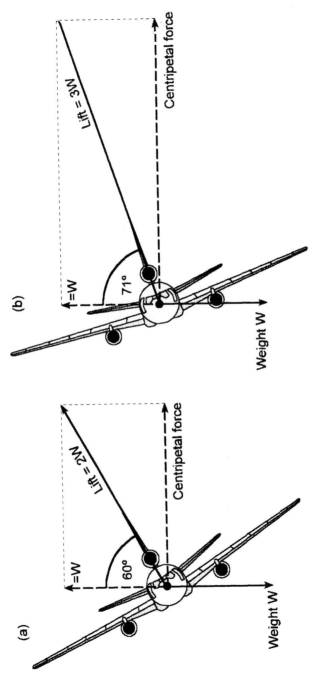

Figure 8.1   Forces on an aircraft in a banked turn in level flight

required in order to achieve a tighter turn[2], i.e. to move along a circle of smaller radius without flying any slower, a greater horizontal component of wing lift is required whilst the vertical component must remain as before, exactly equal to the weight. Thus a steeper bank angle is required, and increased wing lift. This is illustrated in Figure 8.1(b) where the bank angle is 71° and the lift-force equals three times the weight. The aircraft is now 'pulling 3g', and the load factor is 3.

The only agents capable of producing such large forces on an aircraft are the wings, and that is why an aircraft always banks when it is turning from one level flight direction to another. In comparison, the control surfaces with which an aircraft is endowed are (in general) merely very small (compared with the wing area) hinged portions at the back of the tailplane, fin and wing-tips, and these modify the lifting effect of their surfaces by varying the camber. The amount by which the lift coefficient of an aerofoil can be altered by using variable camber is much less than that available through varying the aerofoil's angle of attack. Overall, the forces produced as a result of deflecting the control surfaces are clearly of a very much smaller order of magnitude than the lift-force produced by the wings. Furthermore, if you thought that the rudder was responsible for (or was even capable of) turning an aircraft in normal flight, it is interesting to note that, when a rudder is deflected in such a way as to rotate (yaw) the aircraft in the direction of a turn, the aerodynamic force thus produced on fin and rudder is actually *outwards* from the centre of the turning circle, and so certainly cannot possibly provide the required centripetal force!

Of the three control surface types, only the ailerons act on the main force-producing surfaces, the wings (or rather on a small part of the wings), and these ailerons are designed so that their forces are equal in magnitude and opposite (upwards and downwards) in direction, so that they produce a couple with no resultant force. Furthermore, the control surfaces are always placed on parts of the aeroplane that are as far away from the centre of gravity as possible, which emphasises the fact that they are designed for producing moments *about* the centre of gravity rather than forces *on* the centre of gravity. In fact, ideally they would all produce a pure couple with no resultant force, as do the ailerons, but since there are no equivalent surfaces at the front of the aircraft to match the aft fin and tailplane, this is not possible[3]. The resultant forces produced by both elevator and rudder are an embarrassment (as we shall see later when looking at 'transients')

[2]Not appropriate for the type of aircraft depicted in the figure!
[3]Two exceptions are the Russian Sukhoi Su-27 'Flanker' combat aircraft and the Italian Piaggio P.180 Avanti corporate transport. Each has both an aft tailplane and canard foreplanes.

rather than a requirement, and certainly are not responsible for producing the large centripetal force required.

ROTATIONAL QUANTITIES AS VECTORS

Of course controlling an aircraft does indeed involve rotational motions, and even a simple turn from one direction to another involves a complex sequence of rolling, pitching and yawing, sometimes about the aircraft's axes and sometimes about an axis right outside the aircraft. It is therefore helpful to be able to refer to such rotations in a precise manner in order to be clear what is going on, and to do so it will be helpful to extend our understanding of vector quantities.

In the section of Chapter 2 headed 'Moments and Rotational Motion' we introduced the idea that all linear kinematic and mechanical quantities and principles could be very easily exported to the realm of rotational motions. Each linear quantity had its direct equivalent rotational quantity (moment for force, angle for distance, etc), and by simply substituting the rotational words for the linear ones in the various principles that we met, such as Newton's Laws, we were able to generate a new and exactly parallel set of rotational principles. This meant that the learning work that we had already done did not have to be unlearned but simply reapplied in a new context.

You may have observed at the time that there appeared to be a limitation in this process, since we had become accustomed to thinking of many of the linear quantities as vectors, which have both magnitude and direction. Linear vector quantities could be represented on paper as straight lines in the appropriate direction whose length represented to scale the magnitude of the quantity in question, and hence we could do useful things such as splitting (resolving) a vector into two parts in perpendicular directions, or finding the single vector which represented the combined effect (the resultant) of a number of individual vectors acting at the same time[4]. However, as soon as we switched into 'rotational mode', the new quantities which were the equivalents of our previous vector quantities no longer possessed the essential feature of direction which is characteristic of a vector quantity, and so the ability to combine and resolve them appeared to be lost. They had magnitude, but no longer a unique direction, since they were always going round in circles!

If this limitation were indeed the case, then our assertion that the rotational system of quantities and principles was mathematically

---

[4]The nature of vectors and the processes referred to here are explained in detail in Chapter 2 of *Flightwise – Principles of Aircraft Flight*, under the heading 'Vectors'.

identical to the previous linear system would have been a bit of a fraud. It would have meant that only *some*, but not all, of the mathematics pertaining to the linear system could be transferred to the rotational system, and that we were being dishonest by claiming more for it than that. But our mathematician friends are not wet behind the ears, and you may rest assured that, once they get hold of an idea as promising as two systems which match up to each other so very well, they will not rest until they have extracted the last drop of blood from it. Although our use of vectors in *Flightwise* has been limited to a geometrical treatment of combining and resolving them, mathematicians have developed a complete system of analysing vectors which is every bit as comprehensive as the mathematics of ordinary (scalar) numbers, and includes complex algebra and calculus. So if they are to be able to transfer all the powerful methods that they have developed for systems of linear vectors directly to work on rotational systems, the first requirement is to make sure that those quantities in the rotational system which correspond to vectors in the linear system do behave *in all important respects* like vectors themselves, even if superficially they do not look like vectors.

This sounds like a tall order. Taking linear velocity as a simple example of a linear vector, it means that we also need to be able to treat a rotational velocity (the rate at which something is turning or spinning) as a vector, although it would not appear to have the characteristics of a vector. Can this be done? The characteristics of a vector are that it is a quantity with both magnitude and direction, and by direction we mean a direction along a straight line, which can be defined in relation to a set of fixed axes. For example, a vector may have a direction of 'due East at an angle of elevation of 45° above the horizontal'. Certainly a rotational quantity has a magnitude – the magnitude of a rotational velocity is the angular speed which may be expressed in degrees per second or revolutions per minute – but as for direction we would seem to be clutching at a straw. We cannot define its direction as, for example, the direction along a radius line that is drawn on the rotating object, since its direction keeps changing as the object rotates. Perhaps we could use the direction in which a point on the edge of the rotating object actually travels – but that is no good either, since its direction of motion is a circular path and not a straight line.

Is there any one single and unique line which is specifically related to the rotation of the object, and which does not change its direction as the object rotates? Yes there is, and it is the line of the axis of rotation. If you spin an open umbrella about its shaft, and then incline the shaft, you will alter the plane in which the tips of the canopy are rotating, and so the line of the axis (the shaft) is always normal to the plane of rotation. But maybe it would seem unreasonable to you to *define* the direction of the rotation in this way.

Let us take a step back, and remind ourselves what we are trying to achieve. We are not trying to pretend that a rotation is a linear vector like the others, since clearly it is characteristically different in its nature. What we *are* trying to do is to see whether we could force a rotation into the mould of a linear vector, giving it a direction as well as a magnitude, in order that we could apply to it all the mathematical tricks that have been developed for linear vectors, and so that the answers which emerge in the rotational system will be the direct analogue of the corresponding answers in the linear system. Very conveniently it turns out that, by using the direction of the axis of rotation as the vector's direction, this requirement is precisely satisfied, and rotational speeds and accelerations can in every sense be described as vector quantities.

When we refer to linear vectors, not only do we talk of the direction of the vector, but also we specify the vector's *sense*, by which we mean whether the quantity is pointing one way or the other along the direction line. It is obvious that the sense of a linear vector is the way in which it is acting, but there is no such natural link between the sense (clockwise or anticlockwise) in which an object is rotating and the 'correct' way to define 'forwards' along the axis line. Mathematicians therefore impose a conventional rule which, although initially arbitrary, once declared must always be adhered to in order that the results achieved are consistent with each other, and it may be explained by reference to Figure 8.2. If a toy top is spinning on a flat table, the direction of the rotational speed vector is the vertical spinning axis of the top. By convention, if the top is spinning clockwise, then the forward sense is defined as downwards, and if anticlockwise, upwards, along the axis. The word 'sense' may thus be used both for the way in which the top is spinning – clockwise or anticlockwise – and also for the way in which its vector is defined along the axis line – downwards or upwards.

This convention obeys the same 'right-hand rule' that we met in Chapter 2 and Figure 2.5 when defining the positive directions for the set of aircraft axes. It may help you to remember which is the forward direction along the axis of rotation if you think of using a corkscrew, since this advances forwards into the cork when being rotated in a clockwise sense. Or if you prefer you can clench your *right* fist leaving the thumb extended away from the fingers. If you now orientate your fist so that the curled-up fingers point round in the sense of the rotation, your thumb will be pointing in the forward sense along the axis.

In passing, now that we have clarified the difference between the terms sense and direction, we can be more precise in our use of these

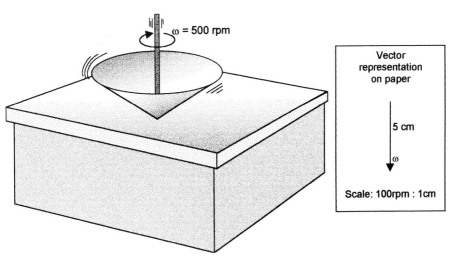

Figure 8.2   The vector representation of a rotational speed

words in future. Up to now, wherever it would not cause any confusion, I have not flinched from using the word 'direction' along a given line, when strictly I should have said 'sense', since the former word is more familiar; but in future I resolve to use the words correctly. Furthermore, since we had not previously defined a linear direction (as we now have) for a rotational quantity, I permitted myself to refer to the words 'clockwise' and 'anticlockwise' as 'directions' of rotation. This was of course strictly incorrect, but now we have clarified the issue we can start to use the proper terminology.

We referred earlier somewhat amorphously to our mathematical colleagues, but it would not be decent to dismiss the enormous mathematical achievements alluded to, which have made possible amongst other things the full analytical treatment of aircraft stability and control, without referring briefly to one outstanding patriarch of the subject, the Swiss mathematician Leonhard Euler (pronounced 'oiler') (1707–83). Having studied mathematics under Jean Bernoulli, he went on to pursue a prodigious career as professor of physics (from 1731) and mathematics (from 1733) in St Petersburg, working alongside Jean Bernoulli's two sons, of whom Daniel is particularly remembered in the field of aeronautics for the equation named after him linking the pressure in a fluid with its velocity[5]. Despite eventually becoming totally blind, Euler published over 800 books and papers, almost all in

[5]*q.v.* in Chapters 4 and 5 of *Flightwise – Principles of Aircraft Flight.*

Latin, on every aspect of pure and applied mathematics, physics and astronomy, including a three-volume non-technical outline of the main physical theories of the time, which was widely read. Some of his publications remained standard textbooks for a century, and a great amount of his prolific output is still essential mathematical wisdom today. In all of his work he displayed an amazing technical skill with complicated formulae and an almost unerring instinct for the right answer. He was more attracted to solving specific problems than to formulating principles with mathematical rigour, and he has left us many elegant and astonishing results. He had a prodigious memory, which enabled him to continue mathematical work even when totally blind, and he is said to have been able to recite the whole of Virgil's *Aeneid* by heart!

Of particular interest in our present context is his study of the motion of rigid bodies in three dimensions. Although a large number of equations and principles in various branches of mathematics and physics bear Euler's name, the 'Euler's Theorem' that concerns us here is a statement of the fundamental principle that rotations may be combined together (and conversely resolved into component parts) like vectors as we have discussed above, and on this foundation he was able to build up the mathematical system for analysing the complex motion that we find when studying aircraft flight.

Things do not always work out quite the way even mathematical giants expect, as Euler discovered when he began to try to apply vector principles to all angular quantities. If you start at the natural starting point, by looking at the most elementary rotational vector quantity, an angular displacement (whose magnitude is angle), and if you try to treat it as a vector quantity using the direction of the axis (the only possible choice, as we have seen) as its direction line, you will find that it just doesn't work – the answers you get by 'adding vectors' are just not the same as what happens in real life. The fact that this is so is illustrated in Figure 8.3. In the sequence of operations shown in the top row two rotations are applied, one after the other, to a box whose faces are clearly distinguishable from each other. The exercise is then repeated (in the lower row) from the same starting position, but exactly the same two rotations are on this occasion performed in the opposite order from the first time. You will observe that the configuration in which the box finishes up is not the same in the two rows of diagrams, which demonstrates that the order in which two (or more) rotations follow each other is highly significant, as it grossly affects the result.

When we combine two vectors together by drawing their vector triangle, it does not matter which of the two vectors we draw first (provided they follow each other sequentially, nose to tail). If we draw

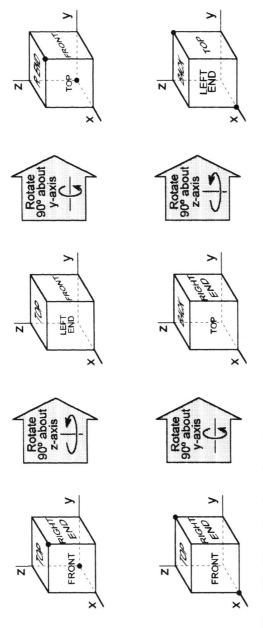

Figure 8.3 The order of rotations affects the result

both of the triangles corresponding to the two different orders in which we can 'add' the vectors, we simply get the opposite halves of the vector parallelogram, but the resultant is exactly the same either way – it is the diagonal of the parallelogram. But we have now just come across a quantity, angular displacement, which certainly has magnitude and a unique direction related to it, but which gives us different answers depending on the order in which we 'add' rotations together.

Let us look again at the rotations shown in Figure 8.3, and see what happens if we try to use a vector approach to describe the process. Figure 8.4 has been drawn on the false assumption that rotations *are* vectors and that they can be combined by graphical vector addition. In both sequences (top and bottom rows of Figure 8.3) the directions of the rotation 'vectors' are in the z-axis and y-axis directions, and so both vector diagrams would lie completely in the y–z plane, as indicated on the left of the two-dimensional Figure 8.4. The rotations are numbered ① and ② sequentially in each case. Each of the rotations is of magnitude 90°, and so all the 'vector' lines are of the same length which represents 90° to scale, resulting in 45° isosceles triangles. As we would expect, the 'resultants' (the hypotenuses) of the two 'vector' triangles in Figure 8.4 are identical to each other in magnitude and direction, because that is the way vectors behave, and of course in both cases this 'resultant' is in the plane of the vectors ① and ②, i.e. the y–z plane. Two rotations performed in sequence *can* indeed be replaced by a single rotation which has the same effect as the combination, but a careful look back at the sequences in Figure 8.3 will show you that this equivalent rotation is not the same in each case, and in neither case is it the same as that predicted by the 'vector' addition of Figure 8.4. In Figure 8.3 small blobs have been added to two opposite vertices of the first and last diagrams in each sequence, indicating the

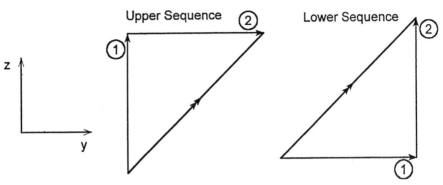

Figure 8.4   Invalid 'vector' addition of the rotations of Figure 8.3

axis line of the combined rotation of the sequence. You will observe firstly that the blobs axis lines are different in the two sequences, and secondly that neither of them lies in any one plane of the coordinate axes but across the three-dimensional space. Thus in neither case do they match the resultants of Figure 8.4, and it is clear that vector addition completely lets us down.

We have heretofore said that a vector is simply a quantity which has magnitude and direction, but in fact these two conditions are not quite sufficient to define something as a vector, since we need to add an additional condition that makes sure that the quantity 'works' in vector mathematics. This third condition is that the order in which the quantities are combined together must not affect the outcome of combining them. In the language of mathematics we say that the combining operation must be *commutative*. Adding and multiplying of numbers are commutative operations, since $5 + 7 = 7 + 5$ and $3 \times 4 = 4 \times 3$, but subtraction and division are not commutative, since $5 - 7 \neq 7 - 5$, and $3 \div 4 \neq 4 \div 3$; and as we have just seen, neither is the combining of rotations. Therefore angular displacement is *not* a vector quantity.

Euler was not one to be easily put off by little frustrations such as this, and the matter was soon resolved. Although large rotations are not commutative, we can easily demonstrate that with very small rotations the order of doing the operations makes very little difference to the outcome. If you hold your model aircraft level, pitch it a small amount nose-up and then yaw it a small angle to the right, it will finish up in very nearly the same orientation as if you had yawed it first and pitched it second. Now the quantities that we are most interested in are not so much angular displacements but rotational velocities and accelerations. To work out approximately the rotational velocity, we can divide a very small change in the angular displacement by the very short period of time (a scalar quantity) during which it occurs, and since very small angular displacements *do* behave approximately commutatively like well-behaved vectors as we have seen, it would seem that the resulting angular velocity would be at least approximately a vector quantity (whatever that means!), as we had hoped.

Furthermore, we can take the process one stage further, and avoid the word 'approximately' altogether. In the section of Chapter 6 of *Flightwise – Principles of Aircraft Flight* headed 'Rates of Change' it was explained that this approximate approach to finding rates of change leads directly into the exact methods of differential calculus. Where we said 'very small' in the previous paragraph, calculus requires us to force these quantities to become so small that they both become infinitesimal, and hence it enables us to get an *exact* answer for angular velocity. Now since a very small angular displacement behaves approximately like a vector, when it becomes infinitesimally small it actually behaves exactly like a vector, and so the angular velocity (a vector divided by a scalar) is itself a true vector quantity. An exactly similar argument may be followed to show that an angular acceleration is also a vector quantity.

So we have established that rotational velocities can be treated (in every respect) as vector quantities, which means that we will be able to add them and resolve them just as we can with linear vectors. We shall find that they are sometimes rather more difficult to interpret and visualise than linear vectors, since we are forced to think in three dimensions. This is first of all because the direction of the rotational vector is not in the same plane as the rotation to which it refers, and secondly because we shall be considering rotations of an aircraft about up to three different axes which are perpendicular to each other. But despite this difficulty, we shall find in the next chapter that the approach of using vectors sometimes gives us an insight into what is going on that cannot easily be gained by other means.

CONTROL DERIVATIVES

When dealing with control-fixed stability of an aircraft, we found it very useful, as a way of structuring and classifying our thoughts, to introduce the concept of aerodynamic derivatives. These stability derivatives were numbers which each related the effect of a certain type of aircraft movement to the force or moment which arose as a result of that movement. Now that we are moving on to consider control, implying that the control surfaces will no longer be fixed but will be adjusted on demand, it will be useful to extend the language of aerodynamic derivatives to include control derivatives as well. But in order to do so, we must first of all decide on a suitable set of symbols and appropriate sign conventions for referring to the amounts (which are nearly always angles) through which the control surfaces are deflected.

To match the three-axis notation that we developed in Chapter 2, we shall require a convenient triple of alphabetic symbols by which we can express the angles through which the control surfaces are deflected. I am sorry to say that, because aerodynamicists have to use such a very large number of different symbols, they have rather scraped the barrel here, and have struggled to find an equivalent set from the Greek alphabet which match our more familiar $[x, y, z]$ set. Although there are direct lower case equivalents in the Greek alphabet for our x and z, they are rather obscure and, to many of us, unfamiliar: they are ξ (*xi*, pronounced 'ksy', as one syllable) and ζ (*zeta*, pronounced 'zeeter') respectively. But there is no direct equivalent in Greek to the English letter y, and so we are asked to use the nearest similar-sounding vowel, which is the Greek letter η (*eta*), usually pro-nounced 'eater' although I was taught at school to pronounce it 'air-te'. It represents a long e sound (as in 'beet') as opposed to the other letter for e which is ε (*epsilon*) representing a short e sound (as in 'bet'), which we used in *Flightwise – Principles of Aircraft Flight* for the downwash angle.

So the triple of symbols representing the control surface deflection angles is $[\xi, \eta, \zeta]$, or 'ksy, eater, zeeter' in that order to match up with $[x, y, z]$. What precisely does each mean, and what is the sign conven-tion? Once again no memory feat is needed here – as I write this I have not yet worked out the answers to the questions – but we simply follow exactly the same rules as before. First of all, since ξ corre-sponds to x, it represents the angle of that control surface (or those control surfaces) which causes rolling rotation about the x-axis. This motion is produced by the ailerons, the surfaces hinged at the trailing edges at the wing-tips. To make the aircraft roll, one aileron must go up and the other down, and the angle by which one goes up and the other goes down[6] is the value of ξ.

As for the sign convention, we simply apply exactly the same 'clock-wise is positive' rule as before. Imagine looking along the control's hinge-line in the positive sense of the axis that the hinge-line is paral-lel to. In this case, that means looking out to the right (positive y-direction) towards the aileron on the starboard wing. If it is deflected downwards, it has rotated clockwise, and so ξ is positive, and thus a positive ξ also means that the aileron on the port wing has deflected upwards. (Do not start thinking about the *effect* of the control when determining the sign of the surface deflection – simply the sense of the actual deflection itself. In fact you will quickly realise that a positive ξ will produce a negative rolling moment.)

Now let us turn to η, which is the angle of the control surface responsible for pitching the aircraft about the y-axis, i.e. the elevator hinged to the back of the tailplane – 'e for elevator', if that helps. Following the same principle, look from left to right (the positive y-direction) along the elevator hinge-line and a clockwise control angle, i.e. elevator down, is positive. (This will actually produce a negative pitching moment.)

Finally, ζ is the angle of the control surface which produces a yaw-ing moment about the z-axis, or the rudder deflection angle. Looking down from above (positive z-direction), a deflection to the left (clock-wise) is positive, and produces a tail fin force to the right, which has a

---

[6]We shall see later that they may go up and down by different amounts, but we will take ξ to be the mean of the two angles.

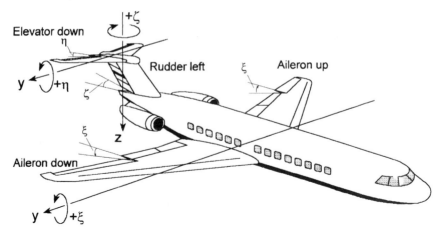

Figure 8.5 Control surface deflection conventions – not a recommended flight condition!

negative, anticlockwise, yawing moment. The conventions are all shown in Figure 8.5.

The most important control derivatives that we shall meet are the most obvious ones, i.e. the three relationships between each control surface deflection and the aircraft moment which it is primarily designed to produce. Using the same shorthand notation that we have grown accustomed to in our stability work, they are L_ξ, M_η and N_ζ. It is interesting to observe that, since the moments are all in the opposite sense to the deflections, the values of the derivatives are all negative, but this will not affect you unless you will be using the derivatives to substitute in equations (which we won't).

The moment produced by any control is worked out (as with the stability derivatives) by multiplying the aerodynamic control derivative, which is 'moment per angle', by the deflection angle of the control. Hence the rolling moment due to aileron deflection is given by $L = L_\xi \xi$, and similarly for the others.

A BRIEF REVISION OF TERMINOLOGY

It will be useful to reassert a few important points of terminology pertaining to angles and rotational motion, before we proceed to look at aircraft manoeuvres in more detail. It may be that the confusion that so often attaches to people's understanding of these rotational concepts is what causes them to regard the subject of aircraft control as difficult, and so let us do our best to dispel any such possible feeling of uneasiness by making sure that we can at least 'call a spade a spade'.

In the previous chapter we laid considerable emphasis on the difference between the two ways in which a side-flow and resulting sideways angle of attack is produced, and although in some cases this is the consequence of rolling, side-flow is essentially a property of the aircraft's motion in the x–y (yawing) plane. We also pointed out the difference between the word 'heading' (relating to the path through the air of the aircraft's centre of gravity) and the direction in which the aircraft's nose is temporarily pointing in the yawing plane due to a disturbance. Earlier, we had drawn attention to the distinction between a rate of roll and an angle of bank, which are features of the aircraft's motion in the y–z plane. All of these distinctions will continue to be met as we proceed, and in addition it will be auspicious now for us to look carefully at some of the notation and conventions that are used in the pitching (x–z) plane.

An angle is a measure of the amount turned through from pointing in the direction of one straight line to that of another. When we consider the pitching-plane motion of an aircraft, we find that we are presented with a formidable set of straight lines, between any two of which there is an angle which may either be important or may be easily mistaken for another one which *is* important. To enumerate, some significant such lines are:

- The horizontal, which is perpendicular to the line through the centres of gravity of aircraft and Earth.
- The flight path, the line along which the aircraft's centre of gravity is moving, which in undisturbed flight also defines the aircraft's longitudinal stability axis.
- The airflow downwash direction behind the wing.
- Alternative definitions of the aircraft's longitudinal axis, arbitrarily defined and often not obvious, but fixed in the aircraft. We will refer to such an axis as a longitudinal inertia axis.
- The chord line of the wing's aerofoil section (or the mean chord line for a twisted wing).
- The chord line of the tailplane's aerofoil section.
- The ground line, which is the line tangential to the bottom of the undercarriage wheels.

You will find, if you pair these together in all possible ways, that between them these seven lines could define 21 possible angles, although only a minority of these are important. There is also a plethora of terms used for these angles, (angle of attack, preceded by various adjectives including zero-lift, overall, effective, geometric, absolute; angle of incidence, rigger's angle of incidence, downwash angle, pitch angle, attitude, angle of climb, longitudinal dihedral angle etc), and so it is clear that there is tremendous scope for misinterpretation and misunderstanding. When it comes to rotational rates, fortunately the scope is more restricted, but there are still two possible rates of rotation to be considered, so that care is needed.

Let us try to rationalise the scene a little. Of the seven lines referred to above, the last four are all fixed relative to the aircraft's body, and so in general[7] the angle defined between any pair of these four is constant. Furthermore, the ground line is of significance only when the aircraft is parked or taxying slowly. It is usually used only in the context of design drawings (see, for example, Figure 14.5), and need not concern us except to be wary of misinterpreting drawings of aircraft in which this line is included. Such drawings are often orientated with the aircraft's longitudinal axis horizontal, so that the ground line is drawn sloping up to the rear on a tailwheel undercarriage aircraft and up to the front where the more modern tricycle undercarriage is used.

This leaves us with three body-fixed reference lines: the longitudinal inertia axis and the chord lines of wing and tailplane. (Note that, although the stability axis is also fixed relative to the body at a given flight condition, it moves relative to the body when the flight condition changes.) Mention was made in Chapter 4 of the angle between the chord lines of wing and tailplane, which is crucial for making an aircraft trimmable, and this angle is usually referred to as the *longitudinal dihedral angle*. I have come across recent literature in which this angle is referred to as the angle of incidence, but this is not common practice. Unfortunately the term angle of incidence is one that has been used to describe a number of different angles, and is therefore a source of confusion rather than clarity. It used to be used most commonly to describe the angle of attack of the wing, i.e. the angle between the flight path (the relative airflow direction) and the wing chord, but there was at the same time another angle referred to as the *rigger's angle of incidence*. This was the angle between the chord line of the wing and a longitudinal inertia axis of the aircraft, and its name arose in the days of biplanes whose wings were braced with struts and stays that could be adjusted by ground technicians. The performance of such aircraft depended very critically on the skill of these 'riggers', whose understanding of aerodynamics was every bit as important as that of the pilot, but today such adjustment is fixed at design.

The term angle of incidence is thus best avoided altogether nowadays, but by contrast the term *angle of attack* is ubiquitous. Even this can cause great difficulties, not only because of the multifarious adjectives by which it is frequently preceded, but also because of the vagueness of definition of the two lines bounding it. Firstly, the difficulty of

---

[7]Except in the case of an all-moving, or slab, tailplane.

defining the chord line of an aerofoil, as discussed in the section headed 'Aerofoil Terminology' of Chapter 9 of *Flightwise – Principles of Aircraft Flight*, is compounded by the problem of defining the mean chord of a twisted wing. Secondly, the relative airflow only corresponds with the aircraft's flight path at a substantial distance ahead of the aircraft, and furthermore this flight path is not easy to observe in climbing or descending flight, since airflow cannot be seen and the aircraft moving along its flight path only describes one point on that path at any instant.

Let us not get bogged down in the difficulties of definition and semantics, but just ensure that we are prepared for the angle terms that are most common and will be used as we proceed. In particular:

- *Angle of Attack* (α) is the angle between the wing mean chord line and the flight path of the aircraft.
- *Pitch Angle* (θ) is the angle between the *undisturbed* flight path and the temporary direction of the longitudinal stability axis of the aircraft during a perturbation.
- *Flight path Angle* is the angle between the flight path and the horizontal (sometimes denoted by γ, lower case *gamma*, or by Θ, upper case *theta*, in other literature, but we will use the full name).

To illustrate the difference between α and θ, it is the rapid oscillations of the angle of attack α that is the most significant feature of a short period pitching oscillation, although the pitch angle θ also oscillates with it. On the other hand, during a phugoid oscillation α remains virtually constant, whilst θ oscillates from positive to negative as the aircraft rises and descends above and below what would otherwise be its flight path if it were not experiencing a phugoid motion.

It is not easy to observe the flight path angle, since only one point on the line is marked by the aircraft's position at any instant. If an airliner has just taken off and is climbing along a steep straight flight path, it will be flying relatively slowly so that it will also be set at a large angle of attack. The only visual reference line is the longitudinal inertia axis, which approximately coincides with the easily observable fuselage centreline. Consequently it will *look* as if the aircraft is climbing much more steeply than it actually is. The best way to achieve a proper perspective on what is happening is to hold up a ruler or a stick at arm's length, inclined so that the aircraft appears to be sliding up it as if up a ramp. By this way the angle of attack (slightly more than the angle between ruler and fuselage – can you see why 'slightly more'?) can be visually distinguished from the flight path angle, the angle at which the ruler is set.

Finally, let us look at what we mean, and what we do not mean, by pitch rate. *Pitch rate* is simply the rate of change of the pitch angle, θ, and is demonstrated in both the short period pitching oscillation (a high rate) and the phugoid (a low rate). But when controlling an aircraft to alter its flight path, for example in a pull-up, there is another rotational rate to be considered, also in the pitching plane but about an axis parallel to the aircraft's y-axis and far above the aircraft. This is the rate at which the aircraft's flight path itself is changing direction, and is completely independent of the pitch rate of the aircraft's fixed axes in relation to the flight path at any one instant. Likewise, whilst flying along a turning flight path (whether level, climbing or descending), there will *also* be a rate of change of the direction of the aircraft about an axis that is perpendicular to the plane in which it is flying but far removed from the aircraft. These two new sorts of rotation are what is different about turning flight compared with straight flight, and must be clearly distinguished from the pitch, yaw and roll rates with which we have been previously concerned. It will be our task in the next chapter to unravel the intricacies of these motions, and to look carefully at how they all interact.

CHAPTER 9
Doing a Good Turn

INTRODUCTION

This chapter is the kernel of the book so far as aircraft control is concerned. It opens by examining, step by step, the surprisingly complicated series of motions and motion changes that are needed in order simply to change an aircraft's flight path in horizontal or near-horizontal flight. It is possible that we shall then raise a few eyebrows as we look at some common misunderstandings of the function of the controls, especially the rudder.

Then and only then shall we move on to consider how the aircraft control surfaces are designed to facilitate the various motions. We shall look at conventional control surfaces and some alternative configurations, initially on the assumption that each type of control does its own job and nothing else, but we shall quickly discover that, although each has a primary function, all controls interact and cross-couple with each other in ways that cannot be ignored in practice even by the most novice of trainee pilots.

Finally we shall look at a variety of aspects of flight, some high speed, some low, and some applying at all speeds, which present pilot and designer with particular problems to be overcome, and at some of the solutions which have been adopted.

Following the *Flightwise* philosophy, the chapter sets out to give understandable explanations of control phenomena based on fundamental principles, so that you will be equipped to answer for yourself all of the many questions that you are likely to meet in the future. Consequently it does *not* set out to compete with those books which seem determined to throw in every conceivable aspect of the subject with an apparent dread of committing the heinous crime of leaving something out. Such an approach results in presenting a parade of items, not with explanations, but with such superficial comments that the items merely become unanswered questions, leaving the reader frustrated or needlessly feeling inadequate because he or she did not understand an explanation – which was not there!

Despite this declared approach, there are a large number of concepts to be got to grips with in this chapter, so that it has resulted in being longer than most. But to help you to take it in digestible chunks you will find that it is liberally subdivided into sections and subsections for ease of reference. In fact it uses one more heading level than most of the rest of the book.

WHAT A TURN IS ...

Let us start by unravelling the details of the most fundamental aircraft manoeuvre, a level turn. You will find it helpful to have your aircraft model at hand as we talk through the various stages of the turn. We will suppose that the pilot is flying straight and level at a steady cruising speed in the direction of due north, and wishes to change the direction of flight to due east. It will be necessary to fly along a circular path of which the centre of the circle is far out to the right of the aircraft in the same horizontal plane. Regarding the aircraft as a particle, this circular motion will require a horizontal centripetal force to the right, which in a tight (small-radius) or high speed turn may be very substantial. As we have already seen, this force must be provided by having the aircraft banked and the wing producing an increased lift force, so that its horizontal component can provide the centripetal force, whilst its vertical component still takes care of the necessary upward force to balance the weight, ensuring that the aircraft does not gain or lose height.

What pilot actions are necessary to make the aircraft transit from its straight path to the required circular path? First of all, it is common knowledge that he must roll the aircraft into the bank, and so he must apply the ailerons, to increase the lift of the left wing and reduce that of the right wing[1]. At first there is no aerodynamic rolling moment to oppose the couple $L_\xi \xi$ created by the ailerons, since before the roll the aircraft's motion was steady and symmetrical, and so there is a rolling acceleration. But as a roll rate p develops, the aileron couple begins to be opposed by the roll-damping couple of the wings, represented by the stability derivative L_p. Fairly quickly the roll damping couple reaches the value of the aileron couple (but in the opposite sense), or $L_\xi \xi = L_p p$, and so equilibrium in the roll is restored, and by Newton's First Law the roll proceeds at a constant rate.

But if you hold your model in front of you facing forward, and if you assume for now that the rolling action due to the ailerons can be treated in isolation from other motions, (an assumption that we shall later dispel,) you will see that the result of applying ailerons is not at all what was required. Instead of banking the aircraft, they simply produce a couple which makes it roll continuously clockwise about the aircraft's x-axis, so that the aircraft will corkscrew along its existing due-north flight path. True, the lift force (which is changing continuously in direction) will vary whilst the weight force has constant magnitude and direction, and so there will be a rotating resultant force at work trying to deflect the aircraft from its straight path. But just as we

---

[1]The mechanism by which the ailerons and other control surfaces operate is reviewed on page 238, at the beginning of the section 'Control Heaviness and Loss of Effectiveness'.

did in the short period pitching oscillation, we can ignore these since the duration of the force in any direction is insufficient to deflect significantly the path of the centre of gravity of the large aircraft mass.

So a further action of the pilot must be to *stop* the rolling motion at the appropriate time. Let us say that we require to carry out a 2-g turn, which involves a bank angle of 60° as we saw in Figure 8.1(a). How does the pilot stop the rolling at exactly 60° of bank? If he merely neutralises the aileron control, the aircraft has a certain roll rate, so that by Newton's First Law for rotational motion it will continue to corkscrew clockwise until the opposing roll-damping moment due to L_p arrests that rolling motion. But at the same time, the aircraft's rolling moment of inertia I_x tries to make the roll rate continue. Both L_p (arresting the roll rate) and I_x (sustaining it) depend largely on the span of the aircraft (or the aspect ratio for a given wing area), and so to a first approximation the rolling will subside in a similar manner on high and low aspect ratio aircraft, and in general the pilot will not need to do anything about stopping the roll rate, except to neutralise the ailerons slightly before the required bank angle is reached. But in the case of a low aspect ratio fighter fitted with heavy under-wing 'stores' (the usual euphemism for weapons) and/or wing-tip fuel tanks, the pilot may need to apply opposite aileron to stop the roll rate, especially if a high roll rate had been set up in order to get the aircraft into the banked attitude as quickly as possible.

So the aircraft is now banked at an angle of 60°, but still flying level in a due northerly direction. It is now flying in the orientation depicted in Figure 6.3 (but banked more steeply), from which we showed that a banked aircraft will sideslip. As we discussed in that section of Chapter 6 (dealing with lateral static stability), if no other action is taken, the aircraft will eventually level out on account of its 'dihedral' (L_v) stability. But at 60° of bank this sideslip would be very rapid – not at all what is required – and a tremendous amount of height would be lost very quickly. So a further action is required of the pilot, and that is to configure the aircraft so that the wings will produce the additional lift that is required, i.e. double the straight-and-level lift value, for a 2-g turn. Without change in speed or height, the only way that this extra lift can be achieved is by increasing the aircraft's lift coefficient very quickly and very substantially, and this can only be done by increasing the angle of attack. To do this the pilot must pull back on his control to deflect the elevators upwards, thus (briefly) pitching the aircraft into a more nose-up attitude. He is not providing a pitch rate to be sustained throughout the turn – which is provided purely by the centripetal component of the wing lift, together with the aircraft's natural stability, as we shall see shortly – but yet he must keep the elevator control in the new pulled-back position since he has had to *retrim* the aircraft to a new, higher C_L value, as we saw in the discussion of Figure 4.12 in the chapter on longitudinal static stability.

This adjustment to the aircraft's longitudinal trim is not in practice left until the aircraft has reached its fully banked attitude, as the foregoing discussion might have suggested as a result of dealing with one thing at a time. If it were, the aircraft would already have sideslipped and lost a lot of height before the extra lift had been applied. Rather, the retrimming is carried out progressively during the roll to the banked attitude, so that at all times during the roll the lift is (at least approximately) correct for the banked attitude reached at that instant. This simply means that the up-elevator control movement is applied progressively as the roll proceeds. But when the required bank angle is almost reached and the ailerons are neutralised, the new up-elevator control position must be maintained.

Looking back at your model in your hand, you will see that we are now banked (not rolling) at 60° to the horizontal, and are applying additional wing lift. If the amount of lift is too little, the aircraft will still sideslip, and thus yaw (on account of its N_v derivative), to the right, and level height will not be maintained but a curving dive will ensue. If the lift is too great, the aircraft will perform a pull-up to the right, since both components exceed what is needed. But if the amount of lift is just right, its vertical component will exactly balance the weight, and its horizontal component will make the aircraft fly in the desired circular path. A *balanced turn* has thus now been fully initiated, and the banked flight in this circular path must be maintained until we are (almost) pointing East.

There is still one further control action that the pilot must take if the newly established turn is to be maintained. As a result of the additional lift from the wings, the aircraft's induced drag[2] is increased, and in the present case of doubling the lift, this increase in aircraft drag is very considerable. Since lift depends on the square of the speed, the effect of a reduction of speed on the balance of forces in the turn would be very marked, and height and centripetal force would rapidly be sacrificed, even with the aircraft at the correct attitude. Thus it is essential that, as the turn is being initiated, the pilot increases the thrust produced by the engine(s) by pushing forwards on the throttle lever(s). If full power was already being used, such a remedy will not be available, and in that case there is no way that the turn can be sustained. For this reason an aircraft's technical data always includes a 'maximum sustained turn rate' in addition to the 'maximum instantaneous turn rate', and the former is always lower than the latter.

---

[2]Induced drag is explained fully in Chapter 12 of *Flightwise – Principles of Aircraft Flight*.

Before looking at the termination of the turn, let us briefly recapitulate what has happened so far. When flying straight and level due North, the pilot wishes to initiate a turn to the right, so that he will eventually be flying due East with no change of speed or height. First of all he must apply a substantial but constant roll control deflection, so that the ailerons produce a clockwise couple and the aircraft quickly builds up to a steady roll rate to the right. Immediately he must start to pull back on the pitch control, but progressively (rather than all at once, as with the roll control) in order to retrim the aircraft longitudinally for the additional lift that will be required during the turn. Simultaneously he must open the throttle(s) to overcome the increase in induced drag. Just before the required bank angle is reached, he must centralise the aileron control, so that the roll damping slows down the roll rate and stops it just as the required bank angle is attained; or, if the roll damping is not sufficient to stop the roll quickly enough, he will briefly apply a little left aileron control. The turn is now established, and will be held with merely an elevator control displacement and an increased throttle setting until almost pointing East.

In order to return to straight and level flight at the end of the turn, the turn initiation routine must be reversed. First of all, the aileron control must be moved to the *left*, in order to roll the aircraft anticlockwise, back towards the level. The roll damping of the wings will now apply a clockwise resistive couple, and when the two couples balance the roll will be at a steady rate. During the roll, the pitch control must be progressively moved forwards, and the throttle lever(s) pulled back, until as the aircraft reaches the level attitude the elevator is back in its correct position for 1-g trim (lift equals weight) and the throttle lever(s) is/are back in the cruise setting. Just before straight and level, the roll control is again centralised, and the roll damping reduces the roll rate to zero as the level attitude is restored.

... AND WHAT IT ISN'T

You will not by any means be alone if you felt frustrated or astonished that during the entire turning procedure described above there was no mention whatsoever of the rudder. We will have plenty to say about the use of the rudder but it is important to appreciate at the moment that the rudder is *not* a primary control surface for carrying out a turn. In order to illustrate this fact, it will be useful to take another look at the motion of an aircraft during the fully established phase of the turn, this time considering only the kinematics without regard to forces and moments. We will draw on the conclusions of our work in the previous chapter, in which we established the Euler Theorem which states that rotational rates can in every respect be treated as vector quantities.

Figure 9.1 shows an aircraft flying along a level circular path at a

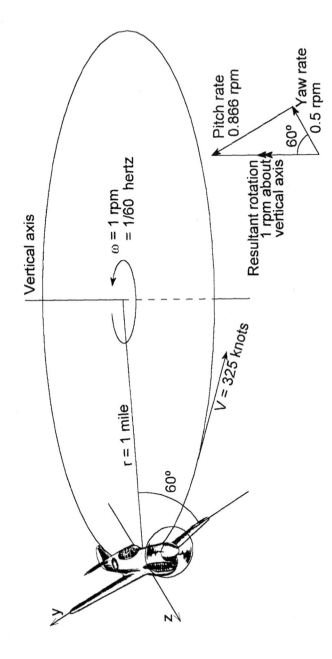

Figure 9.1 Vector representation of an aircraft flying a level circular path

constant speed. In order to match our earlier example, the aircraft is flying at a bank angle of 60°, and in addition it has been specified that the aircraft will take exactly 1 minute to fly a complete circle. The aircraft's speed (325 knots)[3] and the circle's radius (conveniently almost exactly one statute mile) have been calculated on the values of bank angle and time to complete one full 360° turn. The aircraft sketched in the figure is a Curtiss P-40E Warhawk, an American-built Second World War fighter-bomber which was, in fact, not quite capable of achieving our required 325 knots, its top speed being 290 knots at 5000 feet, in straight flight. It was because this performance fell short of that of the rival first-line interceptors at the time that the aircraft was relegated to the rôle of fighter-bomber. The fuselage shape around the radiator under the nose lent itself readily to the shark's mouth design, and this was particularly favoured by pilots in China and the Western Desert, two theatres which were subsequently principle users of the type.

If you imagine that the aircraft is rigidly attached to the edge of a disc represented by the turning circle in the figure, it will be clear that the aircraft (and disc) has an overall rotational motion about the vertical axis through the centre of the disc, the magnitude of which is one revolution per minute, which is equivalent to $\frac{1}{60}$ hertz. But this rotation may be thought of as consisting of two component rotations about two of the aircraft's body axes which are inclined with the aircraft as shown in the figure. This is perhaps easiest to convince yourself of if you pick up your model again, and let it trace out a circular path whilst holding it at a 60° angle of bank. Clearly the aircraft is in a pitching rotation nose-up (about the y-axis), since the nose has to lead the tail around the circular path. But if that were all, the aircraft would be performing a climbing turn, which it is not. There must also be a yawing motion involved (about the z-axis), which tries to rotate the nose down below the level of the turning circle, in order to compensate for its tendency to rise above this plane due to pitching.

So we have two component rotations and one consequent, or resultant, rotation, and if Euler was right we should be able to represent these three vectors by a vector triangle. Let us follow this through in the vector triangle at the lower right of the figure. To start with, we can draw in the resultant rotation straight away, since we know its magnitude (1 rpm) and its direction. Since the aircraft's sense of motion around the circle is anticlockwise when viewed from above, the right-hand or corkscrew rule tells us that the direction of the vector is in

---

[3]Many aircraft speed indicators are calibrated in knots. A knot is a nautical mile per hour, and a nautical mile is the length of arc around the equator which subtends an angle of 1 minute at the centre of the Earth. This distance is 6083 feet, which means that a nautical mile is 1.15 statute miles, and a knot is 0.87 of a mile per hour.

the upward sense along the line of the vertical axis, and so the resultant has been drawn with a double arrowhead pointing upwards.

We do not know the magnitudes of the two component rotations, but we do know their directions and senses, which will be sufficient to construct the entire triangle. First of all, let us consider the pitching motion, which is in the nose-up sense. Its vector direction line is parallel to the y-axis, which is itself inclined at 60° to the horizontal, and its sense is clockwise when viewed in the positive y-direction by the pilot. We can therefore draw in a direction line at 60° to the horizontal (30° to the resultant vector line) passing through either end of the resultant vector – we have chosen the top end – extending some distance each way. We can also pencil in a direction arrow on to it – upwards to the left, pointing in the positive y-direction, although we do not yet know which bit of the new line is going to form a side of the triangle.

We look now at the yawing rotation, and this is anticlockwise as viewed by the pilot looking 'downwards'. Being a yaw, the direction of its vector is parallel to the z-axis, and the sense is in the negative-z sense, i.e. 'upwards'. The z-axis is inclined at 60° to the vertical, and so the yaw rate vector line can now be drawn in, through the other (lower) end of the resultant vector, at 60° to the resultant, and extended until it cuts the pitch rate vector line. The required yaw rate vector is the length between these two intersection points, and its vector arrowhead, pointing in the negative z-direction, can now be drawn in. Furthermore, the pitch rate vector is now completely specified, and its vector arrowhead can also be finally inserted.

So we have shown that a vector triangle can be drawn, with all the segments corresponding correctly with their rotations according to the conventions introduced in the previous chapter. Furthermore, what I call the 'circus elephants' rule for adding vectors, that all the components being added must be connected sequentially nose-to-tail, and that the direct short cut *from* the tail of the rear one *to* the nose of the front one is the resultant, is precisely followed in our triangle.

Well, the clever mathematics seems to work out all right, but, you may be asking yourself, so what? What does this tell us that we did not know before? The answer, surprisingly, is that we can now firmly refute any suggestion that the rudder is a primary turning control. The reason for this is quite simply that, although there is indeed a yawing motion which continues throughout the turn, its magnitude, as revealed by the vector triangle in Figure 9.1, is in fact extremely small (as yaw rates go). The overall (resultant) turn rate is only $\frac{1}{60}$ cycle per second and its periodic time is a full minute. Its vector is the hypotenuse, the longest side, of the right-angled vector triangle, so that each of the components must be even slower rotations than this. The magnitudes (worked out by trigonometry or scale drawing) are in fact shown on the vector triangle in the figure, and the yawing rate is seen to be only half of the overall rate. If the bank angle were increased to more than 60°, the yaw vector in the triangle would become smaller still, until when banked at 90° (not possible without losing height since there is no vertical lift component) the yaw rate would become zero, and all the motion would be purely pitching – like a car in a vertical-sided wall-of-death.

A rudder's job is to produce a yawing moment, and usually doing so will also invoke a temporary yawing rotation until a new equilibrium is established between it and the other yawing moments on the aircraft. Since the rudder affects the lift of the tail fin, which is the parent aerodynamic surface responsible for the aircraft's directional stability, it is to be expected that the order of magnitude of the yawing rates resulting from the application of rudder will be similar to those of directional stability oscillations, in other words of the Dutch roll. But Dutch roll periodic times are, as we have seen, of the order of 2 or 3 seconds, which is very far removed from the required yaw rate to fly in a level circular path, where the periodic time in our example is 2 minutes.

So how is the yaw rate during a turn, albeit very small, achieved, if not with the rudder? Simply by the directional stability of the aircraft, which is capable of coping with far greater departures in yaw from the flight direction (the tangent to the circular flight path) than can ever occur as a direct result of carrying out a turn. It is partly for this reason that stability has been treated in this book before control, because an aircraft's stability is a major (and virtually essential) ingredient of all the normal functions of aircraft control. As a simple analogy, imagine a weather-vane on the top of a steeple pointing into the wind, and then (through some unique quirk of nature) the wind direction moving round smoothly through a complete 360° rotation in 2 minutes. The rate of rotation of the wind is so small that the weather-vane has absolutely no difficulty in pointing into the wind accurately at all times throughout the event.

Exactly the same principles apply when considering the pitch rate during the steady turn. The vector diagram in Figure 9.1 shows that the pitch rate is also less than the overall rotation rate, in this case 0.866 of its value, and once again this is a negligibly small pitch rate compared with that temporarily achievable by deflection of the elevator, which is of the same order of magnitude as that experienced in the short period pitching oscillation. This tends to create confusion in some people's mind, since we have seen that the pitch control has to be held back during the turn, which would appear to be creating a pitch rate throughout the turn. However, this is not the case, and the pitch control deflection is maintained solely for the purpose of keeping the aircraft longitudinally trimmed in the correct attitude (angle of attack) to produce the extra lift required during the turn. The very small pitch rate required as a component of the overall turn rate is delivered entirely (and very easily) by the aircraft's longitudinal static stability, represented by M_w.

Not only do longitudinal and directional static stability come into play in a conventional turn, but so does the aircraft's lateral static stability. When introducing this topic in Chapter 6, we emphasised that one way in which lateral stability is different in kind from longitudinal and directional stability is that the neutral, or undisturbed, position must be regarded relative to the direction of the gravity force, something extraneous to the aircraft, rather than relative to the aircraft's own flight path as in the cases of the other two. 'Wings level' meant 'wings normal to the weight force', and in straight flight this was synonymous with 'wings normal to the lift-force'. In banked turning flight the lateral static stability must try to return the aircraft to the reference position of 'wings normal to the lift-force', since this is the required orientation for a proper (or 'balanced') turn. And this is exactly what it does. If the aircraft were not banked quite enough, it would sideslip outwards and upwards, and due to L_v the resulting sideflow would cause a rolling moment to correct the initial shortfall of bank angle. If banked too much, the opposite would occur. Thus lateral static stability automatically takes care of making sure that the appropriate amount of bank has been applied – provided that the pilot does not interfere, thinking that he knows better!

THE OTHER WAY OF TURNING

There are situations in which the use of a rudder is desirable, and even necessary, during the conventional turn that we have been describing, but such needs arise only when we consider the cross-coupling effects of controls, which we will do in the next section. However, even if you are willing to accept that the rudder is not relevant (as a primary control) in a conventional turn, there may still be lingering in your mind pilots' anecdotes of turning an aircraft by use of the rudder. So let us briefly seek an answer to the question: what happens if the pilot applies just rudder, the yaw control, and nothing else (like steering a boat)? As we saw in Chapter 1, this is exactly what the early pioneers were fruitlessly trying to do, even after the Wright brothers had demonstrated the importance of banking and roll control.

Once again let us consider an aircraft flying due North at a steady speed in level flight, when the pilot wishes to turn to fly due East. If he applies right rudder (and nothing else), a side-force is immediately generated on the fin (and hence on the aircraft) to the *left*! Fortunately this force is small in comparison with the major aircraft forces, but even so the aircraft's centre of gravity is momentarily moved to the left, the opposite of what was required! But being far behind the centre of gravity, the fin force's purpose is to produce a clockwise (nose-right) moment, as a result of which the aircraft's nose will yaw a bit to the right, whilst the centre of gravity continues to travel straight forwards (ignoring the brief left movement mentioned above). Consequently there will be a side-flow from the front left, and this has several effects. First of all, the directional static stability (in the form of N_v) will oppose the yaw, and its straightening yawing moment $N_v v$ will increase until at a certain yaw angle it exactly balances the turning yawing moment of $N_\zeta \zeta$ due to the rudder deflection. (Incidentally, this is fortunately the end of the unbalanced and unwanted fin-force to the left.) If nothing else happened, the aircraft would then fly along its original flight path, but slightly crabwise, yawed but not yawing[4]. However, in addition, the side-flow will create a side-force on the aircraft's fuselage and fin (represented by the derivative Y_v), acting to the right, but the magnitude $Y_v v$ of this force will be far smaller than that potentially available from wing lift, and so the aircraft's path will begin to curve very gently to the right, along a very large turning circle. This would have been the situation experienced by Farman on his Deutsch-Archdeacon Prize flight in 1908, as described in the section of Chapter 1 headed 'Turning Point', and this is also how a boat turns in response to its rudder.

For an aircraft with lateral static stability, the side-flow from the left will have the additional effect of causing a roll to the right, due to the L_v or 'dihedral' derivative, and this roll will make the aircraft tend to take up the accurate banked attitude in the correct sense to allow wing lift to provide some centripetal force. 'Accurate' here means 'with no remaining sideslip', as discussed in the last paragraph of the preceding section. Presumably, since Farman did not have any roll control, such a tendency (although safe and self-limiting) would have been frightening to him rather than desirable, as he would have had no way of preventing what might have seemed destined to develop into a catastrophic roll, and so his rudder-initiated turn would have been a hair-raising experience, to be executed with extreme caution and delicacy of touch on the rudder.

We have just discovered that, by making use of the aircraft's natural stability, it is possible to initiate an approximately correct turn by use of the rudder only. To perfect it for a sustained level turn, when the bank angle has eventually come right the pilot would have (a) to

---

[4]Unfortunately we do not have two words for directional movements which correspond with bank and roll in the lateral motions; hence this slightly clumsy double use of the root word 'yaw'.

neutralise the rudder deflection (to prevent yawing the nose down into the ground), (b) to retrim longitudinally to produce the necessary extra lift (now that the lift vector is inclined) to prevent loss of height, and (c) to adjust the throttle(s) to compensate for the increased induced drag.

There is a situation where initiating a turn with rudder only is an approved, and even recommended, practice for today's pilots, and this is when preparing to land. When an aircraft is gently descending along its approach path, the pilot may find that he is flying parallel to, but not directly in line with, the centreline of the runway. Let us suppose that the aircraft is displaced a little to the left of the intended flight path. In this situation, it is not necessary to go through the entire complex routine of setting up a correctly banked turn to the right, levelling off when flying diagonally back towards the correct approach path, then setting up a second turn this time to the left and finally straightening up when properly positioned and orientated. Rather than all that, a little right rudder on its own will automatically (thanks to the aircraft's lateral stability) roll and turn the aircraft to the right, and before the need arises for longitudinal trimming – the bank angle is only very small – a little left rudder will yaw and roll the aircraft the other way by the same process in reverse, to orientate the aircraft on its original heading, but now in line with the runway centreline. The whole procedure is rather like half of one complete cycle of Dutch roll, deliberately induced and modified by the pilot.

This method is particularly powerful on aircraft with wings that are substantially swept back, and so it can be of benefit to the pilots of large jet transports as well as those of high performance combat aircraft. The reason why it particularly favours swept-wing aircraft is that the 'dihedral' effect of sweepback, which is strong anyway compared with other methods of producing L_v, becomes even stronger when an aircraft is flying at a high overall lift coefficient, as is the case when flying at the slow speed appropriate for approach and landing. The reason for this may be seen from Figure 9.2. Because of the difference between the effective aspect ratio[5] of the wing that is advancing into the side-flow and that of the trailing wing, the lift curve of the leading wing is substantially steeper than that of the trailing wing[6]. Consequently, at a large overall angle of attack, (high C_L, low speed in straight flight), it is clear from Figure 9.2 that the difference in lift coefficient, and thus lift, between the two wings is much greater than it

[5]See the fourth paragraph of the subsection entitled 'Sweepback' in the 'Lateral Static Stability' section of Chapter 6 for an explanation of 'effective aspect ratio'.
[6]This is discussed in Chapter 14 of *Flightwise – Principles of Aircraft Flight*, in the section headed 'Factors Affecting Ride Hardness'.

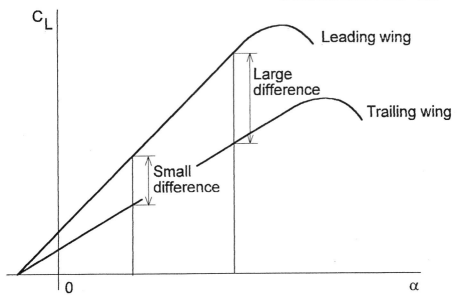

Figure 9.2 The 'dihedral' effect due to sweepback increases with overall angle of attack

is at a small overall angle of attack. Thus the L_v effect of sweepback is greatly enhanced during a conventional approach to land.

TYPES OF CONTROL SURFACES

We have talked about the fundamental rôles of the conventional aerodynamic control surfaces, but we have not yet looked closely at the nature of those surfaces themselves, beyond saying that they work by increasing the camber of the aerofoil section to which they are attached and hence its lift coefficient. After a few words about these conventional surfaces and their nature, we will take a look at some other devices by which aircraft can be and have been controlled.

Conventional or Three-axis Controls

A 'simple' turn for an aircraft is actually far from being a simple procedure, for the reasons that we have seen above and for numerous other reasons that we will come across bit by bit. As well as the aerodynamic complications, there is the additional difficulty, for the pilot, that there are three modes of control to be handled independently, whereas a car driver has only one, handled by the steering wheel, and a train driver has none. The pilot must learn the skill of integrating the movements of these three modes of control, to take account of all the various secondary and cross-coupling effects, and of the substantial variation in the performance of the controls as the aircraft speed is altered, since the aerodynamic forces produced depend on the square of the speed. Through these three modes, the pilot is able to apply turning moments independently about the three orthogonal aircraft body axes, and hence conventional controls are often referred to as *three-axis controls*. This term is mostly used by people who also operate aircraft which adopt alternative means of control, such as hang-glider and microlight enthusiasts, where weight-shifting (which we will mention in a moment) is often preferred to three-axis control.

When an experienced car driver begins to learn to fly a convention-ally controlled aeroplane, there is a fundamental handling difference to be learnt about. To turn in a car, you rotate the steering wheel to a new position to set up the turn. When it is almost completed, you re-centralise the steering wheel and the car stops turning and continues on a new straight line – all very logical and simple. By comparison, the main turning control of the aircraft, the roll control, has to be deflected to initiate the turn and then neutralised as soon as the turn is established. Then, to pull out of the turn, the roll control has to be moved from neutral in the opposite sense to initiate a roll the other way, whereas a car steering wheel simply has to be centralised. Even if one is told about this by one's instructor, the experience of steering a car is so deeply ingrained that often such verbal instruction is fairly ineffectual, and it is not until the new pilot discovers the difference for himself or herself that the full implications are appreciated.

The ailerons are together referred to as a *rate control*. This is because a certain fixed deflection of the pilot's aileron control through a given angular *displacement* will provide the aircraft with a particular *rate* of roll, once the roll damping couple of the wings has built up enough to equal the rolling couple of the ailerons. Remember that the roll damping moment of the wings ($L_p p$), is a paddle-like effect which depends on the *rate* of roll p. As we saw earlier, in the absence of any secondary effects or other control inputs the aircraft would simply corkscrew endlessly about its straight flight path.

By contrast, the elevator and rudder are referred to as *displacement controls*. If the rudder is applied whilst in steady straight symmetrical flight, its yawing moment will be resisted by an opposing yawing moment which grows from zero in proportion to the *angle* yawed through, until this resisting moment equals the rudder's yawing moment. Note that this resisting moment is a result of side-flow fol-lowing yaw ($N_v v$), and is *not* primarily the yaw damping moment due to yaw rate, $N_r r$, since this only makes a brief and trivial contribution. When the yawing and opposing moments are equal, the yaw rate stops[7] and the rudder deflection holds the aircraft at a constant angu-

[7]Strictly there could be an overshoot, but this is usually insignificant if the rudder deflection has been applied at a realistic rate rather than as an instantaneous 'stab'.

lar *displacement.* In a similar way, the elevator adjusts the pitch attitude of the aircraft, thus producing an angular *displacement*, and not (except momentarily) a pitch rate. A sustained turn is produced by wing lift, and the negligibly small pitch rate component of the sustained turn rate is provided entirely by the natural longitudinal static stability of the aircraft. The use of the nomenclature 'displacement controls' further emphasises that the rôle of the elevator and rudder in a turn is not to provide a rotational rate, but something else, as we have already seen and will examine further.

Rudder

Although we have dismissed the rudder from having any primary rôle in a straightforward turn, it does have some important uses in special circumstances. The first of these is the need to be able to control a twin- or multi-engined aircraft against the large yawing moment that results if one or more wing-mounted engine fails so that the remaining thrust is asymmetrically distributed about the x–z plane. The yawing moment of such a thrust force may be sufficient to overcome completely the aircraft's directional static stability, and the pilot may need to apply a very large rudder force to resist it. Indeed, the 'design case' for determining the size of fin and rudder combined on a multi-engined aircraft is usually this situation of asymmetric thrust. Although the pilot could use less rudder yawing moment than that produced by the asymmetric engine and rely on some side-flow due to progressing in a slightly crabwise manner, it is better if possible to balance the thrust moment exactly with the rudder, so that the aircraft's drag is kept low and so that secondary effects such as differential wing lift due to side-flow do not arise. The pilot must otherwise use the ailerons to hold off any tendency to roll.

One other application of the rudder in flight actually takes advantage of the secondary effects due to the wings and of the additional drag that the aircraft experiences if flying crabwise, and this is a technique known as sideslipping. Here we come across another major difference between flying an aeroplane and driving a car. If you want to stop a car (traffic permitting), you simply apply the brakes until the car comes safely to rest. But in an aircraft, it goes without saying that you must put the thing on the ground first, and herein lies a serious problem. In order to descend, the nose must be pointed 'downhill', and then there will be a forward component of the gravity force making the aircraft go *faster*, rather than slower, like a runaway road vehicle on a hill with no brakes. The normal solution to this problem is to minimise the engine thrust and then to limit the angle of descent to such a value that the natural drag of the aircraft, augmented probably by that of flaps and undercarriage, balances the x-direction component of the gravity force at a suitably low speed for landing. However, if the pilot inadvertently finds that the aircraft is too high when preparing to land, he would sometimes like to descend more steeply than the natural drag of the aircraft will permit (without excessive speed). To do this, he needs all the extra drag that he can muster. He may have some 'air-brakes' at his disposal, but even these may be inadequate[8].

This is the situation in which the pilot may deliberately impose a 'sideslip', although it basically involves a side-flow following yaw rather than due to a sideways (y-direction) sideslipping of the aircraft. To achieve this, the pilot applies and maintains a substantial rudder deflection, let us say (for the sake of illustration) to the right. The yawing displacement thus achieved (once the yaw rate has been quelled by the N_v effect) will give rise to a side-flow from the left, and due to the 'dihedral' stability the aircraft would tend to roll to the right. In order to keep the wings level, the pilot applies and holds a left-aileron control input, so that the aileron moment exactly balances the 'dihedral' rolling moment. The aircraft centre of gravity thus proceeds along a straight path, whilst the nose of the aircraft is yawed to the right of this path. The additional drag that is thus produced is due chiefly to the Y_v derivative, which expresses the fact that the side-flow due to yaw exerts a side-force on the aircraft, chiefly on the fuselage and fin, and it is the component of this force in the rearwards flight-path direction, together with the scarcely ever mentioned X_v derivative, that is required. The centre of gravity is still following its initial path in azimuth[9], although now able to descend a little more steeply at the same speed.

If a still more rapid rate of descent is required, the pilot may apply an even greater aileron moment to the left, so that the wings do not remain level but the left wing stabilises at a lower level than the right. (Your model in hand will help you to visualise this.) Now the aircraft will actually sideslip downwards to the left, the centre of gravity will be deflected from its straight path[10], and height will be lost even faster. We now have a situation in which the side-flow is due both to being yawed and to side-slipping, both effects being in the same sense and reinforcing one another. There is consequently a strong tendency for the aircraft to recover to wings-level, and a considerable aileron con-

---

[8]In passing we can at this point dispel another myth. People commonly suppose that the main purpose of air-brakes is to slow an aircraft down, but in fact a much more important purpose is to enable an aircraft to descend steeply and hence lose height rapidly, without gaining excessive airspeed.

[9]Azimuth is an angle measured (from north) in the horizontal plane.

[10]In practice, a pilot will turn the aircraft to compensate, so that the resulting flight path is unchanged from before.

trol force input is required to prevent this and hold the side-slipping attitude.

This is a noisy and unnatural manoeuvre which exerts considerable stress on the airframe and is demanding on the pilot in that the roll and yaw controls have to be used in opposite senses from each other, whilst descending rapidly perhaps close to the ground, but it can be highly effective. It is particularly favoured by pilots of sailplanes, since these aircraft usually have very low drag characteristics and little additional drag from undercarriage or flaps (although they usually have air-brakes), and, furthermore, the option to go round again may not be open to them when committed to land, since they have no power source other than their stored kinetic energy.

Another aircraft with similar low-drag characteristics to those of a sailplane but with a very different mission is the Lockheed U-2 reconnaissance aircraft, shown in Figure 9.3. The high aspect ratio of the wings (for low induced drag) is seen from the plan view, whilst the front view silhouette shows that there is very little frontal area. This aircraft, being optimised for long endurance at high altitude, has received scant concessions from the designer to make it easy to manoeuvre at low speeds and to land. As with most sailplanes there is a central single wheel main undercarriage, and this does not protrude far. Not only does it provide very little additional drag, but with the lack of dihedral the wing-tips are tiresomely close to the ground on landing and take-off. The aircraft is renowned for being difficult to

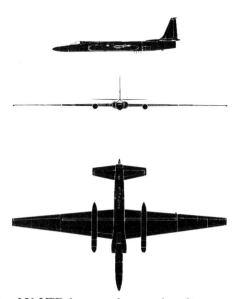

Figure 9.3   Lockheed U-2/TR-1 reconnaissance aircraft

land, since as soon as one pushes the nose down the speed and thus the lift picks up, trying to defy attempts at putting the aircraft on the ground. It would therefore appear to be a prime candidate for losing height through the use of sideslip.

There is yet another very important use which is made of the rudder in flight, and once again this is in connection with the approach to landing, when the wind is blowing across rather than along the runway. For an aircraft in flight high above the ground, the direction and strength of any atmospheric wind that is blowing does not affect the aerodynamics of the aircraft's flight in any respect at all, since the only 'wind' that the aircraft experiences is the airflow meeting it from directly ahead. When a wind is blowing, the entire mass of air surrounding the aircraft, together with the aircraft itself, is all moving as one, and without reference to the ground it would be impossible for the pilot to discern whether there were any wind blowing or not. The aircraft is like a fly flying inside a moving bus with closed windows.

Such a wind does affect the course, or *track*, of the aircraft over the ground, and so for the purposes of navigation it must be taken into account. It is however only when the aircraft comes close to the ground that there is any perceived conflict between the track and the *heading*, the direction of the aircraft's flight path relative to the surrounding air. In Figure 9.4 there is a crosswind coming from ahead and the left as seen by a pilot approaching the runway and intending to land. If the pilot were to fly with the aircraft's *x*-axis parallel with the runway and centreline, as in the upper diagram, the wind's velocity would be superimposed on the velocity of the aircraft relative to the air, as shown in the vector triangle, and the overall effect would be that the aircraft would drift off to the right of the runway along the line of the velocity of the aircraft relative to the ground, which is the

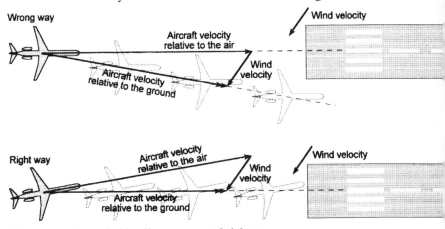

Figure 9.4   Crosswind landing, wrong and right way

vector resultant. Perhaps it would seem desirable for the pilot to anticipate this by starting his approach from the left of the centreline, so
that the aircraft has just drifted on to this line at the moment at which
it touches down on the runway. But this is not practicable, since first
of all the pilot has no visual cue to enable him to judge how far off
centre to start from, and secondly it would mean that ground-based
landing guidance systems would have to be capable of altering the
approach path that they indicated according to the aircraft's speed
and the prevailing ground wind. Furthermore, this wind may be very
localised both vertically and horizontally, so that the wind where the
aircraft is may be different in magnitude and direction from the wind
at the airfield.

The solution, therefore, is for the pilot to fly the aircraft on to the
extended runway centreline early on in the approach, and then to fly
the aircraft on a heading to the left, as shown in the lower diagram, so
that the drift due to the wind keeps the centre of gravity of the aircraft
tracking along the centreline throughout the approach. In terms of the
vector triangle, the wind velocity is (obviously) unchanged in magnitude and direction from the upper diagram, and the *magnitude* of the
aircraft's velocity relative to the air is unchanged. However, the direction of this velocity is modified in such a way that the direction of the
resultant of the two velocities is exactly along the extended runway
centreline. This the pilot can cope with, as he simply adjusts the aircraft's heading in such a way that he is always looking straight along
the centreline, (although not out of the front of his windscreen).

No rudder force is required for this since throughout the approach
the aircraft is flying in a perfectly normal symmetrical attitude relative
to the air. However, at the moment when the aircraft touches down on
the ground, the undercarriage wheels would still be pointing in the aircraft's x-axis direction and not along the runway, and so there would
be a very substantial side-force exerted on the undercarriage wheels
and bogies on touch-down, and a skid or structural damage would
ensue unless the aircraft were yawed to point straight along the runway. To prevent damage, the pilot must use the rudder to apply sufficient yaw *just before* touching down, in order to align the wheels with
the runway so that no side-force is created on them. This takes considerable skill and fine judgement: apply the rudder too early, and the
aircraft will drift off the centreline as in the upper diagram; too late,
and a very uncomfortable and potentially damaging and dangerous
landing will ensue. One or two extremely large transport aircraft have
been provided with rotatable undercarriages to circumvent this problem, but this is not common practice.

Once on the ground, the aircraft must still be steerable, but now
only in a single horizontal plane, so it is no longer appropriate to bank

the wings. Thus the rudder once again comes into its own as an aerodynamic control for steering the aircraft straight up the centreline of the runway against crosswind gusts that would deflect it, during both the landing runs and the take-off. But whereas in flight the aircraft is always at or above its minimum flying speed, when on the runway it is usually moving below this speed, and indeed at any speed down to zero. Thus the effectiveness of the rudder falls off severely long before a landing aircraft has come to rest, and so the undercarriage (usually the nosewheel) must also be steerable both for low speed steering during landing and take-off and for taxying. On a small aircraft driven by a central propeller there can in fact be some aerodynamic steering from the rudder, since it is usually right in the slipstream of the propeller and, so receives an airflow even when the aircraft is itself moving much more slowly.

Alternative configurations

Although trailing-edge camber-modifying hinged flaps are the most common form of aircraft control surface, a number of alternative methods have been devised and are used for controlling aircraft, mostly for applying moments about the aircraft axes as with conventional three-axis controls. Here we will briefly review the most important of these alternative devices, but we will leave until the following section a discussion of the problems which give rise to their use.

Miscellaneous

In place of or as well as ailerons, roll control is frequently achieved by the use of *spoilers* in the wing upper surfaces, plates which on demand either hinge up or protrude vertically out from the top of the wing surface into the airflow with their flat surfaces normal to the oncoming air. A spoiler disrupts the lifting airflow over a wing upper surface, so that that wing loses lift relative to the other and descends. Spoilers are particularly useful in that they serve some additional functions as well. Immediately after a large airliner has touched down on the runway when landing, the spoilers of *both* wings are immediately fully deployed together, in order to kill off quickly as much wing lift as possible and so dump the aircraft's weight firmly on to the wheels. By this means, any tendency for the aircraft to bounce is eliminated, and the effectiveness of the wheel brakes is very considerably enhanced. Although primarily designed for their lift-spoiling function, spoilers clearly also create a very appreciable amount of form drag when deployed, and thus immediately after landing (whilst the air speed is still high) they provide invaluable assistance to the other means of braking the aircraft and bringing it quickly and safely to rest. They are also sometimes used as air-brakes in flight, either to reduce air speed in a hurry or as dive brakes to permit rapid loss of height without increasing speed.

Another method of controlling roll is to use *tailerons*, which are tailplane control surfaces performing the function of elevators and ailerons: together as an elevator and in opposite senses as a roll control. Tailerons have the limitation that the rolling moment arm is very limited, because of the small span of the tailplane compared with that of the wings. Furthermore, the rolling moment applied by the tailerons is resisted by the roll damping of the wings, and thus considerable torsional stress is set up in the fuselage between wing and tail, which must be catered for in the structural design. Another problem is that, when the rolling and pitching modes are used simultaneously, the authority of one of the tailerons may be stretched to the limit since it is serving double duty.

Both spoilers and tailerons are often used in aircraft with high-speed wing sections, in order to free as much as possible (sometimes all) of the trailing edge of the wings for lift augmentation flaps[11]. There are also other reasons associated with high-speed flight which make conventional ailerons unsuitable, which we shall meet in the following section of this chapter.

An alternative tailplane configuration sometimes used is the V-tail, in which the three surfaces of the conventional rudder and tailplane are replaced by two, set with their plane at about 45° both to the plane of the wings and the aircraft's plane of symmetry. In this case, the linkage from the pilot's controls has to be scheduled so that the trailing surfaces on both tail surfaces (which are called *ruddervators*) can act independently in the pitching and yawing senses. Despite the saving in weight and drag, the control linkage complication together with the lack of independence of controls and the danger of unwanted coupling effects have prevented this feature from becoming commonplace. It was, however, made more familiar by the French Air Force aerobatic team, who used to fly the V-tailed Aérospatiale Magister aircraft for their displays; and also by the Beechcraft Bonanza.

Sometimes elevators are replaced by all-moving, or *slab*, tailplanes, in which case the variation in lift is not achieved by varying the camber of the surface to which the hinged surface is attached, but rather by altering the angle of attack of the entire surface, which has no hinged trailing part at all. Since a far greater variation in lift coefficient can be achieved by varying angle of attack than by varying camber, slab tailplanes are powerful control surfaces, and when used as tailerons they tend to overcome the problem of limited aerodynamic

---

[11]Lift augmentation is discussed in Chapter 9 of *Flightwise – Principles of Aircraft Flight* under the heading 'Modification for Flight – Lift Augmentation'.

authority. But of course, as with all aerofoils, they are prone to high angle-of-attack leading-edge stalling[12], especially as they are usually thin aerofoils, with consequently small-radius leading edges.

Canards

Canard foreplanes have a very strong design appeal as pitch control surfaces in place of the aft tailplane and elevators, for a number of reasons that we shall meet at various points later on in this book. We have already seen that aircraft with canards are *not* inherently longitudinally unstable, and furthermore canards are sometimes presented as a design feature which makes an aircraft totally unstallable. This is superficially a justifiable claim, as may be understood by referring to Figure 9.5. In Chapter 4 (under the heading 'Tailless Aircraft') we saw that an aircraft must possess the characteristic of longitudinal dihedral in order to be trimmable, and this principle applies equally to conventionally tailed aircraft and those with canard foreplanes. This means that, as shown in Figure 9.5(a) in which the angles are exaggerated, the canards must be mounted on the fuselage in such a way that they are always at a slightly larger cruising angle of attack (α_c) than the main wings (assuming both aerofoils to have the same camber). If the aircraft's angle of attack α is progressively increased towards the stalling angle of the wings as in diagram (b), the canard will reach its stalling angle first and will stall before the wing stalls, thus losing some of its lift whilst that of the wing is still increasing. This loss of canard lift will cause a nose-down pitching moment to occur, and so the aircraft will pitch nose-down, resulting in reduction of both angles of attack.

The clever bit of this is that the canard should immediately be unstalled again and its required lift restored, so that it should never be possible to reach the overall angle of attack at which the wing stalls. Instead, if speed is not restored, the aircraft will simply fly on a downward-inclined flight path without stalling. Furthermore, if the pilot attempts to reduce the speed still further, the flight path will continue to grow steeper, and the forward component of gravity will ensure that too much speed cannot be lost.

This system has been proved to work very well in practice, especially in some light aircraft designed by Bert Rutan and in business aircraft such as the Beechcraft Starship shown in Figure 9.6. Unfortunately, however, there can be a nasty sting in the tail. When used on high-speed aircraft necessitating the use of thin aerofoils with relatively sharp leading edges, the stalling characteristic of the canard is likely to be a sudden 'leading edge' stall, which means that when the

[12]Leading and trailing edge stalls are discussed in Chapter 9 of *Flightwise – Principles of Aircraft Flight*, in the section headed 'Aerofoil Characteristics'.

(a) Cruising angle of attack

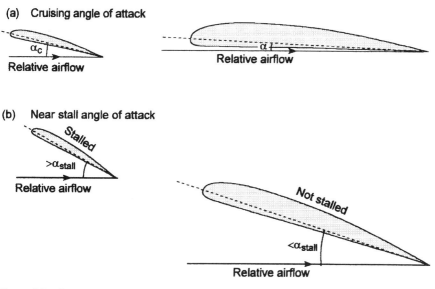

α_c

Relative airflow

α

Relative airflow

(b) Near stall angle of attack

Stalled

$>\alpha_{\text{stall}}$

Relative airflow

Not stalled

$<\alpha_{\text{stall}}$

Relative airflow

Figure 9.5   Stall characteristics of a canard configuration

Figure 9.6   The Beechcraft Starship sporting canards and wing-tip fins and rudders

canard stalls it will very suddenly lose a substantial amount of its lift. This will allow the nose to fall at a very high pitch rate when the canard reaches its stall, with the consequence that, being far ahead of the centre of gravity, the local airflow will approach the canards from below, so that their effective angle of attack is not reduced but further *increased*! So the canards will not recover their pre-stall lift as was hoped, but instead the nose is likely to fall right through the horizontal position into a steep nose-down attitude, resulting in a sudden nose-dive or even a 'tuck-under' which is effectively a somersault. This might be expected to be a subsonic[13] characteristic of the Saab Viggen illustrated in Figure 9.7, a Mach 2 multi-rôle combat aircraft (whose name is the Swedish word for 'Thunderbolt'), except for its saving grace of having a large sweepback angle on its canards, which probably renders their stalling characteristic more docile because of vortex lift[14]. However, such aircraft do have a reputation amongst military pilots for having less than ideal stalling characteristics.

Canards are very much a feature of the rising generation of combat aircraft, as exemplified by their use on the Eurofighter 2000 (Figure 14.7) and the MBB Rockwell X-31A (Figure 14.5). But this is largely because only with the use of sophisticated computer-driven controlling systems can their full benefits be realised, and when the Saab Viggen was introduced in 1971 such systems had not been developed. We will come back and look more thoroughly at this most important and fast-moving subject in the final three chapters of this book.

It might be thought that canards could be used differentially in the same manner as tailerons to produce roll control. Surprisingly, however, this turns out not to be the case at all. This is because canards are placed in front of the wings, and usually they have a relatively low aspect ratio. When a canard produces a large amount of lift in the usual upward sense, it also creates a substantial amount of downwash behind it, which reduces the angle of attack of the main wing in the root region, the main lifting region, and hence some wing lift is sacrificed. Likewise, a canard producing a downward force will create additional upward lift on the wing on its side. Consequently if canards are deflected differentially to produce a rolling moment, the wings unobligingly produce a rolling moment of a similar magnitude in the opposite sense, so that (apart from a torsional stress in the fuselage) nothing is achieved.

Tailless aircraft

When discussing tailless aircraft in Chapter 4, it was stated that the primary motivation towards the desire to produce tailless aircraft was the potential for drag reduction, and that this had especially been so in connection with the search for low transonic drag during the period of

---

[13]Stalling at high angle of attack is not a problem in supersonic flight. This is discussed in the final paragraphs of the section headed 'Expansion Fans' in Chapter 10 of *Flightwise – Principles of Aircraft Flight*.
[14]This is illustrated in Figures 14.4 and 14.5 of Chapter 14 of *Flightwise – Principles of Aircraft Flight*.

Figure 9.7   Saab Viggen

attempting to overcome the 'sound barrier'. Although the abandon-
ment of a tail empennage[15] is not widespread, the tailless layout is to
be found in some high-speed delta-winged aircraft, and in the low-
speed scene it is still pursued by some enthusiasts. Interestingly, the
concept has found a new application in the design of some 'stealth'
aircraft, such as the Northrop B-2 stealth bomber shown in Figure 5.7,
in which a minimum radar signature is a primary design requirement.

A tailless aircraft's wings have to perform the functions both of primary lifting surface and of stabilising and control surfaces. In order to
achieve an adequate moment arm for providing pitching and yawing
moments about the centre of gravity, wing sweepback is normally
required so that the wing-tips are well behind the centre of gravity and
can perform the usual rôle of the tailplane, and washout[16] can take
care of the trimming requirement discussed in Chapter 4. When this is

[15]The word 'empennage' refers to an aeroplane's tail as a unit, including tailplane, elevator, fin and rudder. It is derived from the French word for the feathered flight of an
arrow, which in turn comes from the Latin noun *penna*, meaning a feather or a wing.
[16]Washout is the progressive reduction in wing section angle of incidence (the angle
between the chord and a longitudinal datum axis fixed in the aircraft) from root to tip.
In the case of tailless aircraft it can account for as much as 10° difference between root
and tip.

the case, hinged wing-tip surfaces can provide the functions of both elevators (when acting together) and ailerons (when acting differentially), and they are referred to as *elevons*. In the case of a delta-winged aircraft, elevons sometimes extend over the entire trailing edge of the wing from root to tip. However, the use of elevons is by no means the only possible arrangement for tailless aircraft, and if you are interested in investigating this further may I recommend to you a most interesting and comprehensive book entitled *Tailless Aircraft in Theory and Practice*, written by Karl Nickel and Michael Wohlfahrt and translated by Captain Eric Brown RN into English from the original German. It was published in 1994 by Edward Arnold.

There is also the need for directional stability and control in yaw to be considered, and although some aircraft without tailplanes still have a long enough fuselage to support a tail fin and rudder (such as the Concorde supersonic airliner), some purists of the tailless school insist that tailless means without any components of the conventional empennage at all. Without a fuselage, the main directionally destabilising component of a conventional aircraft is dispensed with, and conveniently sweepback itself produces a fair amount of directional stability. This is because the leading (right) wing in Figure 6.7 (which shows the laterally stabilising effect of sweepback) experiences extra induced drag on account of its additional lift, and hence a restorative N_v effect when the side-flow results from yawing. To control a tailless aircraft in yaw is not of itself a great problem, since the wings provide a long moment arm from the aircraft's z-axis, and a yawing moment can be provided by creating differential drag. Interestingly, the B-2 stealth bomber illustrated in Figure 5.7, with no vertical surfaces at all, uses exactly this principle, and has at its wing-tips splitting drag brakes as illustrated in Figure 9.8. However, all the double functioning required of many of the components of a tailless aircraft leads to many conflicts of interest, cross-coupling effects and often a sacrifice of authority, and in many ways a great price has to be paid for dispensing with an independent empennage.

Although not 'tailless' since it has canard foreplanes, some of the features of tailless aircraft are represented by the Beechcraft Starship (Figure 9.6). Here there is little fuselage length aft of the main wings, and so the fins and rudders have been placed at the wing-tips. As the side elevation silhouette shows, these are as far aft as a conventional tail fin and rudder on account of the wing sweep. They perform essentially the same functions, but also have a number of specialised aerodynamic effects which have to be taken into consideration. Whilst they can reduce induced drag in the manner of winglets[17], they also

---

[17]Winglets are explained in the section entitled 'Winglets and Wing-Tip Sails' in Chapter 12 of *Flightwise – Principles of Aircraft Flight*.

Figure 9.8 Wing-tip drag rudders, as used on the B-2 Stealth Bomber

produce other unique aerodynamic effects. For example, if the rudders are deflected to the right (to produce a yawing moment about the centre of gravity to the right), the right fin is producing lift towards the left, so that immediately to its left, (i.e. above its upper aerofoil surface) there is a region of reduced pressure. This, being above the wing-tip, gives rise to an increase in lift of the right wing-tip and a rolling moment to the left. This is the same combination of motions that we considered above when discussing deliberately sideslipping to lose height, but it is not a desirable feature in normal flight.

Weight shift
At one end of the aircraft spectrum which we have scarcely touched upon are the flexible-winged hang-gliders, microlight or ultralight aircraft (excluding three-axis control microlights) and paragliders. In these craft the weight of the pilot is suspended well below the lifting wings or canopy, and control is achieved by the so-called 'weight-shift' technique. Recalling our earlier discussion about the term 'pendulum stability' when referring to the lateral static stability of high-winged aircraft, we should be wary of the term 'weight-shift', since once again it tends to imply the 'sky-hook' concept which is misleading and not very scientific.

Control by weight-shifting is a major (and very interesting) subject in its own right, but we can only give it the briefest mention here, although by now you will be able to apply the principles of Newtonian mechanics for yourself. All we can say is that, when setting up a turn to the right, the pilot pulls down on the right wing, so that the wing lift vector inclines to the right, hence acting above the centre of gravity and thus rolling the aircraft to the right as well as supplying (immediately) a horizontal centripetal force component. Once the aircraft has established a banked turning circle, the pilot's weight will swing out to the left, 'chair-o-plane'-wise, so that he will once again be perpendicularly below the wing. Really weight-shift doesn't come into it – rather the pilot is adjusting the orientation of the wing, using the inertia of his own mass as an anchor from which to do so. Similar principles apply to pitching the aircraft nose-up and nose-down, for which the pilot ostensibly 'shifts his weight' forward and aft. Sorry – we really mustn't allow ourselves to get further distracted by this fascinating subject!

Vectored thrust

There is one very different approach to the challenge of controlling an aircraft effectively, and that is to use the thrust of the propulsion system rather than aerodynamic forces on lifting surfaces. In recent years much interest and research has gone into developing ways in which the thrust of the engines, particularly jet engines, can be used to augment the authority of the aerodynamic controls as well as providing the required forward thrust.

There are two approaches which have in the past presented themselves, both of which involve ducting some of the accelerated air from the engine(s) in a particular direction, thus producing thrust in the opposite sense (hence the term 'vectored thrust'). First of all, the ducting can be taken to the extremities of the aircraft such as nose, tail and wing-tips, so that moments can be produced about the centre of gravity to produce the same effects as conventional three-axis controls, but without the necessity of forward speed to make them work. The vertical take-off British Aerospace Harrier of Figure 6.13 uses this technique for control in the hover.

But since the thrust of jet engines can be of a similar order of magnitude to the lift and weight forces, there is a much more intriguing possibility presented by the use of vectored thrust, and that is of directly supplying the actual centripetal force to the aircraft's centre of gravity to achieve a change in the velocity vector of its flight, rather than rotating the aircraft so that the conventional aerodynamic surfaces have to provide this force. By this means it should be possible to change the speed and/or the direction of motion of (the centre of gravity of) an aircraft with only scant reference to conventional aerodynamics and the aircraft's attitude, thus opening up all sorts of potentially useful possibilities. Many of these ideas have matured into operational reality in the unique Harrier 'jump-jet' of Figure 6.13 with its legendary capacity for so-called 'VIFFing' (vectoring in forward flight), but there is scope for much further development.

Thrust vectoring is a highly topical subject in the still unfolding picture of aircraft control in today's highly agile fighters. The trend today is to use it for augmenting control surface authority and providing large moments about the centre of gravity, rather than for direct force on the centre of gravity. This subject is a central theme running through Chapter 14.

COMPLICATIONS AND SOLUTIONS

The treatment of an aircraft turning at the beginning of this chapter was a highly sanitised and idealised account for the purpose of explaining the basic principles involved. In practice there are a number of additional features to take into account, which vary widely between different aircraft designs and at different flying speeds. In the remainder of this chapter we shall look first of all at some of the cross-coupling effects that the pilot must take into account in routine flight, and then at the operational and design implications of flying at high and low speeds.

Cross-coupling in Normal Flight

Differential lift in a turn

With model in hand, let us take another look at the aircraft in an established banked turn (let us say to the right) in level flight. If the aircraft has a substantial wing-span, the left wing-tip will be travelling along a larger-radius circle, and hence slightly faster, than the right wing-tip. Since lift depends on the square of speed, the left wing-tip will receive slightly more lift than the right wing-tip, so that the very act of flying in a circle will tend to make the aircraft roll more steeply into the turn. This is an L_r effect, although as we have seen r is small. If this is not corrected, the balance of the forces will be upset and the aircraft will begin to sideslip downwards and in towards the centre of the turn. Consequently it will yaw more into the turn due to N_v, thus amplifying the differential wing lift which started this sequence of events, but at the same time the dihedral stability L_v will tend to oppose this additional roll and to restore the aircraft to its correct bank for the turn. However, some height will be lost due to the sideslip.

We must be careful, when considering secondary effects of controls such as this, to take account of the relative significance of them, since many misunderstandings arise simply as a result of overemphasising one trivial effect in comparison with another which is in fact more significant. In the present case, I have therefore done a quick estimation of the difference in lift force between the two wing-tips of the Warhawk in the turn of Figure 9.1, and it transpires that the extreme outer wing-tip is travelling only about one third of one per cent faster than the inner wing-tip, so that the overall additional lift on the outer wing due to this effect would be only in the region of about half of one per cent. The reason that this effect is so small is that, as we have previously discussed, the yaw rate component of the overall turn is tiny in comparison with typical brief yaw rates generated by the fin through use of rudder or the N_v effect. Furthermore, if the original banking tendency is allowed to grow so that sideslip into the turn follows, the dihedral effect will often prevent this from being a problem. It all depends on the balance of the various effects, as do so many characteristics of aircraft controls, and for this reason it is always unsafe to generalise about the effects of controls. Whatever you say, even with sound reasoning, there will always be a competent pilot ready to contradict with good justification based on experience, and both can be right depending on the nature of the aircraft in question.

If the problem of the bank angle tending to increase occurs during a balanced turn, the pilot must apply a small amount of opposite-aileron (i.e. in the sense to roll the aircraft the other way) throughout the banked turn. Although the effect is very small in the case of the Warhawk in Figure 9.1, it will be greater if (a) the turning circle is smaller, (b) the wing-span is greater, and (c) the bank angle is smaller. This might suggest the scenario of a sailplane circling gently at a low air speed in a thermal up-current, and so it would be expected that in such a situation the need for opposite aileron might be more appreciable.

How does the pilot know whether a turn is properly balanced or not? Having no convenient external visual references when flying, it is necessary for the pilot to be provided with some form of instrumentation to indicate whether the bank angle is correct or not, since the 'seat of the pants' is not sensitive enough. Such an instrument detects the *effect* of an incorrect bank, the resulting sideslip, and is therefore called a *slip indicator*. It consists simply of a bent glass tube with sealed ends, containing a ball that is free to roll along the tube, and in each diagram of Figure 9.9 this is shown on a 'panel' superimposed on the rear view of the aircraft's fuselage, as it would be seen by the pilot. Each diagram represents the aircraft incorrectly carrying out a 30° banked turn, overbanked in the left-hand diagram and underbanked in the right. The position of the ball in the slip indicator is determined by the direction of the 'correct lift' arrow in each case, and to make the indicator's working plain it has been drawn with the centre of curvature of the tube coinciding with the centre of gravity of the aircraft, and a dashed extension of the 'correct lift' line indicating the ball's position. The ball is where it would be if 'hanging' directly 'under' the correct lift line, just like the chair and chains of a chair-o-plane roundabout.

In order to correct the bank, the pilot must apply more aileron control displacement in the direction as if to push the ball back towards the centre. It is *not* normally appropriate to correct the slip indicator reading by applying rudder (as is often thought and taught!), since by doing so one is simply compensating for one sort of side-flow (due to sideslip) by another (due to yaw), and the turn is still not correctly 'balanced'.

Over-banked - sideslipping right   **Under-banked - sideslipping left**

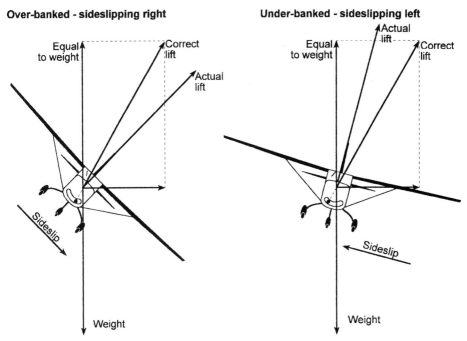

Figure 9.9   Slip indicator in incorrectly banked turns

If you look closely at Figure 9.9, you will see what looks like a wind-screen wiper on each diagram. This short line in fact represents an alternative, much cheaper and in many ways more effective slip indicator which is simpler to interpret. It is simply a short length of string or wool fastened at one end to the outside of the pilot's windscreen, providing a 'head-up display'. Since the airflow due to normal flight streams up, not down, the windscreen, the tuft is fixed at its bottom end and its top is streaming with the flow. If there is any side-flow (resulting from either cause) the tuft will be swept to one side or the other in the directions indicated in the two diagrams of the figure, giving a much more direct indication of the side-flow than the more sophisticated slip indicator. The top of the tuft points to the side that the aileron control should be moved to in order to correct the bank: when correctly banked the tuft streams straight up[18] the windscreen.

Adverse aileron yaw
Probably the most well known and ubiquitous secondary effect of

[18]Unfortunately this neutral position may not be exactly 'straight up', because of the curvature of the windscreen and the three-dimensional flow pattern around it in straight level flight. It is therefore important for the pilot to know what the neutral position of the tuft is, and this can be ascertained by observing it in straight level flight.

aircraft controls is the trying problem known as *adverse aileron yaw*. When ailerons are deflected to produce differential lift at the two wing-tips, they inevitably also produce a difference in induced drag, so that the wing which is required to rise is also pulled backwards because of its extra lift and hence drag. If not compensated for, this unfortunately creates a most uncomfortable response whereby the nose of the aircraft swings out and away from the intended turn. Usually the N_v of the directional stability will prevent this from going too far, but it means that the roll has got off to a very bad start. The problem is most marked on aircraft with high aspect ratios, but tends to be a feature of all aircraft with conventional layout and controls.

If the adverse aileron yaw tendency has not been totally eliminated by any of the designer's tricks discussed in the next paragraph, the pilot will be required on initiating a turn to apply a rudder deflection in the direction of the turn in order to prevent it from occurring. Thus pilots are taught to 'coordinate ailerons and rudder' when entering a turn, but unfortunately this has frequently given rise to the impression that yawing (by means of the rudder) is an integral part of the normal turn, which we have already seen is not the case.

Various remedies can be incorporated into the design of ailerons to overcome at least partially the problem of adverse aileron yaw, but since the severity of the problem depends on the flight condition, no solution can be complete. One approach is to arrange the ailerons so that the up-going aileron (on the down-going wing) deflects further than the down-going aileron, so that it itself produces a substantial amount of form drag to balance out the additional induced drag of the up-going wing. Alternatively (or additionally), the ailerons may be set so that they are both slightly higher than flush with the wing when undeflected, whereby the first bit of downward deflection actually reduces the aileron's form drag. If you sit in an airliner where you can see along the trailing edge of a wing, you will sometimes be able to observe that the aileron is actually deflected a very small amount upwards, even though the aircraft is cruising absolutely straight and level. If you moved across to look at the other wing, you would find that its aileron was also slightly deflected upward.

Another method of tackling the problem is to incorporate a mechanical link between the aileron and rudder controls, so that when ailerons are applied the rudder is automatically deflected as well, but this is not ideal since it sacrifices the preferred independence of the controls. Perhaps the best, and certainly a widely adopted, practice is to use so-called *Frise ailerons*. These are ailerons which are designed with a lip at the lower leading edge, as shown in Figure 9.10, in such a way that this lip protrudes into the airflow under the wing producing

Figure 9.10 A Frise aileron

form drag when the aileron is deflected upwards, but is sheltered inside the wing during downward deflections.

Although primarily introduced to overcome some other problems that we shall see below, the use of spoilers in place of ailerons for roll control often solves the adverse aileron yaw problem completely, and therefore ensures very good roll control at all speeds. This is because only the spoiler on the down-going wing is deployed, and although the spoiler is primarily intended to reduce this wing's lift it also produces additional form drag on the down-going wing, which is just what is required to ensure a small yaw in the appropriate direction.

Low-speed Problems

Reduced control effectiveness at low speed
At low or very low air speeds, the forces and hence the moments produced by all aerodynamic control surfaces are severely downgraded because of the dependence of aerodynamic force on the square of the airspeed. More camber, and hence more control deflection, is therefore required at low speeds than at higher speeds, and so the pilot needs to move the controls a considerable distance to achieve the same effect that a much smaller deflection will achieve at higher speeds. This is particularly significant for the rudder and elevator when the aircraft is accelerating along the runway for take-off, since neither will begin to be effective until sufficient speed has been attained (unless within the propeller slipstream), and similarly their effectiveness will decrease when slowing down after landing. For aircraft with central 'bicycle' undercarriages (such as sailplanes and the U-2 reconnaissance aircraft shown in Figure 9.3) the ineffectiveness of the ailerons means that the wings cannot be sustained level when stopping or starting on the ground, and must either be held by a person running alongside before take-off or must depend on small out-rigger wheels or skids. The Harrier vertical take-off aircraft also has a bicycle undercarriage and outriggers, but in this case it uses pilot-controlled vectored thrust nozzles at the wing and fuselage extremities to control it when it is airborne and does not have sufficient forward speed.

Stalling and Spinning
Much has been said about various types of stall in differing circumstances and on different parts of an aircraft in *Flightwise – Principles*

of Aircraft Flight, and so rather than repeating all of this we will here simply have a look at one or two specifically control surface related aspects of stalling. Before doing so, we must remind ourselves that stalling is not necessarily a low-speed phenomenon, but rather depends purely on the angle of attack of the aerofoil in question. Although a high C_L, and hence a high angle of attack, is certainly required at low speeds, we have now grown accustomed to the fact that it is also a requirement of an aircraft in a turn, at any speed. In fact, at lower air speeds, the structural limit of the airframe or the physiological limit of the pilot is not reached first, but it is the maximum angle of attack, or the stalling angle, of the wing that dictates the maximum load factor and thus the turn rate limitation. Stalling can thus occur at moderate speeds, but the risk of stalling is very much greater at lower or very low speeds.

An aircraft with well-behaved stalling characteristics, as discussed at length in Chapter 13 of *Flightwise – Principles of Aircraft Flight*, is one in which the wing root region stalls before the tip region, and if the wing is not twisted at all this is attainable only with an approximately rectangular planform wing, neither the most structurally nor aerodynamically efficient design. The root region is the safest place for the stall to start for several reasons. Firstly, the turbulent air from the stalled root is likely to strike the tail of the aircraft and cause buffeting, which serves as a natural stall warning to the pilot. Secondly, the ailerons will continue to be effective right up to the stall since the angle of attack reduces towards the tips, so that roll control can be maintained as the stall is approached and even beyond. Thirdly, the loss of lift at the root region will lead to a reduction of downwash in the airflow reaching the tailplane, and so there will be an increment in the lift-force on the tailplane. This will tend to make the aircraft automatically pitch nose downwards, which is exactly the right action to encourage recovery from the impending stall.

Highly tapered and/or swept-back wings both suffer from the problem that, because of the downwash distribution over the span of the wing, the wing-tip region stalls before the root. If this is remedied by twisting, or washing out, the wing the aerodynamic performance is seriously downgraded in the cruise. A compromise is therefore usually adopted by using a small amount of washout. It is undesirable for the stall to start at the wing-tip for all of the reasons that made the stall starting at the wing root desirable. The turbulent wake from the stalled wing-tips will miss the tailplane and fuselage altogether, so that there will be no natural stall warning by buffeting. The effectiveness of the ailerons is reduced once a stall has commenced, and furthermore the conditions are favourable for a strong adverse aileron yaw to develop.

When the aircraft stalls, it is likely that the stall will not develop on both wings at exactly the same rate. If one wing has stalled more than the other, it loses lift relative to the other so that it drops. As it descends its effective angle of attack is increased even further because of the upward relative airflow it experiences, and this puts it more deeply into the stall. At the same time, the other wing rises, so that its effective angle of attack is reduced, and thus it removes itself from the risk of stalling. The resulting rolling motion, which is called *autorotation*, is the basis of many of the more advanced aerobatic manoeuvres, but for the unwary it will precipitate a *spin*, a motion in which the aircraft pirouettes down a tight helical path whose axis is vertical.

Although once thought to be the kiss of death to flying machines since it accounted for so many lives lost, a spin is now regard as an aerobatic manoeuvre, and it is today something which pilots must be trained to cope with. Much height is lost very quickly in a spin, but provided it is executed from a sufficient starting height it is, in most aircraft, a safe and totally recoverable manoeuvre. Being the result of an asymmetric stall, a spin is not a purely aerodynamic phenomenon, since the air speed is very low. At least one wing is fully stalled, and there are high rotational rates involved which give rise to gyroscopic inertia forces which (in a fully developed steady spin) establish an equilibrium with the aerodynamic forces. Spinning is not an erratic, random motion but a steady equilibrium mode of flight in which the axes of the aircraft maintain constant angles (which can vary widely from type to type) with the direction of the centre of gravity's helical path, and this path is itself usually inclined at about 10° to the vertical axis of the spin. The radius of the helix is approximately the semi-wingspan, so that the centre of gravity descends along the helical path whilst the inner wing-tip is approximately moving straight down the axis. The aircraft is continuously yawing in the direction of the spin, pitching nose up (to pull the nose round the helix) and rolling inwards (to constrain the outer wing in its helical path), and the resulting overall rotational motion is the vector sum (after the manner discussed in Chapter 8) of these *three* rotational rates[19], one about each of the aircraft's three axes. The rolling motion is maintained by the continued autorotation which initiated the spin, and the overall centripetal force which keeps the centre of gravity travelling in a circular path (as viewed from above) is provided by the wing lift as it is in a banked turn. Bear in mind that, when a wing is stalled and the angle of attack is not excessively above the maximum lift angle, the lift produced by

---

[19]Unfortunately the vector diagram, having four sides (three components and a resultant) is not a triangle, and so cannot be drawn in a single plane. The three components are all at right angles to each other. Mathematically this presents no problem, but it makes visualisation more difficult.

the wing is still near to its maximum. It is an utter fallacy that stalling implies a major loss of lift straight away. It merely means that the slope of the lift curve changes from positive to negative. However, a stalled wing's drag is very high, and it is the vertical components of lift and drag which together balance the weight, so that vertical motion equilibrium is achieved at a constant downward velocity.

To recover from the spin, the primary requirement is to arrest the rotational motion, and in practice this is usually achieved by tackling the yawing motion first by applying opposite rudder. The nose-up pitch rate is then taken off by pushing the elevator control forwards, and as a result the angle of attack of the wings reduces so that the autorotative rolling motion stops.

Clearly spinning is a manoeuvre to be avoided near the ground where there is no room for recovery. But unfortunately this is exactly the situation in which it is most likely to occur. When a pilot is preparing to land from flying a 'circuit', a rectangular pattern of flying which is used in the vicinity of a runway for flying training purposes, the pilot has to make two 90° turns at the corners of the rectangle in order to line up for the final approach to land. Just before and between making these turns, the pilot's workload is very high for a number of reasons. He has had to select undercarriage-down, adjust his speed and rate of descent by use of throttle and elevator control, and decide whether flaps are appropriate and deploy them accordingly. Meanwhile, he must maintain a very thorough lookout, especially for aircraft which may be coming straight in to land across his bows, and he must communicate with air traffic control to obtain clearance to land. He must also check out all the items of a safety check-list, whilst all the time ensuring that he is maintaining the appropriate speed and descent path.

It is very natural for an inexperienced pilot to want to keep the speed as low as possible, since this would seem to provide more time to carry out all of these actions and checks, but this is exactly where the trouble can start. If the speed is close to the level-flight stalling speed, the angle of attack will be close to the stalling angle, and if a moderately tight turn is executed in this situation the roll into the turn may be enough to stall the inside wing, resulting in an inwards autorotation which can develop into a spin straight into the ground, with no height available for recovery. If recovery is attempted using ailerons, they can produce a strong adverse aileron yaw, the direction of which is into the turn, and if not countered with the rudder, this may itself precipitate the spin. It is for these reasons that one of the first and most important lessons that a novice pilot has to be taught is that, whilst preparing to land, the aircraft's speed should never be allowed to fall below some specified minimum value, typically 10 knots above the stalling speed.

High-speed Problems

Whilst the low-speed problems that we have been considering have been familiar to pilots and aircraft designers since the dawning of aviation, it was not until about the beginning of the Second World War that a completely new and unexpected additional set of problems arose, due to flying at high speeds. Initially such high-speed problems were encountered by the very low drag fighter aircraft that were being developed at that time, when they were put into a steep dive in order to achieve greater speeds than could be obtained by use of propeller engines; but a little later, with the invention and development of the jet engine, such problems became an everyday concern to aircraft designers and pilots alike.

The problems that were being encountered are technically known as 'compressibility effects', but to the man in the street at that time – and even to many uninitiated engineers – there appeared to be a 'sound barrier', an apparently impenetrable wall of extremely high drag forces which would prevent any aircraft ever exceeding the speed of sound and which, if approached, also rendered an aircraft uncontrollable. This is a large subject which, if we were to deal with it here from basic principles, would demand a chapter or two on its own; but instead we must assume that you are familiar with these principles already.

The subject of compressibility is covered comprehensively in two important chapters of *Flightwise – Principles of Aircraft Flight*. The first of these is Chapter 10 entitled 'Supersonic Aerofoils' which deals with the significance of the speed of sound, the cause and nature of shock waves and expansion fans and the implications for the design of aerofoils for supersonic aircraft. The second, Chapter 11 entitled 'Aerofoils in Transonic Flow', builds on the principles established in Chapter 10 and the preceding chapters, and looks at the critical transonic phase of flight in which neither the subsonic nor the supersonic principles of flight can be applied in isolation. After examining the way in which shock waves develop on a subsonic aerofoil as the free stream air speed approaches and then exceeds the speed of sound, the problems that this creates are dramatically illustrated by an account of a test flight in a Typhoon by test pilot Roland Beamont in 1943. The chapter then proceeds to analyse in depth the causes of the various unwelcome transonic effects, before looking specifically at the effects on pitching and rolling controls. We will reproduce here, slightly edited, the passages from that chapter which explain the problems specifically experienced in the use of the elevator and ailerons.

Control Heaviness and Loss of Effectiveness

Before being specific about any particular control surface and the possible problems associated with it, let us remind ourselves of the principle underlying the general control surface concept, so that we can then investigate how a control surface's function is likely to be affected by compressibility.

Conventional aerodynamic control surfaces all consist of the trailing portion of the aerofoil (perhaps about the last third of the chord) being hinged to the front part, like a plain flap. The purpose is to enable the lift of the flying surface (be it wing, tailplane or fin) to be increased by hinging down the flap and hence increasing the camber. When the aerofoil's camber is increased in this way, the circulation around the entire flying surface is modified by adjusting the pointing direction of the trailing edge and hence affecting the Kutta condition[20]. Consequently the pressure distribution around the entire flying surface is modified, and not just that in the neighbourhood of the relatively small hinged control surface itself. By this means much more extra lift can be generated than it would be reasonable to expect the control surface itself to provide or to bear. This principle was well understood by St James, who in his Epistle in the New Testament uses the power of the ship's rudder (which is identical in principle) as an analogy of the power of the tongue to do good or harm. In St James Chapter 3, Verse 4 of the Authorised Version we read:

> Behold also the ships, which though they be so great, and are driven of fierce winds, yet are they turned about with a very small helm, whithersoever the governor listeth.

The reason why this is possible is that information in the form of pressure waves (which travel at the speed of sound) can travel upstream of the rudder through the water in the case of the ship or upstream of the control surface through the air in the case of the flying surface. If, however, any of the air through which this information has to travel upstream has reached the speed of sound, then no information can travel forwards into or through this region, and the region is a zone of silence.

Let us consider the situation (shown in Figure 9.11) of a subsonic aerofoil at a fixed (cruising) angle of attack with a hingeable control surface in transonic airflow conditions, and assume that the free stream airflow speed has been rising and has just reached the speed at which the feet of the two shocks coincide with the hinge-line. In fact this is merely a transitory stage in the process since the lower shock

---

[20]The Kutta condition relates to the direction in which the trailing edge of an aerofoil deflects the airflow downstream, and it is intimately tied up with the explanation of aerofoil lift. This is discussed in Chapter 7 of *Flightwise – Principles of Aircraft Flight*, in the section headed 'Kutta Condition'.

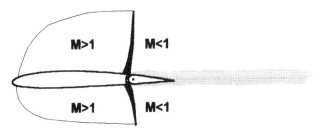

Figure 9.11   Subsonic flying surface in transonic flow, with control surface

progresses very rapidly from leading to trailing edge, but after looking at it we can switch our attention to the before and after.

The control surface is shown undeflected. If it were to be deflected (either up or down) this would change the pressure distribution around it, but because of the supersonic regions upstream of the hinge (bounded by the shock waves) it is totally impossible for the pressure information generated by the control surface to travel forward of the shock waves at all. Consequently, whatever deflection is applied to the control surface can only affect the pressure distribution on the surface itself, and can have no effect on the main portion of the flying surface upstream of it.

Very shortly afterwards as the air speed continues to rise, the lower shock reaches the trailing edge, and the lower surface including that of the control surface is totally immersed in supersonic airflow. At this stage the control surface itself (so far as the lower surface is concerned) is operating as a supersonic aerofoil rather than a subsonic one, and the flow over it will deflect concavely or convexly at the hinge line (depending on the direction of control surface deflection) producing an oblique shock or expansion and a consequent substantial pressure increase or decrease respectively on just the control surface; but once again there is no effect upstream of the hinge line. Not very long afterwards the upper surface shock wave itself reaches the trailing edge, thus immersing the upper surface of the control as well in totally supersonic flow, so that a shock or expansion will emanate from the hinge line up there as well.

There are thus two mechanisms by which the control surface supplies and experiences forces during the transonic phase: that when the control surface itself is in a subsonic flow, and that when it is in a supersonic flow. But in both cases, if the airflow ahead of the control surface is supersonic (as it is in Figure 9.11), then all the required force must be applied by the control surface itself, rather than by the flying surface to which it is attached. Remembering that the area of the control surface may be typically no more than a third of the entire flying surface area, then even with all other things being equal, a force (and therefore also the pilot's control force) of the order of three times the normal control force will be needed to produce the required control effect.

But this is only if all other things are equal, which they are not. During transonic flight there is a severe loss of lift, so that the weight being greater than the lift will pull the aircraft into a vertically curved path and cause it to dive or to steepen an existing dive. Moreover, the serious perturbations that occur in the pitching moment of the wing itself due to the peregrinations of the shock waves are certainly not going to help, being predominantly nose-down, and so the required control force will probably be very much more than three times normal. This accounts for the fact that even pulling on the control column with all the pilot's strength, as was often reported, was not sufficient to sort out the problem.

There is yet another factor to take into consideration, and it is that, before fully supersonic flow develops around it, the control surface is itself operating inside the thick and highly turbulent subsonic eddying wake of the shock stall, as shown in Figure 9.11. This may have a number of undesirable effects on the control surface such as buffeting, but it certainly means that, while in this wake, the control surface's effectiveness will be drastically curtailed compared with what it would be in a clean airflow. It may even flop around a bit inside this wake with no resisting force, which could account for the witness of German test pilot Heinrich Beauvais[21]:

> I had the impression of very high stick forces, which I only applied after due consideration. I believe that I can now [in 1981] remember, however, that some pilots had stated that in the compressibility dive the stick could be moved without force.

Tailplane Problems

The above discussion about large control forces and lack of effectiveness applies to the wing-tips and ailerons and also to the tailplane and elevator (and to the fin and rudder, but this is less important). However, some of the most serious control problems encountered, compounding all of those that we have already discussed, arise from the fact that the tailplane is directly behind the wing. A shock stall occurring on the wing will create a thick turbulent wake which may strike and immerse the tailplane, rendering the tailplane totally ineffective, and also buffeting it very drastically. The buffeting produced by this turbulent wake does not affect only the tailplane, but also the wing creating it, and (close to the wing roots) the aircraft's fuselage. It

[21]Roland Beamont: *Testing Early Jets*, published by Airlife; page 7.

was largely the turbulent wake of the shock stall that accounted for the many and varied reports of rattling and shaking and vibrating that pervade all the early transonic test-flight accounts.

Roll Control Problems

Control surface ineffectiveness and large control forces at transonic speeds create some particular problems in roll control using ailerons, as exemplified by Roland Beamont's report that the port wing of his Typhoon tried to drop. Because of the rapid variation of lift coefficient of an aerofoil during the transonic phase of flight, it would only take a slight imbalance of airflow speed or direction for one of the wing-tips to have lost lift before the other. For example, the propeller of the Typhoon rotated anticlockwise as viewed by the pilot, so that the swirling slipstream would produce marginally more angle of attack on the starboard wing-tip than on the port one. More angle of attack means more circulation, which in turn means relatively less air speed (in the free stream direction) on the lower surface. If this were in fact the case, then it is likely that the other wing, the port wing, would have reached supersonic speed on the lower surface first. And it is this feature of the airflow over an aerofoil's lower surface suddenly becoming supersonic everywhere that causes the lift coefficient to drop drastically.

It is not surprising, from our general discussion above of transonic control problems, that pilots found that they could not resist such out-of-balance rolling moments. But there is one additional widely experienced roll control problem which is known as *control reversal*, and it is perhaps the most celebrated, and certainly the most bizarre, of the many transonic problems that have been experienced.

Have you ever been to a garden fête and been faced with the challenge of riding a certain bicycle a distance of about 5 yards? At 20p a go, and the promise of a £10 prize if you succeed in accomplishing this trivial feat, you have a go, only to discover that when you turn the handlebars to the right the front wheel turns to the left, and *vice versa*. Undaunted, you have a number of attempts at riding the bicycle, but find that it is quite impossible to stay balanced for any distance at all. The £10 prize money is very safe!

Pilots are used to pushing the control stick or turning the control yoke in the direction in which they want the aircraft to roll when commencing a banked turn, and so if the aircraft were one day to perform in exactly the opposite way it would be as unnerving as the cyclist's attempt to ride the rigged bicycle. But that is exactly what happens when transonic control reversal occurs. First of all, for the reasons already discussed, the pilot discovers that the control forces necessary to have any effect at all on the ailerons, and hence to cause the aircraft to roll, become very large. Then, if the pilot persists in applying all of his might to try to deflect the ailerons and control the aircraft, what he actually succeeds in doing is making the aircraft roll the opposite way!

So what is going on here? Control reversal generally only happens with ailerons, and not with elevators, because ailerons are at the ends of long, flexible flying surfaces, the wings. By comparison, tailplanes are short, stubby and stiff. Now let us suppose that the pilot of an aircraft in transonic flight wishes to roll to the right in order to initiate a banked turn. He finds that he needs to apply a very large aileron control force to the right, which he succeeds in doing, so that the left (port) wing aileron is forced to deflect downwards in the teeth of a locally supersonic airflow, and the aileron has to take all of the additional load that ought to be taken by the outer wing. By Newton's Third Law of Action and Reaction, this aerodynamic force must be resisted by the wing itself, and the force is transmitted through the aileron hinge. The hinge is behind the centre of the wing chord, and is being pushed hard upwards by the aileron. Consequently the wing-tip is subjected to a twisting moment which tends to twist the trailing edge upwards and the leading edge downwards. This has the effect of reducing the angle of attack of this region of the wing, which in turn causes the lift coefficient and hence the lift to be reduced. So an action which was intended to increase the lifting effect of the wing-tip region has actually caused a C_L reduction. This will tend to cause the left wing to move downwards rather than upwards, so that the pilot's right stick push results in a roll to the left, which is extremely disconcerting.

High-speed Control Solutions

We will now take a look at some of the ways in which the high-speed problems of controlling an aircraft have been solved, whether it be for airliners flying for most of their operating lives in the transonic region or fighters getting through that region as quickly as possible, thereafter operating at supersonic speeds.

Looking first at the crucial issue of controlling the aircraft in pitch, our attention moves to the design of tailplane and elevators. One of the major problems of flying the pre-transonic aircraft into the shock stall was that the stalled wing wake totally engulfed the tailplane, so that the elevators had little chance of being effective even if they hadn't had problems of their own in a clean airflow. The solution to this problem was to build new transonic aircraft with their tails well out of the line of the wing wake. On low-winged transport aircraft this is usually facilitated by putting the tailplane at the fin root, since this is at the top of the fuselage whereas the wings are at the bottom. In the case of the Buccaneer the tailplane was placed at the top of the fin. On high-winged aircraft such as the English Electric Lightning and many more recent combat aircraft, the tailplanes are mounted well below the wing.

Having decided on the best positioning of the tailplane to avoid externally imposed problems, attention can turn to the design of the control surfaces themselves. The chief problem was that only the rear part of the flying surface, the hinged control surface, took any of the load because information could not be transmitted upstream. The solution to this in the tailplane was found to be to do away with aft-hinged control surfaces altogether and to substitute all-moving, or slab, tailplanes, in which the entire tailplane as one piece is pivoted close to its mid-chord point, so that its angle of attack can be varied rather than its camber. Operating loads were high, too high for pilots to be able to control with manual controls, and so powered controls also became the norm.

Let us turn next to the problem of roll control. A number of different solutions have been successfully adopted in different situations. Some combat aircraft (such as the British Aerospace Tornado) have made double use of their all-moving tailplanes by making the two sides of these operable separately from each other as tailerons, with the limitations that we noted earlier. Because of these limitations, tailerons would not be appropriate for airliners in view of the high aspect ratio wings and the large mass and rolling moment of inertia I_x of the wings which normally hold a lot of fuel and may also carry the engines. Powered hinged ailerons are frequently not suitable for high-speed airliners, since they would be at the trailing edge of a highly swept wing of large aspect ratio where there is a serious problem of aeroelastic twisting of the wing-tip region, which makes the ailerons especially prone to control reversal. Stiffening up the wing is not ideal since it adds weight. However, the moment arm of ailerons at the wing-tips is more than adequate, and the solution frequently adopted (as on the Boeing 747) is to have a second pair of so-called 'inboard' ailerons only half way out along the wings where they are stiffer instead of at the wing-tips, and these are used for roll control in cruising flight. The reduced moment arm is not a problem, since the higher speeds at which they are used ensure that a substantial aerodynamic force is produced even with very small control surface deflections.

Another method of providing roll control in these circumstances is the use of spoilers in the upper surfaces of the wings, sometimes in conjunction with tip or inboard ailerons or with tailerons. Spoilers are used for roll control in the SEPECAT Jaguar, which has no ailerons in order to make room for full-span lift augmentation flaps, and spoilers appear to be achieving increasing popularity with designers of new large transport aircraft. Although intuitively the idea of deliberately destroying the wing's carefully generated lift appears wasteful, spoilers have the very great advantage over ailerons that they always increase drag on the down-going wing, completely eliminating the problem of adverse aileron yaw.

Flutter

Most of our discussion of the quirks and problems of controls so far has been focused on the needs and the perception of the pilot in order that he may safely and effectively handle the aircraft. Beyond implying in passing that there are various operating limits that must be observed, we have paid no attention to the structural implications of using the controls. With the one exception of high-speed aileron reversal, we have found it convenient and adequate to treat the aircraft as a rigid body. However, the fact that aircraft components bend and flex under aerodynamic loads (the feature which is called *aeroelasticity*) gives rise to a phenomenon which is of critical importance to an aircraft's structural integrity even when direct aerodynamic loads are nowhere near their structural design limits. This phenomenon, called *flutter*, is produced by the aeroelastic effects of control surfaces, and can cause the rapid and catastrophic failure of major flying surfaces in flight. The problem can be alleviated by taking appropriate precautions when designing the control surfaces.

Although not exclusive to wings and ailerons, flutter is probably most easily understood by considering how it affects these, since the flexibility of a wing is more plain to see than that of tailplanes and fins. If you pluck the free end of an ordinary 1-foot ruler whose other end is clamped, the ruler will oscillate up and down until the motion is automatically damped out by the internal friction between the molecules, and the oscillations stop. The frequency at which these oscillations occur, the so-called *natural frequency,* is very precise and depends upon a number of factors including the free length of the ruler. If however instead of providing a single pluck you were lightly to tap the free end of the ruler continuously, and if the frequency of this tapping should happen to coincide with the natural frequency of the ruler, the ruler would respond by vibrating up and down in *resonance.* Provided the stiffness of the ruler is sufficient and the externally supplied oscillations are not too great, the ruler will settle into oscillations of a stable amplitude, but there could arise a situation (with sufficiently large taps and insufficient strength in the ruler) in which the ruler's oscillations became large and divergent, until the ruler broke.

Let us transfer this analogy to a high aspect ratio wing of an aircraft, whose free end is capable of oscillating up and down if it is provoked to do so. A single 'pluck' of the wing-tip can be applied by firmly and briefly deflecting and then neutralising the aileron in flight, following which the wing will oscillate up and down at its natural frequency until the oscillations die away through natural structural and aerodynamic damping. But if, instead of centralising the aileron control, the pilot were to apply opposite aileron at the moment when the wing was deflected as far as it was going to go in the first direction, the new aileron input would drive the wing back the other way and tend to increase the oscillation's amplitude next time. If furthermore the pilot were to keep applying oscillatory aileron inputs at exactly the same frequency as the wing's natural frequency, the oscillation would grow and grow, until something very nasty happened to the wing.

Of course no pilot would be daft enough to do this, even if he were capable of keeping up with the natural frequency of the wing, which normally he would not be. But unobligingly a simple hinged aerofoil has a natural tendency to do just this automatically, and to supply an oscillating force input. As the wing-tip rises, it carries the aileron upwards with it, but as it stops rising at the top of its oscillation the aileron (because of the inertia of its mass) tends to carry on going upwards, and becomes deflected upwards so that it exerts a downwards aerodynamic force on the wing-tip, at just the same moment as the natural elastic restoring force of the wing is about to pull it down anyway. The wing-tip then swings downwards, and again the aileron (through its inertia) overshoots at the bottom, deflects downwards and causes an upward aerodynamic force which reinforces the elastic force. In certain circumstances this can cause the wing's oscillation to grow catastrophically, until it becomes overstressed and may even break off. The process is illustrated in the top sequence of diagrams in Figure 9.12, which illustrates an end-on view of a wing-tip in a divergent flutter caused by the aileron.

Since it is the inertia of the mass of the aileron, rather than any aerodynamic feature, which is the culprit, the solution lies in redistributing the aileron's mass. It is because the centre of gravity of the aileron is behind the hinge-line that the aileron overshoots at the ends of the oscillations, and so what is required is rather to locate the centre of gravity in front of the hinge-line. Then the overshooting of the aileron's mass makes the aileron deflect in the opposite sense from before, so that the aerodynamic force opposes the wing's elastic force rather than reinforcing it. The oscillations, and hence also the now favourable aileron deflections, thus grow smaller and eventually die out.

A control surface with its centre of gravity placed ahead of the hinge-line is said to be *mass balanced*. The simplest way of achieving this is by placing a substantial mass on an external boom attached to and extending forward from the control surface and in front of the hinge line, as is illustrated in the second sequence of diagrams in Figure 9.12. On early aircraft this is exactly how it was often done, but

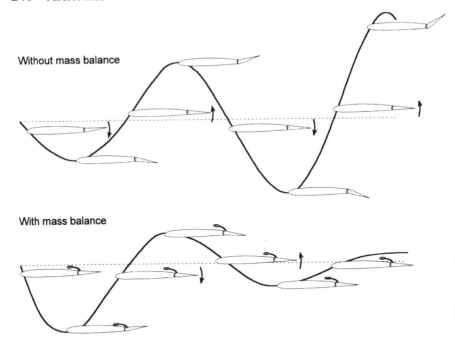

Without mass balance

With mass balance

Figure 9.12 Control surface flutter with and without mass balance

clearly it is not desirable to use protruding bodies because of their drag and their exposure to damage. Consequently the additional mass is usually placed in the leading edge of the control surface itself, and the hinge-line a little further back. Later on (in Chapter 11, The Pilot Interface) we shall be looking at various ways in which control surfaces are modified to help the pilot with the flying task, and will see how mass balance can be incorporated with other requirements at that time.

We have explained flutter with reference to ailerons and wings, but the problem is perhaps most renowned for applying to fins and rudders. Although we have considered the aerodynamic input being caused by a hinged surface, it may also occur due to the aeroelastic deflection of a fixed surface, causing an oscillatory variation of camber and/or angle of attack, but having exactly the same effect. When any new high speed aircraft is being flight tested, a crucial phase of the test schedule is to fly close to the flutter limits of the flying surfaces, to ensure that the structure is safe, since a number of aircraft have in the past met their doom as a result of fins or other surfaces being seriously damaged or even broken clean off as a result of flutter. Fortunately the pilot and passenger can normally rely on the designers and development team to have taken care of this problem and in normal operations need not give it a second thought.

CHAPTER 10
Ups and Downs

INTRODUCTION

If our discussion of aircraft flight control were to be restricted to steering the aircraft around the sky in level (or nearly level) flight as it was in the previous chapter, we might justifiably be accused of adhering to the philosophy of the 'chauffeur' school of thought, which as we saw in Chapter 1 was so stifling to the early development of successful aviation. We would be in danger of getting into a mind-set of thinking of the aircraft merely as an aerial motorcar (or bus or lorry) which could be steered comfortably around above the rooftops.

But aircraft flight opens up to us a complete new dimension, both literally and metaphorically. Just as a sculpture or an artefact or a scale model is potentially far more interesting and valuable (in terms of the information that it presents) than a single painting or photograph or drawing on a flat surface, so the aircraft gives us the freedom to experience a new dimension of our living environment that is totally unavailable to us whilst crawling around on or near to the two-dimensional plane of the Earth's surface. In order to capitalise on the possibilities thus presented, aircraft control must not just allow for steering an aircraft left or right (or to fly northwards or eastwards), but must make ways available by which the vertical dimension can also be fully exploited.

What benefits are to be had by being able to fly at heights other than just above the rooftops? Flying at high altitudes for its own sake is today probably only a requirement of reconnaissance aircraft, wishing to see down without being seen, but even this function has now been substantially taken over by satellites. Before the full development of radar tracking, height was a requirement of bombers, (typified by the British V-bomber fleet of the 1950s and 1960s) which used it as a means of concealment from ground observation.

Today the chief practical reasons for flying at high altitude are more indirect, and arise from the fact that the air density reduces with increasing altitude. The drag of an aircraft varies in direct proportion to the air density, and so flying at altitude is an important means of reducing drag. Furthermore, whereas propellers are more effective in the higher density air at low altitude, jet engines obtain on balance an overall advantage at higher altitude, in particular because of the very much lower air temperatures found there. Overall, the performance requirements of today's high speeds and low operating costs are only to be obtained at high altitude. An additional important advantage is that aircraft can thus fly above most of the turbulence of the atmospheric weather, making flight a more comfortable experience and contributing to flight safety.

In today's scenario of very high speed aircraft (especially but not exclusively combat aircraft), height plays another very important rôle, and that is as an energy storage device. In the same way as on a rollercoaster, potential and kinetic energy may readily be exchanged for each other, and this provides a powerful way of enhancing aircraft performance. Furthermore, by analysing an aircraft's performance on the basis of this concept, the climb of a transport aircraft up to its cruising height and even the cruise itself can be scheduled so as to minimise either the time taken or the fuel requirements and thus the operating costs.

The use of the additional dimension of height presupposes that the pilot has full control over the vertical motion of the aircraft, and this is the subject of the present chapter. We shall be able to break it down into two main sections in a manner closely matching that in which we have seen that longitudinal dynamic stability can be classified. Firstly, we shall consider the aircraft's short-term motion during which it rotates significantly and must be regarded as a rigid body. Secondly, we shall look at the medium and longer term activities such as controlled steady cruise flight, climbing to altitude and making effective use of the potential energy which altitude provides, and for these aspects we will once again treat the aircraft as a particle. We shall close the chapter with a brief look at ground effect, a special feature of flying an aircraft very close to the ground (or water) which can have a significant effect on both its economic performance and its handling.

SHORT-TERM HANDLING
Transients
Before we get round to talking about aeroplanes, join me if you will in a little mental (or practical if possible) experiment in controlling a down-to-earth bicycle or motorcycle. (A motorcycle is preferable because of its greater mass, but the principles also apply on a push-bike, although things happen so quickly that it is less easy to observe them.) First of all, here is a question the answer to which in my experience astonishes even some of the most experienced and hardened of aircraft control engineers: if you are riding along on a motorcycle at a steady moderate speed in an absolutely straight line, and require to do a gentle turn to the right, how do you go about it?

The immediate and instinctive answer of almost everyone who understands the basic principle of doing banked turns is that you lean over to the right, at the same time as turning the handlebars in that direction. But let me show you that it is in fact *impossible* to lean over to the right, and if you want to argue with that you must take it up with Sir Isaac!

Let us suppose that the motorcyclist of Figure 10.1 is travelling in a straight line and wishes to start turning towards his right. In order to do so he requires a centripetal force from left to right to alter his straight path into a circular one. Where is this force to come from? Easy! you may answer; he leans over to the right, and then the horizontal component of the reaction of the road (provided by friction) delivers the required centripetal force. Yes, *if* he were to steer and lean to the right, this would in fact be true – but the problem is, how does he get into the leaning position in the first place?

The rear view diagram of Figure 10.1 shows that, since the motorcyclist is travelling straight ahead, his centre of gravity is directly over the line of contact of the tyres with the road, and the weight and the reaction of the road form an equal and opposite mutually cancelling force pair. There are no unbalanced forces in the plane of this view, just as Newton's First Law leads us to expect, for if there were the motorcyclist would not be travelling in a straight line. In order for him to lean over to the right, his centre of gravity would need to be displaced from its straight line path to the right whilst the tyres are still following the original straight path, and that requires an external force to act on the centre of gravity. Such a force cannot conceivably come from the tyres (yet) since they are still directly below the centre of gravity and so cannot exert a force on it in any direction other than vertically upwards. So where is the side force to come from?

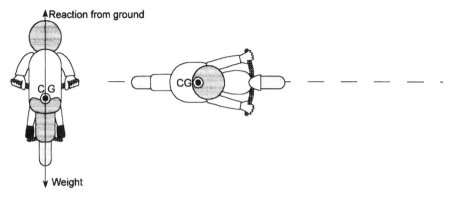

Figure 10.1   Motorcyclist travelling in a straight line

The answer is surprising, and it is that the motorcyclist must in fact turn the handlebars to the *left*! Since he cannot yet get the centre of gravity to move to the right relative to the wheelbase, the solution is to rotate the whole mass (bike and rider as a single rigid body) clockwise about a fore-and-aft horizontal axis through the centre of gravity. This is achieved through moving the wheelbase (being below the axis) to the left of the centre of gravity, by steering that way. The process may be followed from the plan and rear view drawings of Figure 10.2. In the two left-hand views the rider is driving along a straight path (shown by the long-dashed line in the plan view), but has just decided to initiate a turn to his right, which he is now in the process of commencing by turning the handlebars to the left. Initially the centre of gravity continues to move straight forward[1], but the wheels move out to the left from underneath it, as seen in the right hand views. During the transition from the first pair of diagrams to the second in Figure 10.2 the force vector diagram has been modifying itself from the equilibrium situation of Figure 10.1 to the circular path accelerating situation, and the centripetal component of the total reaction of the ground on the tyres (provided by friction) has begun to displace the centre of gravity to the right of its original motion path – just what was initially wished for.

At this stage the motorcycle has attained the appropriate bank angle for a balanced turn (to use aircraft parlance – the situation is directly analogous), and now the handlebars are indeed turned to the right. This provides the necessary yaw rate, a component of the over-

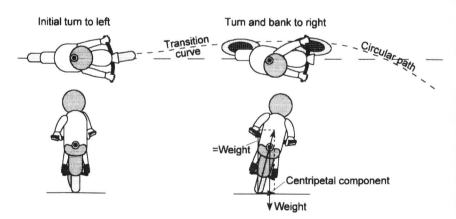

Figure 10.2   Motorcyclist commencing a turn to his right

[1]The centre of gravity will in fact move *downwards* a little, but this is irrelevant to the present discussion and also negligible if the bank angle is small. With steep banking the consequent exchange between potential and kinetic energy will be significant.

all turn rate[2], which as we saw with aircraft earlier is relatively small, so that only a very small handlebar displacement is required – probably less than was initially required in the wrong direction. The normal banked turn is now fully established[3].

In exactly the same manner, in order to straighten up when the motorcycle is almost pointing in the required new direction, the rider must turn the handlebars more tightly *into* the turn, in order to pull the wheelbase in under the centre of gravity, before straightening up on to an even keel again.

I dare say that, even if you have followed the Newtonian logic of this discussion, the claim about opposite use of the handlebars will be so surprising that you will be inclined not to believe that it is really true in practice. If so, I would urge you to try it out. If you do not have access to a motorbike, it can be very vividly demonstrated on a conventional (large-wheeled) pushbike. In either case, ride the machine where you have plenty of room at a moderate steady speed in a straight line, sitting up straight with just the lightest finger pressure on the handle-bars, (effectively riding no-hands). Then *gently and briefly* pull back on the left handlebar, and you will immediately discover that your natural two-wheel balancing instinct will cause the cycle to start to lean and turn to the right. After a short spell along the circular path, a light pull on the right handlebar will recover you to the upright, straight ahead attitude in the new direction. If you try this at very low speed, or on a light bicycle with small wheels, you will find that the lean to the right after initially pulling the left handlebar is so sudden and pronounced that you immediately have to pull on the right handlebar quite firmly to prevent falling off the machine. If you survive the exercise, you have not disproved my point but merely demonstrated it rather too dramatically!

For the cyclist or motorcyclist, this phenomenon actually has a very important practical significance. If you are cycling along a road and you suddenly come across a pothole just ahead of you, it may be extremely difficult to avoid it. If you wish to steer to the right of the pothole, there is nothing you can do but steer to the left first. The wheels will actually track to the left before moving off to the right, as illustrated by the short-dashed path in Figure 10.2, crossing the initial long-dashed straight path one or two bicycle-lengths from the point where the avoidance manoeuvre was started – possibly just at the very point where the pothole happens to be! And of course, the same is true if a child or an animal suddenly steps out in front of you, making avoidance of collision extremely difficult if not impossible.

[2] The other component is a 'nose-up' pitch rate, as with an aircraft.
[3] The circular path is determined by the amount the front wheel is now turned; its centre is the point where the perpendiculars to the tracks of the two wheels intersect.

For those who are saying 'enough about motorbikes – what's this got to do with aircraft control?', we have actually not strayed from the subject at all, but have merely illustrated a most important feature of aircraft control known as *transients*. We have already briefly met one rather trivial instance of a transient effect of a control when we were talking in the previous chapter about using the rudder to initiate a horizontal turn. It was pointed out that the initial overall force on the aircraft resulting from an application of right rudder is actually to the left, so that the aircraft's centre of gravity will initially skid out to the left along a transition path similar to that of Figure 10.2 before any inward aerodynamic force is developed to provide the centripetal force required for the turn. The reason it was trivial was because, as we have seen, using the rudder is not (normally) the correct way to initiate a level turn, so it is not surprising, nor does it matter very much, if it is less than ideal.

The effects of transients are very much more important in the use of the elevator for pitch control. If an aircraft with a conventional tail is flying straight and level at a speed well above the level-flight stalling speed, and the pilot requires to do a pull-up, he pulls back on the pitch control, so that the elevator deflects upwards. The purpose of this control deflection is not (directly) to exert an aerodynamic force on the aircraft's centre of gravity, but rather to apply a pitching moment which will rotate the aircraft's nose upwards about the *y*-axis in order that the wing's angle of attack, and hence coefficient of lift, shall be increased. The additional lift thus created in excess of the weight then produces the required vertically upward centripetal force, so that the aircraft's centre of gravity starts to follow a circular path in the vertical plane[4]. But before the aircraft has had time to pitch nose up, the tailplane with raised elevator is exerting a *downwards* force (over and above any existing downwards trimming tail-force required to maintain the aircraft in level flight), so that the net lift is less than the aircraft's weight. Consequently the whole aircraft moves *downwards* whilst it is rotating into the attitude for the increased lift for the pull-up. This is shown in the sequence of diagrams in Figure 10.3.

On a light aircraft such as the biplane in Figure 10.3 the pitching moment of inertia I_y is small, so that the rotation to the new attitude happens very quickly and the downward transient will often be unnoticeable. However, in the case of an airliner such as the McDonnell Douglas MD-80 shown in Figure 5.3 with a very long and heavily loaded fuselage, or of a very large aircraft such as a Boeing 747, I_y is very substantial, and the pitching motion will take considerably

---

[4]The implications for the subsequent motion of the aircraft in the climb will be considered in the next main section of this chapter. For now we are limiting our thoughts to the few seconds immediately following the control input.

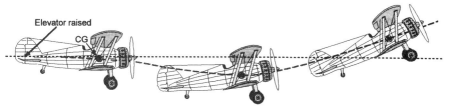

Elevator raised

CG

Figure 10.3   Pitch transient at the start of a pull-up

longer, maybe a few seconds, during which a substantial amount of height will be lost. At normal cruising altitudes this does not matter, but it can become crucially important when an airliner is coming in to land on a straight shallow glide path. If the pilot finds that he has got below the intended flight path, providing he has plenty of speed above the stalling speed in hand he may be inclined to pull back on the pitch control in order to pull up to the appropriate path again. But if he does so the loss of height due to the pitch transient will compound the problem of already being too low, so that collision with obstacles on the ground (or the ground itself) can be a real danger.

Delta-winged aircraft have a particular problem in this respect, since the elevators or elevons are at the back of the wing, just where usually one wishes to install camber-increasing flaps for lift augmentation. Unfortunately these control surfaces must be deflected upwards to pitch the nose up, and this also reduces the wing lift due to camber just when more lift coefficient is required. In fact the principle of what is happening is exactly the same as explained above for the conventionally tailed aircraft, the longitudinal dihedral being provided all within the one flying surface rather than by two surfaces. Furthermore, delta-winged aircraft typically have a high degree of sweepback, and invariably also a low aspect ratio, and both of these characteristics contribute to the slope of the lift curve being much less than for an aircraft with a straight high aspect ratio wing[5]. This means that, to achieve the same increase in lift coefficient, a delta-winged aircraft has to pitch up through a very much greater change in angle of attack than a straight winged, high aspect ratio aircraft. The longer time taken for this means that there is more time for the net downward force to cause a reduction in the aircraft's height.

The pitch transient is also a problem encountered by pilots of conventionally tailed combat aircraft flying fast at the extremely low altitudes demanded by today's tacticians. The purpose of such flight is to penetrate enemy territory without being observed either visually or by

[5]This is discussed in Chapter 14 of *Flightwise – Principles of Aircraft Flight.*

ground-based radar, and the technique demands using the visual and radar cover provided by the trees, hills, buildings and other ground features along the route. Training is usually limited to a minimum height of about 200 feet, but in combat pilots will be expected to fly very much lower than this, so that the avoidance of obstacles becomes a major preoccupation of the pilot (although greatly aided by electronic systems). If a pull-up is the only way to avoid a looming obstacle, the pilot must take into account the fact that he will lose height before gaining it, and so avoiding action must be taken earlier than is ideal.

There is a solution to this problem, and it is simply to use canards in place of the conventional tailplane. To create the pitching moment required for pitching the nose of a canard aircraft up, the canard must produce an increased upwards lift-force rather than downwards, since it is ahead of the centre of gravity. Consequently the net lift-force on the aircraft during the transient motion is greater than, and not less than, the weight, so that whilst the wing's angle of attack is being increased the aircraft is already gaining, and not losing, height. This is one of the major advantages of using canards, which are appearing increasingly on the new generation of combat aircraft.

Although we are concentrating in this chapter on vertical control, we have also seen in the previous chapter that a pitch-up to increase the aircraft's lift coefficient is an essential component of entering a level turn. Exactly the same drawback of pitch transients applies there, and for aircraft involved in air-to-air combat the severity of these transients may be the crucial factor which tips the balance between the superiority of one aircraft in outmanoeuvring the other. But we will return to this most important and fascinating subject in Chapter 12 where we shall look at manoeuvrability and agility.

Configuration Changes

Compared with the relatively secure stability of a four-wheeled road vehicle about all of its three axes, there is on an aircraft in flight a very intricate and delicate balance of forces and moments which is susceptible to disturbance from a host of different causes. We have seen already how the stability modes interact with each other, how a number of at first unexpected secondary and cross-coupling effects come into play when any of the controls are activated, and how some aerodynamic effects are more susceptible to variations in speed whilst others are very dependent on angle of attack and physical features such as sweepback. It is perhaps not surprising then that a full century passed after George Cayley's first 'proper' aircraft flight in 1804 of a conventionally configured glider (Figure 1.2) before the pioneers eventually managed to get sufficiently to grips with enough of these multifarious effects to be able to remain safely airborne in a controllable aircraft. The problems were formidable.

There is an additional complication in respect of the use of the elevator in that it is used not only as a flight control surface for producing pitching rotations to achieve changes in the wing's angle of attack, but also as a trimming device to balance out the variation of pitching moments resulting from the movement of the centre of pressure on the wing. In addition, there are several other variable features of the aircraft and of its flight which we will look briefly at now, which may have a significant effect on the pitching trim of the aircraft, and which the pilot must be prepared to take into account.

Flaps
The subject of lift augmentation, the raising of an aircraft's coefficient of lift beyond the usual operating range for the purpose of permitting safe flight at low speeds especially for landing, has been dealt with at length in Chapter 9 of *Flightwise – Principles of Aircraft Flight*, in the section 'Modification for Flight – Lift Augmentation'. Two differing fundamental approaches were considered there: firstly that of extending the useful angle of attack range to angles greater than the normal stalling angle of the wings by the use of leading edge devices such as slats and slots, and secondly that of increasing the camber (and/or area) of the wings by hingeing downwards and/or extending rearwards a rear portion of the wing. Whilst the first of these has no direct effect on the pitching moment of the wing beyond the usual forward migration of the centre of pressure as angle of attack is increased, the second, the use of flaps, does have an effect on the longitudinal trim of the aircraft, that we must consider here.

When a simple hinged trailing edge flap is deflected downwards whilst maintaining constant wing angle of attack[6], air speed and density, the smoothness of the aerofoil profile at the hinge-line is lost to some extent, and the flap itself acts as a small aerofoil, with its own distinctive effect on the aerofoil pressure distribution as shown in Figure 10.4. If a Fowler flap (a wing area increasing flap which is extended rearwards from the wing's trailing edge) is used, there is likewise a rearwards shift in the centre of pressure. The effect in both cases is to increase the total lift of the wing (as required) and also to increase the nose-down pitching moment. As a result, it would seem that the pilot would have to pull back on the pitch control to apply

---

[6]We continue to define the wing chord line as that joining the leading edge with the position of the trailing edge when the flap is not deflected. Thus the chord line's position relative to the body of the aerofoil section would remain unchanged when the flap is deflected, and so deflection of the flap does not of itself imply an increase in angle of attack.

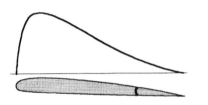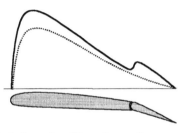

Figure 10.4   Lift distribution over an aerofoil with deflected trailing edge surface

some up-elevator and hence a nose-up pitching moment to compensate.

In practice, however, things are not quite so straightforward. Generally the pilot is not seeking a sudden increase in lift, since at the time of selecting flaps the aircraft will be flying level or on a steady descent in preparation for landing, and a sudden pull-up is not wanted. Rather, the pilot wishes to maintain for the time being a constant value of C_L and hence lift, whilst configuring the aircraft ready for achieving a higher C_L value a little later. The procedure is illustrated in Figure 10.5, which shows the lift curves for the aircraft with and without flaps. The effect of flaps (as far as lift is concerned) is simply to add camber to the aerofoil, and hence to increase the C_L uniformly at all angles of attack (except that the stall occurs earlier), and so the with-flaps line is obtained by sliding the without-flaps line upwards and to the left.

Let us assume that the aircraft is flying at point A on the no-flaps line, when flaps are selected in preparation for providing more lift coefficient shortly but not immediately. The aircraft must move to the point B on the with-flaps line, which is at the same horizontal level as point A, and this means that an immediate reduction in angle of attack is required. The fact that the deflection of flaps produces a nose-down pitching moment is therefore entirely appropriate and welcome, since the pilot will require to take no compensating action. Furthermore, when the attitude of the aircraft has attained that at point B, the tailplane will have risen, so that its angle of attack will have increased in a nose-down sense by the same amount as that by which the wing angle of attack has reduced[7], and the increased downward tailplane force will now be approximately providing the extra nose-up trimming moment required to balance out the nose-down pitching moment produced by the flaps.

Thus provided that the balance of these various effects is roughly right, the pilot will not need to make any compensating trim adjust-

---

[7]We are not referring here to downwash, which is considered overleaf.

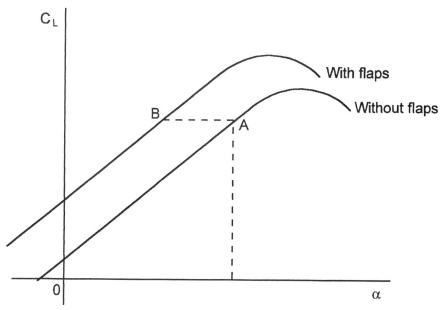

Figure 10.5   Lift curves of an aircraft with and without flaps

ment or short-term control movement as he deploys the flaps, and the aircraft should automatically adjust itself to point B. Following this, the drag will be immediately increased, and so (if the throttle control(s) are not altered) speed will be given up as required, and more C_L can be selected by increasing the angle of attack.

It looks then as though flaps are naturally well-behaved and generally tend to do what is wanted automatically. But we have come across a considerable number of variable parameters in the foregoing discussion, and in practice it is unlikely that the balance between them all will be exactly, or even nearly, right. In addition, there is one other possibly serious effect that we have not taken into account, and that is that the tailplane may be influenced by the downwash behind the wing. When the aircraft moves from point A to point B of Figure 10.5 the lift coefficient, and hence the overall downwash behind the wing, is not significantly changed. However, its *distribution* might be altered because of the different manner in which the C_L value is now being achieved, and this may affect how much it influences the tailplane, since its span and that of the flaps is less than that of the wing. An important design feature of the aircraft is how high (relative to the wings) the tailplane is fixed, and when and to what extent it is immersed in the downwash behind the wing. If the tailplane were to move out of the top of the wing's downwash as the nose pitched down in going from A to B in Figure 10.5, then a cause of down-load is immediately removed from the tailplane, and the nose may have a tendency to pitch down more than is required. Much less desirably, if the tailplane moves up *into* the wing's downwash, or if the redistribution of downwash is such that it affects the tailplane more when the flaps are deployed, this can actually produce a nose-*up* pitching moment when a nose-down one is required, with the very uncomfortable result that the selecting of the flaps pitches the aircraft the wrong way, and the pilot must apply a substantial nose-down trimming input immediately, to prevent what could otherwise lead rapidly to a stall. This undesirable feature is, for example, to be found on the Scottish Aviation Jetstream commuter turboprop aircraft, and may be related to the unusual location of the tailplane half way up the fin, although the precise explanation is not obvious. Here is an example illustrating the considerable complexity of the various interacting influences which come into play when flaps are used.

Drag and Thrust Line Variations
Another necessary preparation for landing is to lower the undercarriage, once again usually during level or nearly level steady flight. In contrast to the rest of the aircraft a retractable undercarriage is not designed to have low drag when deployed, and consequently a lowered undercarriage will often produce as much drag as the whole of the rest of the aircraft. It is inevitable that the line of action of this new rearward force is considerably below the aircraft's centre of gravity, so that it produces a nose-down pitching moment. As with the deployment of flaps, this is essentially a desirable feature. If not compensated for by the pilot applying a nose-up trim adjustment, the resulting nose-down pitch rotation causes a reduction in wing lift, and thus a deflection from the level into a descending flight path, in which the forward component of gravity usually more than compensates for the additional drag of the undercarriage, so that speed increases as the aircraft descends. If, however, the pilot does apply a corresponding nose-up trim change when selecting undercarriage down, the aircraft will temporarily remain in level flight, but the additional drag will call for additional thrust from the engine if level flight is to be maintained.

Although we have assumed all along that the thrust of the aircraft acts through the centre of gravity, this is not always the case. On aircraft such as many of today's large airliners with low wing configuration and underslung engines, the thrust line is substantially below the centre of gravity, so that increasing the engine power produces a nose-up trim change. Since increasing power is usually the prelude to climbing or reducing the rate of descent, this trim change is fortuitous, since it pitches the nose up ready for the climb or out of the dive. But seaplanes and float-planes necessarily usually have their engines mounted very high up above the centre of gravity, in order to keep them out of the water spray, and the nose-down pitching moment produced by these when power is increased is highly undesirable, and must be compensated for by a substantial nose-up trim adjustment by the pilot.

Subsonic/supersonic trim

It was shown (and discussed in some detail) in Chapter 11 of *Flightwise – Principles of Aircraft Flight* in the subsection entitled 'Longitudinal Trim Changes' that when an aircraft accelerates from subsonic to supersonic flight, there is a very substantial rearward movement of its aerodynamic centre from about the quarter-chord point (as discussed in Chapter 4 of this book) to about the half-chord point, because of the nature of supersonic pressure distributions which was explained in Chapter 10 of *Flightwise – Principles of Aircraft Flight*[8]. The sizeable nose-down change in pitching moment which results has to be seriously taken into account when designing a supersonic aircraft. If the tailplane is designed and set appropriately for balancing out the small nose-down pitching moment at subsonic speeds, then at supersonic speeds when the centre of pressure has moved a long way backwards, a substantially greater down-load will be required by the tailplane, which will bring with it a considerable amount of additional drag, the last thing wanted when designing for supersonic flight. The solution adopted on the Concorde supersonic airliner is to shift the centre of gravity of the entire aircraft aft as the aircraft is accelerating through the speed of sound, and to move the centre of gravity forward again as it slows down through Mach 1 in preparation for landing. Rather than moving all of the passengers and baggage backwards and forwards in flight, the centre of gravity shift is achieved by means of mechanically pumping a large volume of fuel between forward wing tanks and tail fin tanks. The elaborate system required for this perpetual fuel transference is just one of the many complex necessities built into Concorde to enable it to do its job successfully. Clearly further trimming problems may be encountered if the total amount of fuel on board is allowed to fall below a sufficient minimum to enable this retrimming process to take place whilst decelerating before landing.

MEDIUM-TERM MANAGEMENT

In a number of the discussions of the previous section we were just broaching the longer term effects of applying an elevator input when

---

[8]There is also likely to be a change in the zero-lift pitching moment of the aerofoil, the nature of which will depend on the supersonic characteristics of the aerofoil.

we broke off, or merely made brief passing reference to what would happen next. As we now turn to examining these longer-term consequences of pitch control, and bring into the arena the additional variable of altitude in a substantive manner, we shall need to add one more pilot's control to the inventory that we have chiefly concentrated on so far, namely the variation of engine power, and hence thrust, by the adjustment of the throttle[9]. This is because, if we wish the aircraft to do other than continuously sacrifice energy (potential or kinetic) to the atmosphere as a glider does, we require a source of energy, the engine and propulsion system, which must be controllable in order to be able to manage the third dimension of altitude effectively.

We shall from now on be regarding the aircraft (on the whole) as a particle rather than a rigid body, since we are looking beyond the immediate rotational responses of the aircraft to pitch control, and considering the interaction of all the overall forces on the aircraft's centre of gravity. We shall need to call on the concepts of kinetic and potential energy extensively, and so if you are not very conversant with these ideas, may I recommend you to brush up on them, for example from the first few pages of Chapter 4 of *Flightwise – Principles of Aircraft Flight*.

Speed and Height

When we were looking at what was involved in carrying out a level turn in an aircraft, we contrasted the task of the pilot with that of a car driver, since many more people have the latter experience than the former. Now that we are taking on board the vertical element of flight, such a comparison is once again quite informative. Supposing that the road route that a car driver will follow is already decided, he or she has no choice about whether to go up or down, since the contours of the road unyieldingly dictate this. But what will change, if the driver takes no compensatory action, is the car's speed, which will decrease or increase according to whether the car is ascending or descending a hill. To maintain a steady speed, the driver must constantly adjust the power being supplied by the engine to the driving wheels by using the accelerator pedal and perhaps the gears.

How important is it for the car driver to maintain a steady speed? In the past, it was perhaps usually not very important, but today one's

---

[9]To obviate the pedantic and annoying use of the indecisive word 'throttle(s)' from now on, we shall stick to the singular form of the word, which may be taken to imply 'throttles' or 'power levers' for a multi-engined aircraft. Likewise we shall use the word 'engine' as a portmanteau word for 'powerplant or powerplants', including propellers if appropriate.

speed is very rigidly constrained either by the law or by the speed of other vehicles in front. I have been made painfully aware of the importance and difficulty of precisely observing imposed speed limits. On a 40-mile trip that I regularly make near my home the imposed speed limits change frequently and abruptly between each of 30, 40, 50, 60 and 70 mph, and they are policed by cameras at various strategic points. There is one such camera concealed round a bend at the bottom of a substantial hill as one approaches the end of a village, still inside its 30 mph limit. After maintaining 30 mph through the level part of the village, it is necessary to brake quite substantially while descending the hill to avoid being caught out by this camera and receiving an unwelcome letter through the door a week or so later! Whether it was this camera or another that caught me out, I am now obsessively aware of watching my speed, especially on this route, arguably to the detriment of overall road safety.

An aircraft does not, however, have an external influence like a tarmac road under it to dictate its ups and downs, and so as well as watching speed the pilot has the additional task of deciding on and controlling the vertical motion of the aircraft. This makes a very substantial additional demand on the pilot of an aircraft compared with the driver of a car. Speed and height are both fully controllable, but there are two controls (pitch control and throttle) which each affect both variables in a complex interactive manner. The aircraft pilot has therefore to learn the skill of coordinating the use of these two controls in order to achieve the required results. After mastering the ailerons with their unexpected behaviour in a turn, the novice pilot has the considerably harder task of learning how to manage height and speed.

On the road, one's altitude is determined by ancient geology and recent earthworks, whilst one's speed is usually governed by a legally imposed speed limit, traffic jams excepted. Speed limits should not be regarded so much as maximum speeds but as target speeds, since it is recognised good practice to drive as close to the limit as possible (other road conditions permitting). In the air, it is much more common for a specific flying *altitude* to be demanded by an external authority, air traffic control, in order to separate aircraft safely into non-conflicting 'flight levels'. In some instances (such as approaching to land at busy airports) speed is also dictated by air traffic control, but more often the speed of flight is determined by the aerodynamic requirements of the aircraft, depending on its size and the power available, and what the flying objectives are for the current phase of flight. For example, one may wish to fly at the best speed for obtaining the maximum *specific air range*, which is a measure of the amount of fuel required per unit distance travelled, analogous (but in inverse form) to the 'miles per gallon' of a road vehicle[10]; or for obtaining maximum *endurance,* i.e. remaining airborne for as long as possible for each unit of fuel burnt. One may require to fly as fast as possible compatible with the sustained running rpm limit of the engine. During a climb, different speeds are appropriate (for a given aircraft) according to whether, for example, one requires to achieve (a) the best angle of climb (for clearing ground obstacles), (b) the best rate of climb (to gain a certain height in as short a period of time as possible, often the aim of an interceptor aircraft), (c) the most economical rate of climb in terms of fuel utilisation (the usual transport requirement), or (d) compliance with local noise regulations. When preparing to land, the recommended speed is commonly 30% above the level-flight stalling speed. These and other speeds are laid down in each aircraft's operating manual. Usually the 'right' way to approach the task of flying an aeroplane is first of all to establish and maintain the appropriate speed, according to the circumstances as discussed above, and then to maintain the desired flight path, whether level or descending or climbing.

Cruising

Let us first of all consider what is involved in establishing and maintaining the aircraft in level flight at a desired height and speed. Either the speed or the height (or both) might be not quite right, and the pilot has two primary controls each of which has an influence on both speed and height. Now the natural inclination, thinking in terms of the short-term response to pitch control and of the car driver's experience of using the 'accelerator' on the level, would be to adjust the height by means of the pitch control and the speed by varying the throttle setting. But to the frustration of the car driver, this is not the best way to do things when flying.

To understand why not, we must think in terms of energy. In steady level flight, the aircraft's kinetic energy $\frac{1}{2}mU^2$ is constant since the speed U is constant[11], and also its potential energy mgh is constant since the aircraft is being flown at a fixed altitude h. Thus the aircraft's total energy (the sum of potential and kinetic energies) is not varying, and so the power of the engine (i.e. the rate at which it is providing energy) is exactly matched by the rate at which energy is being lost to the air as a result of the aircraft's drag.

---

[10]Range, economy, height and endurance are discussed briefly in the subsections under these headings in Chapter 1 of *Flightwise – Principles of Aircraft Flight.*
[11]Although the mass m is slowly decreasing on account of burning fuel we can ignore this in the short to medium term.

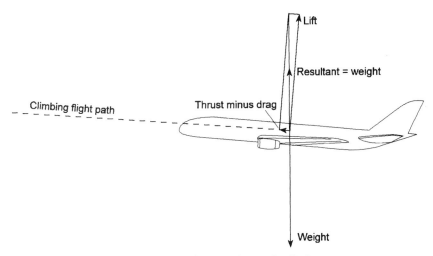

Figure 10.6   The forces on an aircraft in a steady gentle climb

If we suppose that the speed is correct and constant but rather than flying level the aircraft is very gently climbing (indicated by the altimeter needle rotating clockwise[12]), it means that the engine is producing too much energy, and the surplus is being converted into potential energy. The forces on the aircraft are shown in Figure 10.6. Since thrust and drag are in line with each other (treating the aircraft as a particle), it is convenient to combine them into the single force [thrust minus drag] in the flight direction. The tiny shortfall in the lift force's component in the vertical direction is made up for by the equally tiny vertical component of the relatively small [thrust minus drag] force, and the resultant of [thrust minus drag] and lift is equal and opposite to the weight. This ties up with the fact that, even though climbing, the aircraft is in steady, non-accelerating flight so that by Newton's First Law all three forces must be in equilibrium. Thus there is no force *accelerating* the aircraft upwards, but nevertheless it is gaining height, and hence potential energy, due entirely to the excess energy being generated by the engine.

To try to correct the climb by pitching the nose down using the pitch control would merely mean that the lift vector would rotate forwards so that its rearward component would disappear and the excess

[12]An aircraft usually also has a rate-of-climb indicator, but because of the principle on which this works there is always a lag in its reading. Therefore when adjusting or trying to steady the rate of climb it is generally preferable to use the altimeter.

thrust over drag would cause the speed to increase, which we do not want. The only way to arrest the climb without altering the speed is to reduce the throttle setting by an appropriate amount, so that the engine stops producing too much thrust. When this is done, the [thrust minus drag] force disappears, thrust now equals drag, and the aircraft quickly and automatically adopts the required level flight path because there is no surplus energy available to sustain the climb. It is true that the rearward component of the lift force would initially cause a small rearwards acceleration of the centre of gravity according to Newton's Second Law, but because of the mass and hence the inertia of the aircraft and because the lift force tips forward to vertical whilst the thrust is reducing, the correction to the climb is completed almost before any speed change has occurred at all.

During this correction, the alteration in lift force is negligible and the speed is unchanged, and so the lift coefficient must remain unchanged. Therefore there is no requirement to retrim the aircraft in pitch (unless the thrust line is above or below the centre of gravity, as discussed in the previous section), and so no pitch control adjustment is required at all.

If we started off with the aircraft flying at the desired speed but gently descending rather than climbing, exactly the same arguments would apply in reverse, and the pilot must (contrary to intuition) open the throttle to provide more engine power to maintain level flight, again maintaining a fixed-pitch control position. Furthermore, if we wish to climb or descend to a new required flight level, without change in speed, this may be achieved simply by adjusting the throttle accordingly, and restoring it to the appropriate setting for the new altitude just before that altitude is reached. We have thus demonstrated in theory, and practice bears this out, that:

The primary height control is the throttle.

Let us now change the scenario, and suppose this time that the aircraft is flying level at the desired altitude, but that we wish to slow it down to a new lower constant speed, with no change in height. Again we have too much energy, this time in the form of kinetic energy, and so it might seem logical that, as before, the pilot should reduce the throttle setting. But by the discussion in the previous paragraph we have seen that if he does so it is the potential energy that will be sacrificed rather than the kinetic energy, and so all that will happen will be that the aircraft will start to descend, still at the original speed, and this is not what we want.

What then is the solution? The other possible control to use is the elevator, but if the pilot pulls firmly back on the pitch control the aircraft will do a pull-up and will start to climb, which we don't want. Subsequently speed would certainly be lost as kinetic energy was converted into potential energy in the ensuing climb, but this would mean that we had altered both the speed and the height, whereas we only wanted to reduce the speed.

The answer is that the pilot must ease *gently* back on the pitch control, so as to retrim the aircraft in pitch, not moving the control fast enough to cause an appreciable pull-up. The idea is to increase the aircraft's angle of attack and hence C_L by a small amount *in preparation for* the lower speed which will follow. The aircraft's speed will not change abruptly because of its inertia but the aircraft's drag will immediately increase a little, on account of the extra induced drag resulting both from the greater wing downwash at the higher angle of attack, and also from the tailplane's greater down-load. Consequently the speed reduces, and as a result the *profile* drag of the aircraft reduces more rapidly than the induced drag was increasing, being dependent on the square of the speed, so that the overall aircraft drag reduces. There is now a little excess thrust, so to obtain a new equilibrium and prevent climbing the throttle setting must also be reduced slightly, so that the thrust equals the new value of drag. This agrees with the fact that there has been an overall reduction in energy because of the loss of kinetic energy, so that less engine power is required.

Let us follow what has happened by reference to Figure 10.7, the graph of drag against air speed which we first met in Chapter 2 when dealing with speed stability, in which the drag curve consists of the sum of two contributory curves (not shown here), one of induced drag (falling to the right) and one of profile drag (increasing to the right).

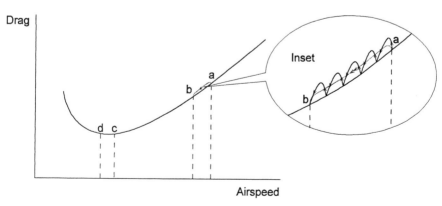

Figure 10.7 Drag and speed changes during retrimming to a lower speed in level flight

Let us assume that we wish to reduce the aircraft's speed from that at point *a* to the lower speed at point *b*, whilst maintaining a constant altitude. The inset shows this part of the graph more clearly, but the heights of the humps are greatly exaggerated. The overall change from *a* to *b* has been broken down into five small steps implying five small incremental upward movements of the elevator matched by five small reductions in the throttle setting, but in practice of course the two control movements would normally be smooth and continuous from *a* to *b*. We will look at one incremental step on its own at first.

From *a*, as the pitch control is eased backwards, the aircraft's operating point temporarily moves off the drag curve upwards, as the induced drag of wing and tailplane is increased, and follows a path rather like the curved hump closest to *a* until the new speed and drag values are established. The throttle must be reduced accordingly, so that thrust equals drag, or else the aircraft will climb. In the figure the procedure is repeated five times until point *b* is reached, but in practice the process would be smooth, and the change would take place along a curve something like the dotted one from *a* to *b*. Ideally, the reduction of throttle setting should be so accurately coordinated with the pulling back of the pitch control that the dotted line from *a* to *b* will lie almost along the drag curve itself, but a little deviation is inevitable for the process to work.

For reasons of speed stability and performance requirements, it is usual for flight speeds to lie to the right of the lowest point of the drag-speed curve, as do points *a* and *b*. However, it is quite possible and acceptable to be flying at a point such as *c* on the graph, very near to the minimum drag speed. If it is required to reduce the speed from that at *c* to some lower point such as *d* where the drag is scarcely changed from that at *c*, the adjustment will be made simply by means of a gentle easing back on the pitch control, and no throttle movement will be required at all. Furthermore, if the pilot continues to pull gently back on the pitch control after *d* has been reached, the drag will increase and an *increase* in throttle setting will be required to maintain level flight. It is at this stage that the aircraft enters the regime of speed instability, as discussed in Chapter 2, and continuous adjustments to the throttle setting will be needed to maintain equilibrium at all points on the curve to the left of the minimum drag point.

So we have seen that, when an aircraft is cruising at a constant height,

> **the primary speed control is the pitch control, and the throttle compensates (if necessary) for the resulting change in drag.**

It is therefore appropriate to refer to trimming the aircraft to a particular speed (in level flight), and this exactly corresponds with our discussion in Chapter 4 on trimming an aircraft longitudinally. There we concentrated on trimming for the appropriate lift coefficient, and here for the appropriate speed. The lift equals the weight and so must remain constant, the wing area S is fixed, and at a given altitude the air density ρ also remains constant, and so in the lift formula $L = C_L . \frac{1}{2}\rho U^2 S$ there is one and only one speed which corresponds to each C_L value, and *vice versa*.

Overall, controlling an aircraft once it is established in cruising flight at the appropriate speed and height requires constant monitoring of speed and height. Any departures in speed are corrected by gentle use of the pitch control, pulling back to reduce speed and pushing forward to increase speed, whilst making small compensating movements of the throttle to ensure that the aircraft does not gain or lose height. Departures in altitude are easier to deal with, since they can be corrected simply with the throttle, without retrimming the aircraft in pitch. However, although this sounds quite tidy in theory, the practical reality of having two interdependent variables controllable by two interdependent controls allows plenty of scope for error, and the proper coordination of throttle and pitch control is a skill which takes considerable time to master, and is very demanding of a novice pilot.

Normally, in cruising flight, some degree of tolerance can be allowed both in speed and in height. However, flying in tight formation behind a lead aircraft reduces the acceptable tolerances virtually to zero, so that very rapid and continuous small and properly coordinated adjustments of both throttle and elevator are demanded of the pilot. Good formation flying is extremely exacting of a pilot's skill.

Climbing

Although we have considered how to deal with the need to change height during a cruise, the procedure to be adopted during a sustained climb, such as after taking off, is somewhat different. Frequently either full power or a fixed high proportion of it as recommended in the aircraft's operating manual is used, and so the elevator is the only longitudinal control left for the pilot to vary at his or her discretion. In this case, as when varying the speed during a level flight cruise, the elevator control is used for the purpose of trimming the aircraft to the appropriate climbing speed. The recommended speed will vary according to type of engine (piston or gas turbine), whether it is required to climb at the fastest possible rate (i.e. vertical component of the aircraft's velocity), the steepest angle, or for maximum overall fuel economy, and in this last case it will also depend on the proportion of the flight which will be spent in the climb up to the cruising altitude, compared with the overall distance to be flown.

Descent

A steady descent such as that during the approach to land is managed somewhat similarly to the cruise. As we have already seen, it is the aircraft's air speed which is crucial and is predetermined, being as low as possible for a comfortably low landing speed and short length of ground run (unless a higher speed is demanded by air traffic control), whilst remaining sufficiently above the level flight stalling speed to keep the aircraft well out of the danger of stalling or spinning. But whereas in the cruise the altitude is also kept constant, during the descent this requirement is replaced by the need to fly down a recommended flight path at a fixed angle, typically at about 3° to the horizontal, without deviating far below or above it.

Whereas the constancy of altitude in the cruise is observed from the altimeter, the line of the descent flight path is far more difficult for the pilot to discern precisely. It may be done simply through learning by experience what the runway looks like from too high or too low an angle, or there may be automatic coded lights by the runway which indicate to the pilot whether the aircraft is above or below the recommended flight path. Most aircraft, apart from the very simplest, are fitted with sophisticated instrumentation which responds to ground-based radar transmitters and informs the pilot of the aircraft's position (both above or below, and left or right) in relation to the recommended flight path. But our concern here is not with how the information is obtained, but what the pilot must do with it.

Just as in the cruise, the pilot must maintain speed by re-trimming[13] the elevator with the pitch control, and height and attitude relative to the intended flight path by use of the throttle, as shown in Figure 10.8. Unfortunately this requirement is in sharp conflict with the basic instincts of an untrained pilot, since one's natural inclination is to pull back on the pitch control if descending too steeply and aiming for the ground short of the runway. But this action would produce exactly the opposite response from that which is required. Apart from the already mentioned and not inconsequential effect of the pitch transient which *immediately* pushes the aircraft further downwards and away from the intended flight path, the longer-term effect of a firm pull-up is to initiate a climb in which speed will rapidly be sacrificed to potential energy, and a stall is likely to ensue. If engine power is increased at this late stage, the response (especially that of jet engines) will usually be too slow to save the situation. If on the other hand, in an attempt to correct an over-steep descent, the elevator control is eased back gently, the aircraft will be retrimmed to a lower speed setting, and if as is very likely it is flying at around point *c* of Figure 10.7, all that will

---

[13]In the technical sense rather than the pilot's sense, as discussed on pages 68 to 70.

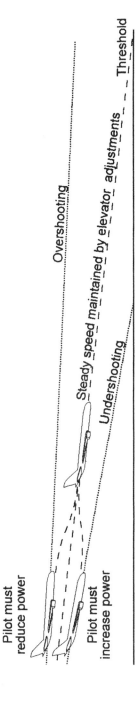

Figure 10.8   Correcting the flight path during approach to land

change will be the speed, to too low a value, with no recovery to the correct flight path. The correct (and only) solution is to apply more throttle.

If during the approach the speed drops to too low a value, the correct action is to push gently forward on the pitch control, even though this seems to be diving the aircraft into the ground. But if operating near the bottom of the drag-speed curve of Figure 10.7 where drag is approximately constant, this will not occur, and speed will be recovered without departing from the flight path. If operating on the right-hand side of the drag–speed curve, some increase in power will also be required.

We said that the approach angle is typically about 3° to the horizontal, but whilst this is usual for instrument approaches, very often a considerably steeper approach angle is more desirable, perhaps for obstacle clearance or for visual landings, or for added safety in the event of engine failure. Air-brakes may be used to enable this to be achieved without excessive aircraft speed. Flaps and other lift augmentation systems, on the other hand, are primarily intended to enable the aircraft to fly at a given approach angle at a lower safe air speed than would be possible without flaps. Trailing edge lift augmentation devices also have the advantage of producing the same lift coefficient at a lower angle of attack than without them, giving the pilot a better view ahead over the coaming of the instrument panel, whereas devices such as leading edge slats and slots which obtain a C_L increase by allowing a larger angle of attack to be used than the unaugmented stalling angle have the opposite effect, and may on their own make landing very difficult because of the reduced pilot visibility of the runway ahead and the risk of scraping the tail on the ground. This is one reason why the two types of system are usually used in conjunction with each other.

Energy Height

While we have been restricting our discussion chiefly to relatively demure modes of aircraft flight such as cruising and approaching to land, the balance between potential and kinetic energy has played only a minor rôle. However, when considering aircraft which have a very large operating range of both speed and altitude, the principle of interchanging potential and kinetic energy can be extremely useful, both for improving mission performance and for maximising the specific air range. This possibility has given rise to a way of analysing aircraft performance and of flight planning known as the *energy height* method or the *energy state* approach. Although this is strictly in the realm of aircraft performance rather than control, it will be instructive to look at its implications here, since the answers it yields can directly influence the way in which the aircraft is controlled.

The central variable to be used in the method will be one which expresses the total mechanical energy of the aircraft, i.e. the sum of its potential and kinetic energy. Let us have a closer look at this variable. The aircraft's potential energy is given by the expression mgh and its kinetic energy by $\frac{1}{2}mU^2$. However, it is more convenient to work in terms of so-called specific energy (potential, kinetic or total) which is the energy that each unit of weight possesses rather than that of the entire aircraft, and by this means the theory is more general in its application. To get these quantities, we divide both expressions by the weight mg, which gives h and $\dfrac{U^2}{2g}$ for the specific potential energy

and specific kinetic energy respectively.

The specific potential energy h is not only a measure of energy per unit weight but also, by definition, the height at which the aircraft is flying. Therefore, since the specific kinetic energy $\dfrac{U^2}{2g}$ is exactly the

same kind of quantity dimensionally, it may also be thought of and interpreted as a height: it would be the *additional* height that an aircraft flying at a speed U and height h could attain if all of its kinetic energy were to be converted into potential energy (without loss), so that its speed became zero. Theoretically this extra height could be obtained by zooming[14] the aircraft upwards until its speed was zero.

If we add together the specific potential energy and the specific kinetic energy, we obtain the specific total energy, which is in fact just called the specific energy, of the aircraft. But because of the argument of the previous paragraph, an easier way to think of this is that we are adding together two heights: the height at which the aircraft is flying plus the additional height available if all speed were to be converted into height. Consequently an alternative name for the aircraft's specific energy is its *energy height*, for which we will use the symbol h_e, and it is this term that we shall use from now on, since it is more descriptive and understandable. We can express the relationship between the three specific energy terms, or the three heights, as follows:

$$h_e = h + \frac{U^2}{2g}$$

The concept is very reminiscent of the frictionless roller-coaster analogy that we have used in the past, where the aircraft is the roller-coaster. Kinetic energy can be easily converted into potential energy

---

[14]This is the word that is actually used for this process.

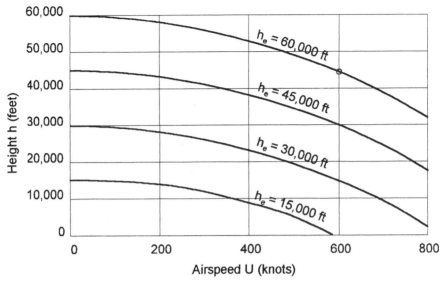

Figure 10.9 **Lines of constant energy height**

simply by pulling the aircraft into a climb until it has no speed left at all, and *vice versa* by diving it. If there were no drag and no engine power[15], then the aircraft could repeatedly dive and zoom back up to its energy height as often as you liked. The starting height of the roller-coaster with zero speed is the equivalent of the aircraft's energy height h_e.

It will help us to visualise the relationship between these three quantities if we use a graph. Let us start by drawing a pair of vertical and horizontal graph axes to represent height and speed respectively, and mark off on them suitable ranges to include all the values of each variable that we are interested in. This we have done in the grid of Figure 10.9, in which each point represents a height-speed combination. What we will do is to choose a value of h_e and find all the points on the grid at which the potential energy height (the vertical axis value) and the kinetic energy height (calculated from the horizontal axis value) add up to give this particular chosen value of energy height h_e. We can do this by rewriting the h_e formula with the altitude h as the subject, thus:

$$h = h_e - \frac{U^2}{2g}$$

[15]We will come back to look at this proviso in a moment.

For illustration, let us show how the points of the top curve (labelled $h_e = 60,000$ ft) have been evaluated. At a range of air speeds (say every 100 knots) and for the chosen value of h_e (60,000 feet) we calculate and plot h (first of all ensuring that U and g are in feet per second and feet per second squared respectively). For example, a speed of 600 knots[16] is equivalent to $\dfrac{600 \times 6083}{60 \times 60}$ or 1014 feet per second, and $g = 32.2$ feet per second squared, and so at $h_e = 60,000$ feet the value of h from the formula is $60,000 - \dfrac{(1014)^2}{2 \times 32.2}$ or 44,000 feet. Hence the point ($U = 600$ knots, $h = 44,000$ feet) is plotted on the graph as one point of the $h_e = 60,000$ feet curve, and the remaining points of this curve are calculated and plotted similarly. The procedure is repeated for other constant-h_e curves. (We have chosen 45,000, 30,000 and 15,000 feet.)

You will observe that all the resulting curves in the graph pass through the same height on the vertical axis as the energy height which they represent, and this is because the speed on this axis is zero and all the energy here is potential. It is analogous to the roller-coaster sitting at the top of its first incline, ready to descend but not quite moving. As the roller-coaster descends down the first plunge, on the graph it moves out along its constant-h_e line as speed increases and height reduces, and when in real life it climbs up the next incline, on the graph it moves back along the same line (assuming no friction) towards the $U = 0$ axis.

Let us suppose now that a particular aircraft is to take off and then climb as quickly as possible[17] to a given height, and when it reaches that height it must be at a specified speed. This might be an airliner preparing for cruising flight, or it might for example be a combat aircraft on an interception mission. The question we wish to answer is, what is the best speed to be flying at, at each height during the climb? To answer this question, we must introduce another variable, which is the rate of change of energy height, or in calculus notation $\dfrac{dh_e}{dt}$, for it is this value that we must make as large as possible at every moment during the climb in order to gain energy height as quickly as possible. Here we are talking about the *rate* at which the engine supplies

[16]A knot is defined in footnote 2 in the section '...And What It Isn't' of Chapter 9, in the discussion of Figure 9.1.
[17]The method can also be adapted to solve other similar problems such as how to climb in the most economical manner.

energy, and this prompts us to introduce formally the concept of *power*, a physical quantity so far only used loosely but not precisely defined in *Flightwise*. Power is simply defined as *the rate of doing work*, or in other words *the rate of providing energy*, and like energy it is a scalar quantity.

In order to make an aircraft climb and accelerate, the engine has to provide energy at a sufficient rate to accomplish two different requirements: first of all, throughout the flight it has to balance the rate at which energy is being given up to the air as a result of drag, and secondly it must produce additional energy which is being converted into energy height. The first component of this need not worry us, since all it does is ensure that this part of the thrust equals drag throughout the flight, and it was for this reason that a few paragraphs back we were able to contemplate using a method of analysis which assumes no losses. We said that 'if there were no drag and no engine power'; in fact of course there is drag, and there must be power to produce thrust, but if we consider the drag to be equal to the thrust produced by this *initial portion* of the engine's power, then they cancel out corresponding to the 'no drag and no thrust' condition of the perfect roller-coaster. Thus it is merely the *excess power* (i.e. that which is being produced by the engine over and above what is required simply to overcome drag) that is of interest to us in providing the aircraft with energy height. Since energy height is a *specific* quantity (i.e. energy per unit weight), we must also deal with the engine power in specific terms. We are therefore talking about 'the rate at which the engine is producing power, over and above the requirement to overcome drag, per unit weight of the aircraft', and this is very logically and naturally given the name of *specific excess power*, which we shall sometimes abbreviate as SEP.

Now h_e is not only a height but also a quantity of specific energy, as we know from its derivation. Therefore $\dfrac{dh_e}{dt}$ is the rate at which the aircraft's specific energy is being increased, and since this is exactly supplied by the specific excess power of the engine, it follows immediately that $\dfrac{dh_e}{dt}$ *is the same thing as the specific excess power.* Very conveniently, since it is also a rate of change of height, it can simply be expressed in feet per second, and it directly represents the rate at which the energy height can be increased by the engine's excess power.

Looking back at the graph of Figure 10.9, we should like to know how much specific excess power the engine of a particular aircraft can produce at full power at every point on the graph grid, because then we shall be able to choose a path of points on the graph to give us the best rate of climb. In order to work out these values we need a formula for the engine's specific excess power in terms of quantities which can be determined from other information. Power is rate of doing work, which is $\dfrac{\text{Force} \times \text{Distance}}{\text{Time}}$, and in turn this can be written as Force × Speed. In the case of the aircraft's specific excess power, the force is simply Thrust − Drag, the speed is the aircraft's air speed, and we must divide by the weight because of the word 'specific'. Remembering that specific excess power is also equal to $\dfrac{dh_e}{dt}$, we can write

$$\frac{dh_e}{dt} = \frac{(\text{Thrust} - \text{Drag})(\text{Speed})}{\text{Weight}}$$

Now the thrust and drag forces depend on a very large number of factors, such as height, speed, coefficient of lift, the size of the aircraft and the nature and size of the powerplant (whose performance also depends on height and speed). If we had access to all the relevant data, it would be possible (but a large job) to use the above formula to work out the value of $\dfrac{dh_e}{dt}$ at every point on the grid of the graph in Figure 10.9. In a moment we will take a look at the typical results and usefulness of this exercise in Figure 10.10, but before we do so it is important to emphasise a difference between the two sets of results that we are plotting on the graph. The curves of constant energy height that we plotted in Figure 10.9 were found by using an equation which was simply based on the energy conservation principle 'total energy is constant', and the results were completely and utterly independent of whether we were referring to an aircraft or a bullet or a bird. This must be the case, since we were able to work out the specimen value of h for a random value of $U = 600$ knots without having any particular aircraft in mind. But now, on the other hand, although we are going to plot curves on the same axes as before, the set of curves that we will get is totally dependent on the particular aircraft and propulsion system in question, because of their dependence on the quantities thrust, drag and weight. The first set of curves is universal and purely kinematic in its derivation, whereas the second depends also on the mechanics of the system, and so the two sets are different in nature.

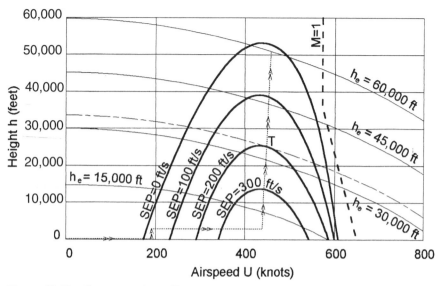

Figure 10.10 Contours of specific excess power superimposed on lines of constant energy height

After calculating the aircraft's specific excess power at *all* points on the graph, contour lines, each joining all points which have the same value of SEP, are interpolated from the results, giving typically the new set of curves shown in Figure 10.10. These represent a high-performance subsonic combat aircraft, although in practice there are very few with as high a performance as this. The best way to visualise what is going on is to think of these new curves as the physical contours of a hill, as drawn on a map, so that we have as it were a spur of high land rising out of the sea (which is outside the 'SEP = 0 ft/s' curve) and protruding northwards from the southern border of the map.

Our quest now requires us to find the quickest way for the aircraft to reach, let us say, an energy height level of 60,000 feet, starting from rest on the runway at zero feet. To do so, we must choose a path on the graph grid such that, as we cross every energy height level, we are operating at the point of maximum specific excess power. This path, which we will now investigate, is shown by the fine dotted line in Figure 10.10 with the double arrow-heads on it.

Starting from the origin (zero speed and height) with zero energy-height, the first requirement is to get onto the highest point of the SEP 'hill' as soon as possible without gaining more energy height than is necessary. This involves taking off and climbing to the lowest acceptable flying altitude and then accelerating up to about 430 knots. We now have maximum SEP available from the engine, and so we are ready to gain energy-height as quickly as possible, which means that we must cross every constant energy height curve at the highest possible point of the specific excess power contour 'hill'. The fine dotted line shows how this works out in practice, but in order to understand precisely how it can be plotted we must remember that only a selection of the possible energy height curves, and only a selection of the specific excess power contours, have been plotted. In fact, through *every* point on the grid there is an energy height curve and through all points inside the SEP = 0 ft/s boundary there is a specific excess power contour. (The aircraft would not have enough power even to sustain level flight outside the SEP = 0 ft/s contour.) In general, the energy height curves cut the specific excess power contours either at two points or not at all, but the points that we are interested in are those at which an energy height curve meets a specific excess power contour at only one point; in other words, the points at which they are tangential to each other. This is illustrated in Figure 10.10 by the inclusion of one additional energy height curve (the dashed-and-dotted line) corresponding approximately to h_e = 34,000 feet, which is tangential to the SEP = 200 feet-per-second contour, and the tangent point is labelled T. To see why the point T must lie on the required path, imagine standing at point T on the specific excess power 'hill'[18]. If you were to walk either way along the dashed-and-dotted line, you would be walking downhill, so T must be the 'highest' point on this dashed-and-dotted line. If, on the other hand, you were to stand at the left-hand one of the two points at which the h_e = 30,000 feet line cuts the SEP = 200 feet-per-second contour, you could then walk to a higher point on the 'hill' by following the energy height line to the 'east', and so you were not at the point of highest possible specific excess power for that energy height level. Thus the tangent points of the two curves are the points forming the required performance path.

So we have found the quickest performance path by which to achieve 60,000 feet of energy height. The pilot, after reaching about 430 knots at low altitude, zooms into a climb such that his speed continues to increase a little, but most of the engine's excess power is used in providing height. From the graph the aircraft finishes up flying at about 460 knots at an altitude of about 51,000 feet. But what if this were not in fact the combination of speed and height that was eventually required, even though the energy height is what was wanted, (i.e. almost the maximum attainable, since very soon afterwards we run out of SEP contours)? In this case the pilot must simply convert some speed into height by zooming upwards (moving to the left along the h_e = 60,000 ft curve), or some height into speed by diving (moving to

---

[18]Remember that the SEP 'hill' rises out of the plane of the paper. It is not the peaks of the SEP curves as viewed in the drawing – those curves are 'contour' lines.

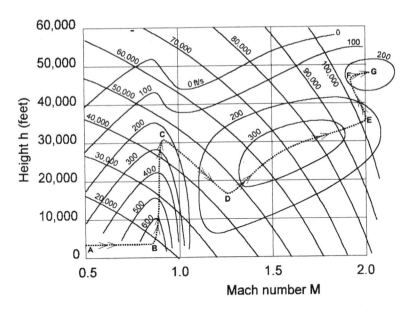

Figure 10.11 Energy height curves and specific excess power contours for a super-sonic aircraft

the right on the curve). In fact his scope for doing so is very restricted because of the engine's performance limitations. He can only sustain level constant speed flight whilst remaining inside the SEP = 0 ft/s curve. The limits are about 53,000 feet at 410 knots or 50,000 feet at 490 knots.

As we mentioned, Figure 10.10 applies to a subsonic aircraft, but in practice it is very rare for a subsonic fighter to have a service ceiling (i.e. maximum height at which it can fly straight and level) of over 50,000 feet, as is the case here. The dashed line labelled $M = 1$ shows the speed of sound at all altitudes. (Its slope below about 36,000 feet, the tropopause[19], results from the change in the speed of sound with the temperature lapse rate of about 2°C per 1000 feet up to this altitude, since the speed of sound is proportional to the square root of the absolute temperature[20].) The results that we have obtained from applying the energy height analysis to a subsonic aircraft are not particularly interesting or dramatic, but if the method is extended to a typical supersonic aircraft a fascinating result emerges.

Figure 10.11 shows a similar graph to Figure 10.10, but this time for a supersonic aircraft, and Mach number is plotted instead of air speed

[19]The tropopause is discussed in the section headed 'So What?' in Chapter 11 of *Flightwise – Principles of Aircraft Flight.*
[20]This is discussed and absolute temperature is explained in the section headed 'The Speed of Sound' in Chapter 10 of *Flightwise – Principles of Aircraft Flight.*

along the horizontal axis. Note that Mach numbers below 0.5 have been omitted and, to avoid overcrowding, the units have been omitted from the numbers labelling the curves, but they are the same as before. When the specific excess power contours are plotted, a considerably more complex picture emerges than in the subsonic case, and this is partly to do with the dependence of the engine performance on speed and height, and partly because of the very high drag that the aircraft experiences in the transonic phase, so that there is very much less excess power available at that phase. The SEP = 200 ft/s 'island' near the top right-hand corner reflects the dependence of engine performance on temperature, which is here constant with altitude, and air density, which continues to fall with altitude.

Following the same principle as before of picking the points of maximum specific excess power (where the curves are tangential to each other) at each energy height reached, a surprising quickest-climb path emerges, shown as before by a dotted line with double arrowheads, with the addition of reference points A to G, the last representing the desired cruise or mission condition.

As before, the aircraft accelerates at a low altitude from A to B, and then zooms up into a climb from B to C at virtually constant Mach number, during which the engine's excess power is almost entirely being converted into potential energy. When an energy height is reached whose curve is tangential to the same value SEP contour to the right of Mach 1 (i.e. at D) as to the left (i.e. at C), (about the 45,000 feet curve in the example graph), the aircraft is put into a powered dive from C to D, during which the aircraft accelerates through the transonic region and gives up nearly 15,000 feet of potential energy to kinetic energy, crossing the 'valley' of reduced specific excess power at a constant energy height. Then once at the highest point at which this h_e line crosses the new SEP hill (point D), the aircraft climbs and accelerates to point E, using the highest specific excess power available at each point in that region of the graph. At E the aircraft zooms up into a steeper climb, sacrificing speed, again at a constant energy height, to get to point F in the small region of high specific excess power surrounding the operating point, and then once again climbs and accelerates from F to G.

An interesting example of a well-known aircraft which uses the energy height technique is the Concorde supersonic airliner. It follows a climbing schedule based on the energy height analysis, but does not actually dive through the transonic region, partly because this would cause undesirable complications for air traffic control, and also out of consideration for the passengers, who might be somewhat alarmed to enter an accelerating dive so soon after taking off! Since this modification means that points C and D are more nearly on the level than they are in Figure 10.11, it means that energy height is still being added during the transonic phase. Additional specific excess power is obtained by boosting the thrust of the engines with the use of reheat. One reason why the Russian supersonic airliner has not seen passenger-carrying service is that it required to use reheat in cruising flight, whereas Concorde only requires it to boost the specific excess power available for a brief period whilst passing through the transonic regime.

Ground Effect

To close this chapter on the vertical control of aircraft, let us descend from the sublime to the ridiculous and look briefly at a special aerodynamic feature of aircraft flying extremely close to the ground, which is called ground effect. By extremely close, we mean in general considerably less than a wing-span above the ground, so of course the situation only arises in conventional aircraft during landing and take-off.

The feature of the ground effect has given rise to considerable speculation down the years about the possibilities that it might offer for designing a flying machine which would be a quantum leap more aerodynamically efficient than the conventional aeroplane. At the very end of Chapter 12 of *Flightwise – Principles of Aircraft Flight*, the chapter dealing with the downwash behind a wing and the resulting induced drag, we speculated about ways in which this downwash effect with its accompanying persistent requirement for the aircraft to be continuously flying effectively uphill, could be circumvented. However, the nearest that we got to a solution was to observe that migratory birds have overcome the problem by flying in the *upwash outside* the wake of the bird in front, by means of forming up on each other in echelons. Only tongue-in-cheek did we suggest the idea of airliners crossing the oceans in close formation!

All that is required to reduce a wing's downwash significantly is to place an infinitely large horizontal ground-board close by under the wing, lying parallel to the free stream airflow, and this is exactly the situation which prevails when an aircraft is flying very close to the ground. This has the same effect as greatly increasing the aspect ratio, since although the wing-tip trailing vortices are still present, their axes are deflected upwards (relative to their usual direction) so that the downwash between the wing-tips is substantially reduced.

As an immediate result of this, the relative airflow in the vicinity of the wing is restored to nearly horizontal, so that the induced drag, the rearward component of the lift-force, is largely eliminated. Not only is the drag reduced, but there is also an appreciable increase in the lift of the wing, provided the angle of attack is not altered. This is because of the effective increase in aspect ratio and the accompanying rise in the lift curve slope[21], which has the effect that at any given angle of attack the coefficient of lift is increased. So since both the drag is reduced and the lift is increased at a given angle of attack, the lift:drag ratio of the aircraft is substantially raised, which is a primary indicator of the flying efficiency of the aircraft.

On the face of it, everything sounds good, but we must look at this in the appropriate context. Normally these effects only occur during landing and very briefly at the moment of take-off, and it is handling considerations that are more important than flying efficiency at such moments. If we look at the influence of the ground effect on the longitudinal handling of the aircraft during landing, we find that some significant problems are created. In the first place, the increase in lift means that the aircraft tends to 'balloon' back up into the air just as it is supposed to be touching down, which of itself would seem to demand some deft forward control movement by the pilot to reduce the angle of attack. But the pilot is already in the process of pulling further and further back on the pitch control in order to produce more and more coefficient of lift as the speed reduces, aiming to let the aircraft settle gently on to the ground approximately as the stalling speed is reached. Herein lies a conflict of demands.

This conflict is further aggravated by another factor. As a result of the reduction of downwash behind the wing due to the ground effect, the airflow meeting the tailplane is in a less downward direction than in normal flight. Therefore the pilot must pull further back on the pitch control to maintain an unchanged nose-up pitching moment, independent of the considerations of the previous paragraph.

The balance between these three pitch control demands, (pulling back to retrim as speed reduces, pushing forward to compensate for the additional lift produced by change in lift curve slope, and pulling back to trim out the change in flow direction at the tailplane) varies appreciably between different types of aircraft, and whilst in some cases they may present no appreciable problem, in others very serious handling difficulties may be experienced. Making matters worse, as discussed earlier, is the pitch transient effect which means that, whatever pitch control action is taken, the initial response of the aircraft's centre of gravity is in the opposite direction to that which is demanded.

Mention of the pitch transient problem reminds us that we cannot regard the aircraft as a particle when it is so near to the ground, since a small angular displacement about either the longitudinal or the lateral axis will make different parts of the aircraft come closer to the

---

[21]This is discussed in Chapter 14 of *Flightwise – Principles of Aircraft Flight*, in the section headed 'Factors Affecting Ride Hardness'.

ground than other parts. This is particularly significant in the case of a delta-winged aircraft, since here there can be an additional aerodynamic effect. As the trailing edge comes close to the ground, it creates a narrow passage for the airflow between the wing and the ground, and this acts as a venturi[22], increasing the air speed and reducing the pressure. Thus the trailing edge of the wing is sucked down towards the ground, giving rise to a reduction in lift towards the trailing edge. But in a delta-winged aircraft the overall increase in lift due to the change in lift curve slope tends to be a dominant (and problematic) result of ground effect, so that the chief consequence of the downforce on the trailing edge due to the venturi effect is to provide a stronger nose-up pitching moment, which must be trimmed out by a nose-down pitch control input – one more to add to the previous list of conflicting pitch control demands.

So during landing the ground effect can be a nuisance or even a danger, especially for pilots changing between aircraft types. During take-off the problems are not so acute, since the aircraft is leaving the ground and there is not the same urgency to correct for transient longitudinal trim changes (which do still arise) as when the aim is to put the aircraft gently and safely down on to the ground. But is ground effect of any interest to aircraft designers and operators other than during take-off and landing? Is it possible to take economic advantage of the substantial increase in lift:drag ratio which ground effect undoubtedly bestows? There have been a number of proposals in recent decades, notably from Russia, for large-scale ground effect vehicles to be built and operated as passenger or cargo carrying aircraft, the operations of such aircraft being envisaged over a calm sea or very flat terrain. But the problems of ensuring no contact with the ground, coping with rough seas or uneven ground surfaces, ingestion of and damage by spray or dust or other debris, finding safe uninterrupted high-speed routes clear of conflicting traffic, and accessing these routes from useful flight termination locatians, have together rendered the idea little more than a pipedream.

Despite the drawbacks from the point of view of a conventional aircraft, the wing-in-ground-effect vehicle is currently arousing particular interest amongst the offshore fast ferry fraternity, who are thinking of it as a boat which can climb just out of the water, rather than as an aircraft that can fly very low. Two firms are now reputedly at an advanced stage of preparation for the launching and marketing of such vessels. Sea Wing International of Tasmania are

---

[22]The venturi principle is introduced and explained in Chapter 5 of *Flightwise – Principles of Aircraft Flight*, in the section headed 'Continuity and Bernoulli Combined'.

Figure 10.12   Wing-in-ground-effect 20-person ferry proposed by 'Sea Wing'

proposing various craft including the 20-passenger Sea Wing 05 shown in Figure 10.12, initially for passenger operations in South-East Asia, and Wingships Inc. of the USA are developing a 'Hoverplane' to the US Coastguard's specification. The protagonists are confident that wing-in-surface-effect vehicles (as they are also called) are the transport of the very near future, so we may 'watch this space' with interest.

But that is not quite the end of the story. One type of aircraft, whilst not conventional in the sense that we usually mean, is undoubtedly a ground effect vehicle, and that is the so-called 'ground effect machine', the hovercraft. Conceived initially as a vehicle which might fill the gap between, on the one hand, the large load-carrying capacity but low-speed seaborne vehicles and, on the other, faster aircraft with their limited load-carrying ability, it has achieved limited success, particularly in situations where no other form of transport is suitable, and also as a ferry over water. Being airborne it can only be controlled by aerodynamic controlling forces, which are much more tricky to produce than on a conventional aircraft, due both to its inability to bank and also to its very much lower air speed. We will look at hovercraft control in the next chapter. Despite these difficulties the hovercraft principle has survived commercially and is still used in a number of situations where it is appropriate.

CHAPTER 11
The Pilot Interface

INTRODUCTION

We have talked extensively about *what* the pilot has to *achieve* by way of manipulating the controls of an aircraft, but the emphasis throughout has been on the aerodynamic effect of the various control surfaces. We will now bring the discussion round to the human level, and give some thought to the question of linking the machinery of the aircraft's control surfaces to the mind which has to make the decisions. In between the machinery and the mind must lie the answer to the other question of *how* the pilot in the cockpit physically interacts with the controls, and how they are designed to make the challenging tasks as intuitive and safe as possible, whilst being agreeable and comfortable to use.

Whilst dealing with the three-dimensionalism of aircraft flight, it has proved constructive on occasions to consider affinities with and differences from other forms of vehicle such as unconventional aircraft, cars and even bicycles. When we look at the way aircraft pilot's controls have evolved, it is interesting to look at how the same questions have been tackled in other means of transport. Since both waterborne and wheeled vehicles predated the aircraft very substantially one would expect that the two-dimensional solutions developed for these vehicles would have been very seriously considered for adoption and extension by the pioneer designers in the three-dimensional realm.

We will therefore start the chapter by looking briefly at the way in which the control interface problem has been tackled on some land and waterborne vehicles, so that we can spot the similarities and dissimilarities that the aircraft manifests, and how these have been dealt with. Then, when we have discussed the conventional arrangement for the primary controls of an aircraft, we shall extend the investigation of the evolutionary process forward from the aircraft, and will see to what extent the well-established solutions adopted for aircraft proved satisfactory for a more recent form of flying machine, the hovercraft with its unique *modus operandi*.

We shall then move resolutely back into the aircraft cockpit, and consider two very important problems that have emerged and how they have been overcome: firstly that of the pilot being undesirably and continuously occupied with maintaining the controls in the required positions for flight even when changes in direction or speed are not called for; and secondly that of the finite-sized human pilot not having the strength to cope with ever larger and larger, and faster and faster aircraft, in which the forces on the control surfaces have become far greater than a person could cope with unaided.

The story will not be concluded in this chapter. After looking at some of the more advanced control requirements of combat aircraft in the following chapter, we shall be in a position in Chapter 13 to draw the various threads together, and to develop the ideas into a discussion of what may be achieved when ingenuity and mechanics and aerodynamics are enriched by the ascendancy of today's state-of-the-art computer technology. Finally, in Chapter 14, we shall look at some examples of the state of the art today.

ERGONOMICS AND RATIONALE OF VEHICLE CONTROL
Land-locked Vehicles

From the very earliest days of the motorcar, it has been more or less taken for granted that the hands should have control of the direction of travel, and this left the feet (which are generally less sensitive) to deal with speed control. Whether this is sensible or not, it probably derives from the fact that it has always been the hands that have held the reins of a horse, whilst the primary methods adopted for controlling its speed were urging forward with the heels (on horseback) and slowing down by means of a foot-operated brake (in horse-drawn carriages). Before the universal adoption of the idea of a steering wheel, some of the early 'horseless carriages' had a hand-operated tiller to steer the front wheels, and nobody (to my knowledge) has ever seriously proposed a foot-steered car. In my youth I recall electric dustcarts which were steered by a crank handle on one side of the driver's seat-pad and which had another crank handle on the other side for controlling power, reminiscent of tramcar control in which of course steering was not required. There were also three-wheeled electric milk floats which had a tiller (shaped like quarter of a large steering wheel) directly connected to the front wheel for steering, and the intriguing Messerschmitt three-wheeler bubble-car of the late 1950s with its single road wheel at the rear, a hinged canopy, a saddle seat for two to sit pillion, and handlebars for steering – more suggestive of a motorcycle with an aircraft cockpit than a conventional car!

But from the very early days of the motor vehicle the steering wheel has been almost universally adopted as the 'right' device for yawing a car, yawing being the only mode of control required. Its purpose is to turn the front wheels (rear-wheel steering is unstable in yaw, as driving fast backwards will quickly demonstrate) about a nearly vertical axis so that the axes of all the road wheels pass through a common point out to one side of the vehicle, and friction on the tyres then takes care of providing the centripetal force. The use of a full-wheel steering wheel allowed it to be geared to rotate several times from full lock to full lock, thus reducing the driver's force needed as cars got bigger and tyres broader, but this meant that rapid steering was not practicable because of the large angle (sometimes several full rotations) through which the wheel had to be turned.

Since both the yawing of the car and the turning circle are rotations in the horizontal plane, their axes are parallel (vertical) and there is no rotational vector component other than yaw rate contributing to the turn rate, as there is on an aircraft as we saw in Chapter 9. Hence the steering wheel is a *displacement* control (as opposed to a rate control like ailerons), the angular displacement of the wheel being directly proportional to the tightness of the turning circle[1], and thus steering is very logical and easily learnt. Whether the axis of the steering wheel is more or less vertical (as on lorries and buses) or nearer to the horizontal (as with most cars – remember the Bond Minicar with its horizontal steering wheel axis and absolutely vertical wheel?), the direction of turning is very intuitive and logical, except that it gives some novice drivers a bit of difficulty when learning to manoeuvre in reverse.

Whereas the steering control of a motorcar is very straightforward, the control of its forward speed is particularly complicated. The use of the internal combustion engine which can produce high torque only over a limited rpm range (and none at all close to zero) has created the need for variable gearing and a clutch, and so it is perhaps surprising that our less versatile members, our feet, have been called into service for controlling the speed. Not only are there three pedals[2] to be operated by only two feet, but each pedal behaves in a distinctively different manner from each of the others, and their use has to be closely coordinated with two additional hand controls, the gear stick and the handbrake. Thus speed control of the motorcar is by far the most difficult aspect of driving to master, yet the task is still given primarily to the feet, whilst the more capable hands mainly just operate the much simpler steering control.

Bicycles have always, since the days of the 'hobby-horse' and the 'penny farthing' (more properly known as the 'ordinary' bicycle), had a direct link between the rotation of the steerable front wheel and the steering control, the handlebars. I have a silly childhood memory of wanting to replace the handlebars on my bike with a steering wheel, but since no gearing is involved the continuous rim of the wheel would

[1]Or, to be more mathematically rigorous, inversely proportional to the radius of turn.
[2]I look back on the days, not so long ago, when there was a fourth pedal (to the left of the clutch) which was the dip-switch for the headlights.

be superfluous, and would merely get in the way of one's knees. The handlebars perform essentially the same function as the steering wheel of the car, providing a yawing angle which is directly related to the yaw rate, but since a bicycle banks like an aircraft, there is also a pitch rate component during a turn. The intuitiveness of the turning direction of bicycle handlebars is absolutely essential, since fine rapid adjustment is often required to coordinate the yaw rate with the bank angle, as competing in a 'slow bicycle race' (in which the last rider to reach the end of a straight track of narrow lanes without putting a foot on the ground is the winner) quickly demonstrates. If you have ever tried to ride a bicycle which has had the handlebars doctored with gears so that the front wheel turns in the opposite sense from that in which the handlebars are turned, you will almost certainly have found it impossible, and a sure way of making a good profit at a garden fête is to offer people a substantial prize for riding such a machine for a few yards!

Whereas the lateral (rolling) stability of a car, provided by the difference in the reaction force between the ground and the tyres on the two sides of the car, makes it unnecessary for the driver to do anything about 'coordinating' a turn, it is critical for the bicycle rider to coordinate the turn correctly. In a banked aircraft, the only result of not coordinating a turn is to sideslip, but the effect on a bicycle would be that the rider would fall off. The coordination is sensed by the rider feeling the reaction force of the road on the tyres acting directly through the centre of gravity, and is largely adjusted automatically by the usual arrangement whereby the forks are inclined forwards so that the contact point of the front wheel with the ground is a little way behind the point where the pivot axis of the forks meets the ground, as shown in Figure 11.1. By this means the wheel trails behind the pivot line like the castors on a piece of furniture, always following in the right direction. (The curvature of the forks is not provided for this purpose but to give a measure of springing for comfort and good handling over bumps, since scarcely any springing is available from the wheel or the frame. This curvature actually *diminishes* the castor action somewhat.) Because of the built-in castor action, it is possible to ride a bicycle hands-off, even whilst gently turning, but the handlebars are available for providing an overriding yawing input if required to correct for imbalance, and for managing tighter turns. The speed 'control' (or power input) on the pedal-bicycle is once again given over to the legs and feet (perhaps reminiscent of spurring a horse) and although hands are usually used for braking, some bikes are provided with a back-pedal brake on the rear wheel.

The development of motorcycles provides a rather intriguing case study of the way in which the speed and steering control problem has

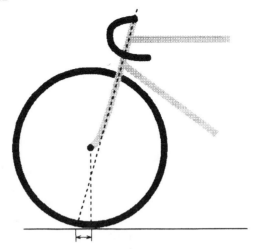

Figure 11.1   Castor action on a bicycle

been tackled. Whilst handlebars are used for steering, the conventional speed controls have evolved into an arrangement which seems to be very little influenced by intuition, even if ergonomic. The primary speed control, the throttle, is usually a twist-grip in the right hand, which the rider turns towards himself or herself to accelerate – an action which can sometimes be dangerously accentuated when the cycle accelerates hard, throwing the rider backwards and opening the throttle further. The twist-grip throttle is also to be found on helicopters (in the pilot's left hand), but it is virtually unknown apart from in these two applications. However, it is the braking and clutch and gear control on a motorcycle which is such a surprise. Brakes are usually operated by one hand (in addition to the throttle) and one foot, whilst the other hand and the other foot are used for clutch and gear control respectively. One would think that there ought to be a better way!

If a boat is propelled with a substantial outboard motor which is yawed relative to the boat to produce a turn and the line of action of the propeller is below the centre of gravity, the sideways component of the propeller thrust produces a rolling moment, and the boat may bank inwards during a turn. But in all boats with a conventional rudder there is (to a good approximation) no banking and a turn occurs purely in the horizontal plane, as with a car. In either case, whether banked or level, the centripetal force is produced *only* by the sideways force of the water on the hull as the boat sideslips. (The yawed outboard motor propeller actually applies an *outward* force, making even greater demands on the side-force due to sideslip.) On shallow-draught sailing boats a deep keel or a centreboard is virtually essential for producing sufficient side-force when sideslipping, both during a turn and also to resist the sideways component of the wind force on the sails. Without it the boat will be scarcely controllable, but will just skid across the surface of the water.

Boat rudders are controlled by directly coupled tillers or linked steering wheels, any such device being referred to by the old Norse-derived word 'helm'. On rowing boats the coxswain is often some distance from the rudder at the stern, and in this case a horizontal transverse bar may be attached to the top of the rudder, with a pull-cord attached to each end of it, and these cords are taken forwards to the hands of the cox who sits facing the front. If the cords were to be crossed over, the movement of the hands of the coxswain would be identical in sense to that of the handlebars on a bicycle, which as we have seen is very intuitive – to yaw to the right, push the left hand forward as the right hand moves backward – which is also the same way that the hands move on a steering wheel of a road vehicle. But in practice the cords are usually not crossed, and this means that the coxswain's action has to be exactly the opposite from that of the cyclist – as on the rigged garden-fête machine – and the right hand must move forward to yaw the boat to the right! Clearly a completely different thought process is involved, so perhaps it is just as well that the balance of the boat is not dependent on the cox's coordination.

Aeroplanes

With this very diverse range of ways of tackling the left-right fast-slow control challenge of terrestrial vehicles, the designers of the first aeroplanes had a wealth of different ideas to draw upon. Which should they use? Or, since they now had to add up-down to the inventory, should they start again from scratch? The primary objectives must surely be intuitiveness and consistency, since the pilot has a large number of different considerations to deal with at any one time, and as with a bicycle a quick and appropriate response demands not having to perform a tortuous mental exercise to work out what to do.

Arriving at the correct answer (if there be a correct answer) to this question must depend on analysing what differences the addition of the extra dimension makes, particularly in carrying out the basic manoeuvre which corresponds to steering a terrestrial vehicle, that of doing a horizontal turn[3]. The first difference is that an aircraft must

[3]Incidentally, a rudder-induced turn as discussed in the section of Chapter 9 headed 'The Other Way of Turning' corresponds closely with a turn on a car or a boat, since the centripetal force and yaw rate are both produced automatically, but as we have seen this is aerodynamically not the most efficient way to turn an aircraft. This makes it clear why so many people wrongly regard the rudder as a primary turning control of an aircraft.

bank to achieve its centripetal force from the wing lift, but in this it differs little from a bicycle, except in the way the roll into the bank is achieved, which we have already dealt with thoroughly in each case. But the second difference is that, whereas the magnitude of the centripetal force provision (through friction) is self-determining for a road vehicle, it must be controlled in an aircraft by altering the lift coefficient. So the continuous yawing action required of a car is replaced by the temporary rolling followed by the sustained alteration to pitch trim on the aircraft.

So what should the designer do? Experience dictates that the hands (rather than the feet) should be the primary steering control operators, but steering wheels and handlebars are conventionally displacement-type yaw controls, and yaw control is not a primary requirement in turning an aircraft. In fact the only sustained control input during a turn is the pitch trim change, and since this is a symmetrical operation unaffected by whether turning right or left, its control will not satisfy the needs of telling the aircraft which way to turn.

The answer seems to lie in approaching the problem from a fundamentally different standpoint. The pilot must get right away from thinking in terms of a turn as a sustained yaw rate, but rather must think of the aircraft as a projectile which can fly in any direction, either in a straight line or a curved path, and the controls are simply the devices for orientating it correctly for this required flight path. Since this requires being able to rotate the aircraft about any one or more of the three perpendicular axes, three different modes of directional control are required. That seems a lot to demand of the hands (although not impossible), and so use of both hands and feet seems appropriate.

Rudder-bar or Pedals
Which mode should be assigned to what type of hand or foot movement? Since yawing is essentially not a primary aircraft control requirement, it seems reasonable to relegate its control to the feet, and hence the rudder is, and has traditionally been, controlled by what might be thought of as handlebars operated by the feet, a rudder-bar or a pair of pedals linked to act differentially in the same manner as a handlebar. The choice then arises as to which sense they should be made to operate in: like a bicycle's handlebar, which as we have seen is undoubtedly highly intuitive, or like the uncrossed rudder-cords of the rowing boat, which act in the opposite sense and seem to be contra-intuitive? Much to the surprise of many people, the latter choice has been made for the aircraft rudder-bar or pedals, so that the right foot, like the coxswain's right hand, must be pushed forward to yaw to the right. Some pilots will say that this is intuitive, but bicycle-riding

and lorry-driving and bus-driving experience would suggest, rather, that the operation of aircraft rudder pedals is a learned skill. When on the ground the steering of an aircraft corresponds much more closely with turning a car, and independent undercarriage wheel brakes and/or a steerable undercarriage wheel are linked to the rudder pedals (or similar closely integrated foot controls) in order to allow the feet to steer the aircraft when taxiing. Here the control movement is quite decidedly more akin to that of the rowing boat than that of the car or bicycle.

Column or Yoke

Since the pitching and rolling control of the aircraft have to be integrated so closely for carrying out turning manoeuvres, a combined hand control has been found to be the best solution. It would be very satisfactory if the movement of the control inside the cockpit could mimic the response of the aircraft to that control relative to its surroundings. Conveniently a simple vertical stick, universally jointed *below* hand level, does this very nicely, as it can be pulled (rotated) back to resemble pitching the aircraft nose-up, or pushed forward for pitching nose-down; and it can be tilted to the right (or left) to correspond with the aircraft tilting (rolling) to the right (or left). Thus the conventional control column, with fore-and-aft movement coupled to elevators and side-to-side movement linked to ailerons, emerged as the standard. There have even been some aircraft with control columns mounted at the top of the cockpit and projecting downwards, but although movements to front, back, left and right were conventional, the resulting rotation of the column about the overhead pivot was in the opposite sense from that of the resulting aircraft rotations, so the system could be confusing. (A good analogy would be steering a car with your hands on the bottom of the steering wheel rim, which demands a non-intuitive input.)

Perhaps because of the desire to use two hands on the control, perhaps to clear the space above the pilot's knees of obstruction, but I suspect chiefly because it offers a greater air of dignity and conformity with the conventional and customary steering wheel of a ground vehicle, the control column has been and is very frequently replaced by a device similar to the steering wheel of a car (not of a bus or lorry), which is called a yoke. The yoke is rotated clockwise about a fore-and-aft axis to activate ailerons for a roll to the right, and *vice versa*. It is moved forward or backward (either on a sliding shaft, or by being mounted at the top of a column pivoted at the base) to operate the elevators, in the sense corresponding to that of a control column.

The aeronautical meaning of this word yoke does not appear in many dictionaries, but it is clearly derived from the nautical meaning in which it refers to the cross-piece (mentioned earlier) which is attached to the top of a boat's rudder, and to which steering cords, or 'yoke-lines', are fastened. Thus the idea is closely associated historically (but inappropriately) with the handlebar concept. Occasionally a full-circle wheel has been used, as on some early big transport aircraft and seaplanes, but large rotational movements are not desirable since the control must be centralised once the turn is initiated, and must be turned in the opposite direction to produce a roll out of the turn. Therefore yoke rotations today are limited to around 90° each way, making the continuous rim of a full-circle wheel unnecessary because the hands never need to move away from their starting position. This means that the top of the wheel can conveniently be cut away to give better forward visibility of the instruments or over the coaming, and the bottom to create more leg-room. As a result the yoke today more closely resembles handlebars than a steering wheel, except that its axis of rotation is nearer to horizontal than to vertical and its function is very different from either.

Speed Controls

So, with both hands and feet occupied with the directional control of the aeroplane, what about speed control? This is not as continuously demanding as on a car, and fortunately it is usually possible to handle the control column or yoke most of the time with one hand, and so in flight the control of an aircraft's speed is entirely assigned to the hands[4]. This is a major departure from the conventional practice of using the feet (perhaps augmented by the hands) for controlling the speed of virtually all land vehicles since the horse, but corresponds with the usual practice on boats, probably because, as in an aircraft, boat speed control is not continuously demanding. The helmsman of larger boats have traditionally worked standing up so that feet are not readily available for control, but in the case of the aeroplane it seems that the pilot's feet are remarkably underutilised even though he or she is sitting down. One wonders whether this is a throwback to the misunderstanding about the way in which an aircraft is turned, and that the rudder-bar assumed too much significance in the thinking of the early designers. In earlier aircraft much more rudder compensation was in fact required because of adverse aileron yaw and other asymmetric effects, and the legs were the strongest limbs for holding an aircraft against the yawing moment resulting from a failed engine on one side. But today with better aerodynamic design, more reliable engines and power-operated controls, one wonders whether pilot interface development has been unnecessarily held back by the

---

[4]Toe- or heel-operated foot brakes operating on the undercarriage wheels are often used for braking control on the ground.

ingrained tradition of the pilot's feet operating rudder pedals and nothing else. It is not inconceivable to incorporate rudder control into a yoke, (rotating it about a vertical axis) or even into a control column, which has the extra dimension of twist available to the designer, and so perhaps there *might* be alternative and better ways of designing the pilot interface than we have grown accustomed to, utilising the underoccupied feet either for speed control or for some other tasks. However, tradition dies hard, and ours is not to speculate, but to deal with the *status quo*.

We have seen already that there are two primary flying controls whose action has to be coordinated to control the speed and height of flight – the pitch control and the throttle. There is also a variety of additional controls, varying considerably according to type, which in one way or another affect the speed (or height) of an aircraft, and these can be basically classified into two groups: those which are power related, performing engine and propulsion system management functions such as propeller pitch, reverse thrust and carburettor choke and heating controls; and those which alter the aerodynamic configuration of the aircraft such as flap, air brake, spoiler and undercarriage selectors. But as a general rule they all have two things in common: firstly, they are all hand operated; and secondly, they all (where possible and appropriate) adopt the convention that 'forward is faster and backward is slower', except in the case where the controls are replaced by elecrical switches.

Once again it is debatable whether this convention is intuitive or not. It certainly follows the example given by the control column or yoke, which is pulled back to trim for lower speeds and pushed forwards for higher speeds, and it is almost certainly this which led to the convention being adopted in the first place. Furthermore, to move something along, on wheels or sliding on the ground, one pushes in the intended direction of motion, and if it is running away one pulls back on it (as also on the reins of a horse) to slow it down. However, a motorcycle's throttle twist-grip works the other way: with wrist and back of hand over the top of the twist-grip, the rider must pull back with the arm in order to open the throttle, and it could be argued that this is more intuitive than the other way, since it is the natural way the body moves as a result of the acceleration of the bike beneath the rider. Perhaps on balance the 'forward is faster' rule is the more intuitive, in which case once again the motorcycle finds itself out on a limb!

To enable the 'forward is faster' rule to be implemented, aircraft throttle (or power) controls are usually either quadrant levers (on larger aircraft) which rotate about a pivot below the handle in the same way as a control column, or push-pull knobs on stems which slide into and out of the instrument panel in front of the pilot. There is no consistent rule as to which hand should operate them, but often there is only one (or one set), placed between the two pilots' seats so that the hand to use depends on which side the pilot is sitting. Gliders, which have no power control as such, treat the air brake or spoiler control in the same manner as a throttle, and therefore pulling back deploys the air-brakes or spoilers, and pushing forward retracts them. This is perhaps a little confusing in the case of air brakes, since they are usually used to achieve a steeper dive without undue increase in speed, and of course diving is more naturally associated with pushing a control forward. Flap control levers and (when operated by a mechanical lever) undercarriage deployment controls also adhere to the same principle: since both are associated with slowing down, both are deployed by pulling the control rearwards.

Hovercraft

In 1955 Christopher Cockerell, an electronics engineer and amateur boat-builder from Suffolk, patented his forward-looking invention of the hovercraft, or air cushion vehicle, which offered the possibility of carrying the loads associated with large ships at far higher speed, by means of staying just above the water and so avoiding the substantial drag penalty of ploughing through it. By 1968 the concept had been sufficiently developed for the introduction of large passenger-carrying and vehicle-carrying hovercraft, the first being the SR-N4 (the initials standing for 'Saunders Roe', the makers, and the 'N' simply for 'number') which was then licensed to carry 254 passengers and 30 cars across the English Channel, and this was quickly followed by a handful of others.

It is indisputable that a hovercraft is an aircraft, and that its motion may properly be called flying, since its entire support, propulsion, stability and control are all provided purely by aerostatic and aerodynamic forces. But from an aircraft point of view its shape is very unconventional. Since its lift is achieved by fan engines maintaining a small excess pressure above atmospheric pressure over its entire underside, its weight must be kept as light, and its plan area as large, as possible, and for this the best planform shape is a circle, in stark contrast with the cruciform shape of an aeroplane. Although thrust for the hovercraft could, as on aeroplanes, be provided by propellers, its means of producing lift meant that the craft could not bank to produce a centripetal component of lift for turning. Consequently its method of achieving aerodynamic control had to be thought out from scratch, as did the pilot interface through which it would be handled.

This gave rise to a very interesting debate. Being an aircraft, it was perhaps natural to lean towards the customary arrangement of aircraft

controls rather than those of land vehicles. But there were several crucial differences. First of all, it was limited to motion in two dimensions, a flat surface, so that no variation in height was called for, which
might perhaps have drawn the developers towards the control philosophy of a land-locked vehicle. Secondly, there was no natural fore-
and-aft axis, no keel or any other feature to constrain motion against
any tendency to sideslip, and no aerodynamic reason why the hovercraft should go in any one direction rather than in any other. Had it
not been for the desirability of having a 'front' where the flight deck
could be permanently placed with the pilot looking 'forward', and for
the way in which a compass fixed in the craft always gives the heading,
or 'forward'-pointing direction, of the craft itself (rather than the
direction of the vehicle's track over the sea or ground), maybe the
hovercraft could have been exactly circular in planform, and designed
never to need to yaw at all, always being orientated in the same direction, with the ability for its thrusting propellers to be orientated
through a full 360° in azimuth to propel it in any required direction.
Thirdly, whereas a flying aeroplane is always moving forward at a substantial air speed, a hovercraft can hover with no forward speed, and
therefore needs to be fully controllable in the hover – fore-and-aft,
sideways, and rotating about its centre – even when hovering on a
slope such as a landing ramp. No previous vehicle apart from the helicopter had presented a similar control challenge, and the solutions
adopted for the helicopter very firmly reflect the fact that it also has to
cope with the third, upward, dimension. Despite these differences, the
hovercraft developers still decided that the pilot system should as
closely as possible correspond with that of a conventional aeroplane,
perhaps believing that aeroplane pilots were the best breed of people
to fly these new machines.

Very few commercial hovercraft have ever been built, and so the
control philosophy has never had the opportunity to mature in the
same way as that of conventional aircraft. In fact the solutions
adopted for the SR-N4, whether optimum or not (which is doubtful)
are the only ones which can today be considered, since the two
machines of this class (now larger than at first due to body 'stretching') plying regularly between Dover and Calais are the only two
operational large car-carrying commercial hovercraft in the world.
They still perform a successful commercial operation since the speed
and convenience are desirable to customers, but it is unlikely that hovercraft design will ever develop to its full, simply because hovercraft
economics is being outstripped by that of other (waterborne) vehicles
which have the potential to provide similar advantages at lower initial
and operating costs.

General Control Principles

So what were the solutions arrived at, as adopted in the SR-N4? In answering this, let us look first at the means provided for aerodynamic control, which are very extensive and (probably) more than adequate. The approximately rectangular plan view is about twice as long (fore-and-aft) as it is wide, and near the corners of the roof are four large aircraft-type propellers mounted on pylons uniformly dispersed about the hovercraft's centre. These pylons, and hence the propellers' thrust lines, can each be independently yawed through an angle of plus or minus 35°, although usually they yaw as a forward pair and an aft pair. Also each of the propellers is equipped with variable pitch controlled by a separate hand lever, by means of which its thrust can be smoothly varied from full ahead to not-quite-so-full astern[5]. Thus the thrust vector of each of the propeller units can be varied both in magnitude and direction in a very versatile manner. In addition to these propeller-pylon units, there is a pair of large vertical fins mounted immediately behind the rear propellers in their slipstream, and these fins can be deflected through 30° both clockwise and anticlockwise. A number of configurations are shown in Figure 11.2, the first (diagram (a)) representing the positions of the pylons and fins in the normal setting for forward motion. In these planform figures, forwards is up the page, the rectangular lip at the top representing the bow loading ramp and the egg-shape just behind it the flight deck which is on the roof. The 'rudder'-bar and yoke are represented in grey superimposed on the flight deck, the 'rudder' being in its true orientation but the yoke being shown as viewed by the seated pilot. In diagram (a) these are both shown in their neutral positions.

Before discussing how this multiplicity of angular parameters is linked to the pilot's controls, let us see what the requirements are, and how these are achieved with the various adjustments that are available. I suggest that you ignore the cockpit controls in this our first look through the various diagrams of Figure 11.2, and afterwards we will revisit the diagrams with emphasis on the pilot's actions. First of all, because it is closer to our familiar stomping ground, let us see how the pylons and fins are used to control the hovercraft in normal cruising flight with a substantial forward air speed. As in a conventional aircraft a sideways (centripetal) force at right-angles to the forward velocity vector is required to maintain the craft in a circular path during a turn, and the very small yawing rate during the turn (which is the same magnitude as the turn rate) can be easily taken care of by the

---

[5]Interestingly the rear propellers have a slightly higher maximum positive pitch, probably because in straight-ahead cruising flight they operate in the slipstream of the front propellers, so that the axial velocity of the air reaching them is somewhat higher than the hovercraft's air speed.

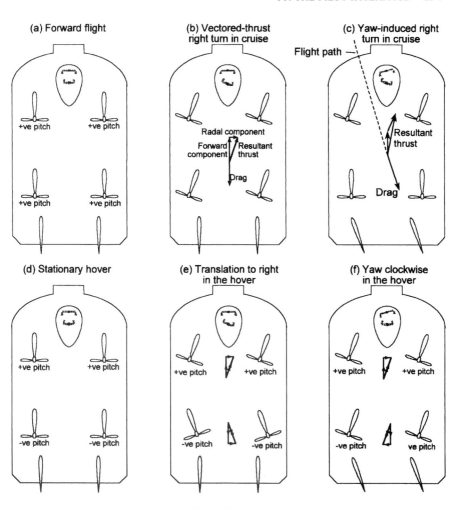

Figure 11.2   Hovercraft control configurations

directional stability provided by the fins without any deflection. This may be achieved by simply pointing all the pylons to one side in unison, as shown in Figure 11.2(b) for a turn to the right. This produces a sideways component of thrust from the propellers, and being equally dispersed about the centre of gravity, or more accurately the turning centre[6], they will not exert any yawing moment. The uninitiated

[6]This turning centre is theoretically the centre of gravity, but in practice its location is modified by the fact that the hovercraft must be maintained level by varying the lift in different regions of its plan area, with the consequence that some asymmetric water-interference drag occurs.

(unlike you) might suppose that this would produce a linear velocity in the direction of the propeller axes, or in other words a resultant velocity consisting of forward and sideslip velocity components, but this is not the case. The total thrust vector (of all four propellers combined) is shown split into its forward component and its sideways component in the velocity triangle superimposed on the centre of the roof in diagram (b). Now in a constant-speed cruise the forward component of thrust is exactly balanced by the total drag of the hovercraft[7], so that fore-and-aft the craft is in equilibrium and Newton's First Law of no acceleration applies. But there is no sideways force opposing the sideways component of the thrust, and so this component produces the required centripetal force to cause an inward radial acceleration, and thus maintain a circular flight path.

Just as there is with an aeroplane, there is an alternative approach to turning the hovercraft to the right during forward flight, and that is to yaw it clockwise from its flight path about its centre of gravity, which may be achieved by orientating front pylons as shown in diagram (c) of Figure 11.2. The fins are aligned with the new flight path as shown, so that the N_v directional stability will provide the small sustained yaw rate of the turn, exactly as with an aircraft. In a conventional aircraft the secondary effects which are produced by a yaw automatically produce a bank angle, so that wing lift provides the centripetal force required, but that can't happen here. Instead, in the case of the hovercraft, the propellers are producing a thrust component along the dashed flight path, and are also providing a centripetal component normal to this flight path. In other words, the overall thrust has been redirected inwards by yawing the craft itself (rather than just the pylons, as in the first turning method), producing a centripetal force component to the right so that a circular path is followed.

Although the first approach is the proper one for a conventional aircraft with its ability to bank, this second method is actually better than the first in the case of the hovercraft, as may be understood by considering the forces acting on the passengers during the turn. The first method is exactly analogous to a car going round a bend, the longitudinal axis always being directed along the tangent of the curved path, and as in a car it is the sideways friction between seats and bottoms which provides the passengers with their own personal centripetal force, so that they feel as if they are being thrown outwards, which is uncomfortable. On the other hand, by the second method some of the centripetal force is provided as a component of the thrust

---

[7]This total drag is ideally purely aerodynamic, but in practice it will include an element of water interference as the skirt scrapes along the water, especially in choppy conditions.

force which acts directly forwards through the passengers' backs, by pressure from the seat-back, so that there is less sense of sliding outwards on the seat. We may therefore regard this second method as a proper, or more balanced, turn for a hovercraft, somewhat analogous to the banked turn of the aircraft.

Now let us turn our thoughts to the stationary hover, for which the pylons and fins are all aligned straight ahead as shown in Figure 11.2(d). Remember that all the propellers are spinning, so if they all had positive pitch the craft would be accelerating forwards, which we do not want just yet. If they were all set to zero pitch, they could not be used to provide other forces and moments to manoeuvre the hovercraft in the hover, and so that would not do either. Instead, the front propellers are set at about half maximum forward pitch, and the rear ones at about half maximum reverse pitch, trying to pull the front and back of the hovercraft apart.

From this static hovering position it is required to make the hovercraft capable of moving without rotation (*translating*) in any direction, and also of rotating about its centre, since total control is a combination of these abilities. For this the pilot requires control over the fore-and-aft force, the side-force and the yawing moment about the centre of gravity. Fore-and-aft force is controlled simply by varying the pitch of the propeller blades, but the other motions involve manipulation of the pylon and fin yaw angles as shown in Figure 11.2 (e) and (f).

Diagram (e) shows the arrangement required for translational motion to the right. Both front and rear propellers must exert an equal force component to the right, so that their yawing moments about the turning centre cancel out. The front propellers have a positive pitch setting, so they must be yawed clockwise to produce this force component, but the rear propellers are in negative pitch and are pulling backwards, and so *they* must be yawed anticlockwise. Front pair and rear pair force vector diagrams are shown to illustrate the resulting sideways forces which translate the hovercraft to the right without yawing. If this motion were continued for a sustained period, the fins would provide a side drag at the rear and thus a clockwise yawing moment, so that the craft would begin to turn towards the direction of its motion.

The pylon arrangement required for yawing the craft clockwise about its centre of gravity without going anywhere is shown in diagram (f), in which all pylons are rotated clockwise so that the front ones produce a side-force component to the right and the rear ones, because of their negative pitch, pull to the left. You will notice that the fins are also deflected, in the same way as they would be for a yawed flight path in forward cruising flight, but in fact in the hover they are not achieving anything.

The Hovercraft Pilot Interface

We now bring in the pilot, whom we would like to equip with controls which, it has been decided, should be as similar as possible in function to aircraft controls. In the aircraft, the pedal bar produced yawing (although only of peripheral usefulness), rotating the yoke produced rolling (but not turning) and pushing and pulling on the yoke gave pitch control. The pitch control requirement would seem to be redundant on the hovercraft since this craft does not need to vary lift in the turn, nor does it have to climb or descend or to be trimmed longitudinally to cope with changes in speed (except that drag exerts a nose-up pitching moment which is speed dependent). However, some control over the undesirable pitching motion on a swelling sea is required, and so a feature is incorporated by which the lift distribution between front and back can be temporarily adjusted by power sharing between the lift fans and thrust propellers, and to match the aircraft pilot's customary control movement this is controlled by pushing the yoke fore-and-aft. But this need not concern us, since it is not a primary turning control mode.

That leaves turning the yoke by hand and pressing with feet on the pedal bar. Certainly the yoke cannot be a roll control as on aeroplanes, so do we need two controls? Are there two distinct functions to be performed? Let us examine this question firstly for the forward cruising case, as depicted in diagrams (b) and (c) of Figure 11.2. We can indeed identify two distinct modes of control: firstly the *side-force* without moment which in diagram (b) is producing the centripetal force whilst the craft is pointing along the path's tangent; and secondly the *yawing moment* which produces an angle between hovercraft longitudinal axis and flight path. The first is exactly like steering a car (as we have already seen), and so the yoke, reminiscent of the steering wheel, is found to be an appropriate control for achieving this as shown superimposed on the flight deck in diagram (b). As with a car steering wheel, it is a displacement control, to be held in the turned position throughout the turn and then centralised when the turn is completed, rather than being a rate control (like the aircraft's roll control) which adjusts the rate of entering and of exiting from a turn.

So in the cruise the hovercraft *can* be controlled exactly like a car, in which case the passengers and crew experience the same feeling of being thrown sideways as they do in a car. (The rate of turn is limited by the angle to which the pylons can rotate, and thus the amount of centripetal force available, but if pylon angles were allowed to be greater there would be too much of a sacrifice of forward thrust.) But we saw earlier that this is not the best way of turning a hovercraft, and tighter and more comfortable turns may be achieved by yawing it in towards the centre. The pedals (reminiscent of aeroplane rudder pedals) are provided for the purpose of yawing, and on their own (in the cruise) they would transiently turn the front pylons inward and the rear ones outward, (not shown in Figure 11.2), using the quaint but standard convention of right foot forward to yaw to the right. In practice, however, although eliminating the side-force on the passengers, this would give a compass heading (direction in which the nose is pointing)[8] inside the required curved flight path, which would be less visually acceptable to the pilot than pointing along the tangent path – the tighter the turn, the more inward-pointing would be required. It would also sacrifice too much forward thrust.

Therefore a compromise is adopted of using 'some of each', a right turn of the yoke coupled with a right foot forward on the yaw pedal bar, by means of which the pilot can obtain a good 'balanced' turn, as shown in diagram (c). Aeroplane pilots brought up in the 'coordinating stick and rudder' school through the need to compensate for adverse aileron yaw were therefore happy that the new skill did not involve a major rethink, but merely getting used to a somewhat different feel.

How do these conventions carry over to the hover? Fore-and-aft movement is controlled by the use of hand-lever-adjusted variable pitch. Yawing on the spot is, instinctively for the aeroplane pilot, achieved by operation of the pedals in the conventional way, as shown in diagram (f). Sideways motion, however, has no direct analogy in any other type of vehicle (except for the helicopter), and so it is found quite convenient to adopt the same control motion, the turning of the yoke, as used to achieve a side-force and hence a car-type turn in the cruise. Thus the hovercraft in diagram (e), with yoke turned to the right, will be travelling directly to the right without yawing (until the fin drag becomes effective).

So, in all, a fairly complex system of variables has to be linked to a combination of yoke, hand levers and foot pedals in such a manner that all the required functions are achieved when the appropriate control demands are made by the pilot. The complexity involved in this is well illustrated by a comparison between diagrams (b) and (e) of Figure 11.2, where exactly the same yoke command achieves different pylon orientations simply as a result of there being a different distribution of propeller blade pitch settings in the two cases; or between diagrams (b) and (c), which shows that the pedal bar is not just a

---

[8]Since during the turn there is a fixed yaw angle, the direction that we have here called the compass heading is not the hovercraft's heading by the usual definition of the word. The actual heading is the direction of the flight path relative to the air, which is the tangent to the turning circle, and for clarity this is sometimes referred to as the 'heading made good'.

'rudder'-bar but also has an influence on the pylon orientations[9]. So we cannot say that the yoke controls this whilst the pedal bar deals with that and the pitch variation levers cope with the other – rather, the inputs from all the pilot's controls are mixed through a very sophisticated control mixing box, and thence transmitted to the hydraulically operated mechanisms.

Maybe if the hovercraft were assured of a more secure future the means of controlling it might mature in a way that departed from its not entirely appropriate modification of conventional aircraft controls. But, sadly, it is likely that the hovercraft is a dying breed, and although Hoverspeed hope to be able to operate the two SR-N4s for another 25 years, eventually they are likely to be mere museum exhibits reminding us of a fascinating and successful experiment in manned flight. However, the time we have spent considering their *modus operandi* is far from wasted, since the hovercraft control concepts illustrate very well yet another manifestation of the dynamics of a body subject to Newton's laws, and reflecting on them can help to hone our minds to a sharper awareness of these principles. Becoming 'flightwise' involves delving beyond the facts to understand their significance, and I for one have added to my understanding of aircraft control through making this comparative study, as I hope you have. But enough: we must get back to conventional aircraft.

TRIM (PILOT'S MEANING)

We have been using the word 'trim' freely and fluently for a number of chapters now, and have become familiar with thinking of the word as used by the engineer rather than the pilot. But now that we are discussing control very specifically from the pilot's point of view, we must switch over and adopt the pilot's usage of this word. Near the beginning of Chapter 4 on Longitudinal Static Stability, there was a section headed 'Trim', in which the difference between the two uses of the word by engineers and pilots was explained in some detail, and it is on the foundation of that section that we develop the discussion further now. A reread of that section may be helpful to you, but as a link we will repeat its final paragraph here before going any further.

An engineer considers an aircraft to be trimmed if there is no resultant moment (about the axis in question) and thus the aircraft is in rotational equilibrium. The pilot, on the other hand, says that an aircraft is trimmed (about a given axis) if the moments are balanced out, and *if in addition* the aerodynamic trimming devices are adjusted cor-

---

[9]The pilot is provided with the alternative facilities of locking two or all four of the pylons in the straight-ahead position in the cruise, and using just the fins controlled by the 'rudder'-bar for steering. But in practice this mode of operation is not usually used.

rectly so that the pilot himself is not having to apply trimming moments through his controls.

By far the most important control surface to be equipped with some form of trimming device is the elevator, since as we have seen the elevator has to be routinely adjusted to different positions, so as to produce different aerodynamic forces, depending on the aircraft's speed in level flight, and on the tightness of a turn in manoeuvres. Thus without a trimming device the pilot would nearly always need to be exerting either a steady push or a steady pull on the control column, unnecessarily occupying both hand and mind. On the other hand, except during a turn (which is a short-lived state) the ailerons should be in a neutral position, and any need to trim them will be against a constant asymmetry of load, probably weight, such as more fuel in one wing's tanks than in the other. Likewise, the rudder will only need to be trimmed against any steady asymmetry in the thrust or drag forces on the two wings. In both of these latter two cases, once set the trimming devices will only need to be adjusted occasionally. But just as elevators, ailerons and rudder all work on the same fundamental principle, so the methods of trimming them can be applied to any of the three.

The need is to replace a pilot's force on a control surface by another force which is adjustable by the pilot but is applied automatically. One obvious way in which this can be achieved is to provide an arrangement of friction or springs acting on the control column and rudder-bar in the cockpit, but this immediately implies that the pilot needs to apply an additional force when moving the controls to overcome the resistance, and as we shall see later, efforts have to be made to reduce the control forces required. Therefore an alternative solution is required.

The solution is to use aerodynamic force to do the job, and this is achieved by the use of *trim tabs*. Just as the lift on a flying surface such as a wing, fin or tailplane can be increased or decreased by the use of a control surface hinged at the back of it, so the force on the control surface can itself be increased or decreased by attaching a smaller hinged flap, known as a tab, to its rear edge, as shown in Figure 11.3. In this figure, a downward force is required to hold the main control surface in its downward-deflected position against the additional lift-force that

Figure 11.3   Trim tab

it is generating (a large proportion of which is created by the control surface itself, as shown in Figure 10.4). The required downward force on the control surface is achieved by deflecting the tab, the smaller control surface, *upwards* as shown. Now of course the resulting downward aerodynamic force on the control surface itself produced by the tab is in opposition to the overall additional upward force that the control surface is supposed to be generating, but this is small by comparison and is of little concern. The important outcome is that the moment (called the *hinge moment*) required to hold the main control surface in its deflected position is easily provided by the tab because the tab is located far behind the control surface hinge line.

A linkage is required between the cockpit and the trim tab so that the pilot can control the tab completely independently of the control surface to which it is attached. No attempt has been made in Figure 11.3 to show the mechanism by which the trim tab is controlled, but suffice it to say that there must be a pilot-operated control for each trim tab, and that these controls should have a mode of movement in the cockpit which is intuitive and directly associated with the sense of the related primary control. The trim tabs must be capable of very fine adjustment, which means that considerable gearing down must occur between the trim control and the trim tab. For this reason handwheels are frequently used which turn through a number of full circles and can be rotated by light hand force.

The use of such trim wheels provides a natural approach for their intuitive orientation, each wheel's axis being aligned parallel to the aircraft axis about which its related control surface(s) produces moments and rotations. Thus a rudder trim wheel has its plane horizontal and axis vertical like the steering wheel of a bus or lorry, the aileron trim wheel is orientated like that of a car, and the elevator trim wheel rotates fore-and-aft about a transverse axis. Usually the trim controls are made physically smaller than the related primary controls, but on some large airliners and transport aircraft of the past three very large trim wheels the size of steering wheels have made the flight deck look a bit like a boiler-room with large hand-valves. A number of alternatives to the trim wheel are also used, such as small levers or for electrically operated tabs rocker-switches which may be mounted on the control column. Occasionally the pilot is not helped by having a thoroughly non-intuitive trim control, such as a ceiling-mounted rotatable handle reminiscent of the control for opening the sun-roof of a car. Perhaps this might be appropriate for a rudder trim tab control, but when used (as it has been) for pitch trim one is totally at a loss to see any possible link between the sense of rotation and the resulting pitch-up or pitch-down trim change.

In passing before we leave the subject of trim tabs, mention must be made of the fixed tab. This works in exactly the same manner as the pilot-controlled trim tab, but is not linked to the cockpit at all and can only be adjusted when on the ground. Very often a fixed tab is simply a small strip of flexible metal riveted to the trailing edge of the control surface which can be bent by hand. Its purpose is simply to trim out any imbalance of the controls which the pilot has reported from a previous flight. As such it would be inappropriate for the elevator, but can be useful on the rudder or ailerons of aircraft on which pilot-controlled trim tabs are not provided for these controls. A bit of careful logical thinking (and understanding of the aerodynamics involved) is required of the ground technician or pilot in order to adjust the fixed tab in the correct sense according to the imbalance reported in flight. For example, if the pilot has been having to maintain continuous foot pressure on the right rudder pedal during flight, the clockwise yawing moment that the rudder is required to produce necessitates a leftward force on the fin and so a deflection of the rudder to the right. To achieve this the fixed tab must be bent a little to the left. By similar reasoning, work out for yourself what would be required if the pilot reported the aircraft to be flying left-wing-heavy.

In Chapter 9, under the subheading 'Miscellaneous' in the section 'Types of Controls: Alternative Configurations' (page 220) it was mentioned that all-moving, or slab, tailplanes are sometimes used for the all-important pitch control of the aircraft. Very often this is the case in transonic or supersonic aircraft, and these all-moving tailplanes are operated by power systems. This has given rise to the use of an alternative approach to trimming in pitch, which is sometimes known as the *flying tail*, and consists of an all-moving tailplane combined with a hinged elevator surface at the rear as well. Variation of the angle of attack of the all-moving tailplane is used for trimming the aircraft and the power supply for this is managed by the pilot's trim wheel or control, whilst the hinged elevator is operated by the pilot's primary cockpit control for short-lived control inputs in manoeuvres. By this means the drag produced by trimming the aircraft in pitch can be kept to much lower values, since an uncambered aerofoil at an angle of attack produces a considerably better lift:drag ratio than a cambered aerofoil producing the same lift, especially as the airflow disruption of the hinge-line is eliminated.

LARGE CONTROL FORCES

As aircraft grew larger, the force which a pilot could exert on the cockpit controls began to become insufficient to cope with handling the control surfaces with their ever increasing aerodynamic loads and consequent growing hinge moments. The first and most obvious solution might seem to be to provide better leverage or gearing to the cockpit controls themselves. A control column simply needs to be twice as long from its pivot upwards in order to halve the force required to achieve the same result at the control surface, and by replacing a yoke with a wheel it can be geared down to rotate through a full turn or more without having to cross the hands over. The trouble is that there is a limit to the amount of hand (and foot) movement which is acceptable, or even possible, within the confines of the pilot's seat or the cockpit. The top of a double-length column moves twice as far (from side-to-side or fore-and-aft) for the same control surface deflection angle; it just takes too long to turn a steering wheel round and round, twice as often as when steering a car because of also having to roll *out of* a turn; and there is a physiological limit to the distance a seated pilot's feet can move forwards and backwards.

As with trimming the controls, once again aerodynamic solutions were sought, and a number were found and have been adopted. The techniques used are collectively referred to as *aerodynamically balancing* the controls. Because an aerofoil's lift is distributed in the manner of Figure 10.4, one very direct solution is to move, or *inset*, the hinge-line of the control surface away from its leading edge and back to some intermediate point along its chord, so that its nose overhangs the hinge as shown in Figure 11.4, tending to deflect the control sur-

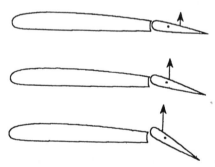

Figure 11.4 Aerodynamic balance by off-setting the hinge-line

face further. At the same time the control surface's cross-sectional shape may be improved a little to that of a better aerofoil profile, since its leading edge is now going to become exposed to the airflow and thereby aerodynamically active every time the surface is deflected. In plan view the insetting of the hinge may be implemented on an aileron by insetting the hinge-line in the manner shown on the left of Figure 11.5. A similar effect is achieved by the use of a *horn balance*, as shown on the right of the same figure, in which the tip of an elevator or rudder protrudes beyond the tailplane or fin tip, providing a substantial part of the aerodynamically active surface forward of

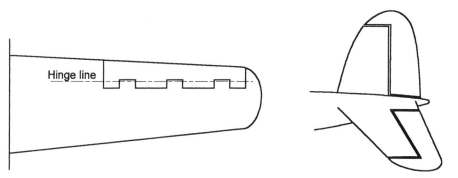

Figure 11.5   Inset hinge (left) and horn balance (right)

the hinge-line. The concept of the inset hinge provides ready accommodation for a mass to be placed inside the nose of the control for the purpose of preventing control flutter, as discussed at the end of Chapter 9.

The question arises as to how much overhang should be used, or how far the hinge-line should be inset, but unfortunately there can be no simple right answer. As the deflection of the control surface is increased (at a constant air speed), so the aerodynamic force on it not only grows but also moves forwards towards the leading edge, in the normal fashion of the migration of the centre of pressure of an aerofoil, as shown in Figure 11.4. At first during this movement the force grows and its distance from the hinge-line decreases, so that the moment, the product of the two, does not change too drastically. But when the centre of pressure passes in front of the hinge-line, the sense of the aerodynamic moment fairly suddenly changes to a negative value. *Now* the aerodynamic moment is trying to deflect the control surface further, and the pilot will have to apply a force on the cockpit control *back towards neutral* in order to restrain the control from being swept over to its full deflection. Furthermore, as the deflection continues to increase beyond this point, both the force and its distance from the hinge-line grow larger together, so that the decentralising moment may very rapidly become too large to be held by the pilot. This situation is known as *overbalance*, and is clearly a totally unsatisfactory state of affairs, since if the pilot does not firmly constrain the control it will cause a potentially very hazardous situation by going to full deflection, (known as a *hard-over* condition). Even if the pilot does hold it the resulting instability of the control deflection is a very undesirable feature from the pilot's point of view, and so the hinge-line should not be placed so far back as to allow this to occur.

The choice of best hinge-line position is further complicated by other considerations. First of all, if exposed to the airflow the leading edge of the control surface will produce large local suction forces when the control surface is deflected, in the manner of any aerofoil with a rounded leading edge, and this has the effect of bringing the centre of pressure forward. Thus both the degree to which the leading edge of the control surface is shielded by the main flying surface, and also the shape of the leading edge itself, will have a substantial influence on the centre of pressure position and movement. Secondly, greater control surface deflections are required at low air speeds than at high air speeds to produce the same moments, and so the extent of forward migration of the centre of pressure, and hence the optimum position for the hinge-line, will also depend on the speed of flight. But the speed of flight varies, whereas the hinge-line must be fixed, and this imposes very severe limitations on the usefulness of the inset hinge approach.

A variation of the inset hinge is to use an *internal balance*, as shown in Figure 11.6. In this case the portion of the aerofoil extending for-

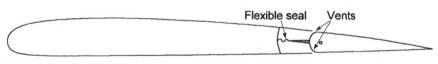

Figure 11.6   Internal balance

ward of the hinge line is in the form of a beak or paddle attached to the control surface's leading edge, which moves in a cavity between the upper and lower surfaces of the wing, tailplane or fin, and is connected to it by a flexible seal which prevents any flow of air between the upper and lower chambers of the cavity. Aerodynamic balance is obtained as a result of the difference in pressure between the upper and lower surfaces when the flap is deflected, and this pressure difference is transmitted to the cavities through the vents. This method has the advantage that the smooth contour of the flying surface does not need to be disrupted at the control surface leading edge, and virtually no air actually flows into and out of the cavities. Consequently quite a considerable saving in profile drag can be achieved. In the past the internal balance has been quite a common device, but being totally hidden from view it is not immediately obvious to the casual observer, and so is less familiar than other forms of aerodynamic balance. It does not address all of the problems discussed earlier with the inset hinge balance, and one additional disadvantage is that it limits

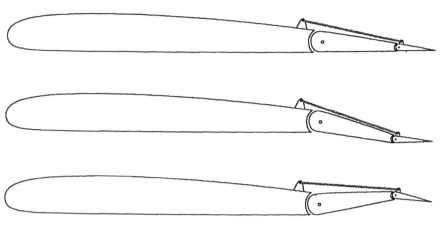

Figure 11.7   Geared tab

the maximum deflection angle that the control surface can move through.

Alternative approaches to the problem of balancing controls were therefore sought, and the most successful has been the use of tabs in one form or another. We have seen how the pilot-controlled trim tab can be used to replace the pilot's control force by aerodynamic force when a steady deflection is to be maintained, and so it is a natural extension of this idea to use a tab to provide some of the force needed to deflect the controls during manoeuvres. The simplest system is the *geared tab*, as shown in Figure 11.7, in which the tab is automatically controlled as a result of the control surface deflection. The main control surface is operated in the normal way by the pilot (the control linkage not being shown), and the fixed-length grey rod which is pivoted at its ends to brackets on the main flying surface and the tab automatically causes the tab to deflect in the opposite way to that of the control surface, thus achieving the required result. The gearing of the system may be adjusted by varying the height of the bracket on the trim tab. Furthermore, such a tab arrangement may easily and conveniently be used to act as trim tab as well as balance tab, since all that is necessary is for the pilot's trim control to be linked to the tab mechanism in such a way that it either alters the length of the grey rod or moves its supporting bracket backwards and forwards on the main flying surface.

If you have been inclined to feel deep down that really the idea of the tab is asking a bit much, since we seem to be getting something for nothing, you may be even more sceptical to be told that the concept can be extended even further. Why limit the work of this tab to just

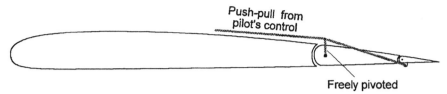

Figure 11.8   Servo or flying tabs

doing *part* of the pilot's task for him if it works so well? Why not go all the way and let the tab drive the control surface entirely on its own? Then all the pilot would have to do would be to control the tab itself, and there would be no need for any linkage from the cockpit to the primary controls at all!

Tabs of this sort which are the sole means of operating the control surfaces are called *servo tabs*, but since this name has now and then been applied to other variations on the theme in the past, the alternative name of *flying tabs* is sometimes given to this system. The operating system, illustrated in Figure 11.8, shows that a push-pull rod linked to the cockpit control operates on the end of a short crank arm freely pivoted on the hinge line of the control surface, so that it has no direct effect on the control surface when the operating rod is moved. Instead, in a somewhat similar manner to the geared tab of Figure 11.7, another pushrod links the end of the crank to an offset boss, this time on the *opposite* surface of the tab. If the main pushrod is moved aft, the linking pushrod will deflect the tab upwards, and consequently (provided there is a sufficiently fast airflow) the aerodynamic force on the control-surface-tab combination will cause the control surface to deflect downwards.

Why is the pivot point of the linkage on the servo tab in Figure 11.8 on the opposite side of the tab from that on the geared tab in Figure 11.7? To answer that, let us look at what would happen if we tried to use the geared tab arrangement of Figure 11.7 to act as a servo tab, moving the pushrod by sliding fore-and-aft the larger boss on the main flying surface. To make the control surface deflect downwards, the tab must deflect upwards, which means moving the larger boss *forward*. That's OK at first – we simply connect to the cockpit control the other way round. But then, just as with the geared tab earlier, the deflection of the control surface automatically makes the tab deflect further in the same way as its initial deflection, which would tend to create a situation of control overbalance, and make for a very sloppy feel for the pilot. If the arrangement of Figure 11.8 is adopted, on the other hand, for any fixed position of the crank (e.g. when the pilot has applied and is holding a small deflection), the deflection of the control surface resulting from the imposed tab deflection will tend to undo the tab deflection, thus providing less aerodynamic balance. The main control surface does not itself experience any hinge moment at all in the usual manner of a torque about the hinge-line, since the deflection is created instead by aerodynamic force on it, and thus absolutely no aerodynamic balance at all is required in the normal way. So any aerodynamic balance such as that produced by the linkage arrangement in Figure 11.7 would be too much and would imply overbalance, and in order to produce a positive feel in the pilot's controls the cross-linkage approach of Figure 11.8 is adopted instead. Even with this feature to make the operation of the controls more positive, a characteristic of servo tab control is that the controls usually feel 'spongy' to pilots, with whom they are therefore usually unpopular because they lack the crisp response provided by a more direct system.

Servo tabs have been used to very good effect on a number of large turboprop transport aircraft, such as the Bristol Britannia and the Short Belfast heavy freighter, and have appeared on at least one turbojet aircraft, the four-engined British Aerospace 146, in order to preclude the need for powered controls and to keep the aircraft systems simple. One problem with servo tabs is that the control surfaces require a substantial airflow to make them operate properly. When the aircraft is parked, therefore, they just flop limply or flap in the breeze, and it is impossible for the pilot to carry out the conventional preflight checks of 'full and free movement of the controls'. The aircraft must be moving close to flying speed down the runway before the pilot can have proper aerodynamic control[10].

Returning to the more general use of tabs for aerodynamic balancing and trimming of controls, the fact that aerodynamic force depends on the square of the air speed means that more aerodynamic balance is required at higher air speeds, but providing enough for this scenario tends to mean that the controls present a sloppy and overlight feel to the pilot at low speeds. To cope with this difficulty, a number of different tunes have been played on the basic theme of the control tab, by means of the use of more complicated linkages and the incorporation of springs.

One successful solution used on many aircraft has been the *spring tab*, which is illustrated in Figure 11.9. To understand how it works,

[10]Another interesting feature of the Britannia was that its propellers were powered by free turbines, and so had no mechanical connection to the main shaft of the gas turbine engines. Consequently, not only would the control surfaces have the tendency to flap in the breeze, but also the propellers could rotate at considerable speed like windmills when the aircraft was parked with engines not running, had not 'parking locks' been embodied in both systems to obviate this happening.

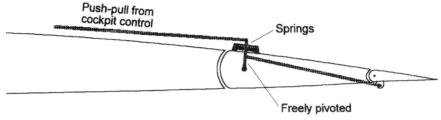

Figure 11.9   Spring tab

first of all imagine that the two little springs are extremely stiff, so stiff as to be unyielding, so that the crank whose lower end is pivoted at the hinge-line is effectively attached rigidly to the control surface by the springs and can only rotate together with the control surface. In this situation, the pushrod from the pilot's control directly actuates the main control surface, and the tab becomes totally inoperative, producing no aerodynamic balance at all. Now think of the opposite extreme situation, in which the springs are so weak that they are to all intents and purposes not there at all. If this were the case, we would have exactly the same circumstances as that of the servo tab in Figure 11.8 (apart, perhaps, from the gearing having been altered); the pilot's input would bypass the main control surface altogether and would only operate on the tab, which would do all the control-deflecting work just like a servo tab. In practice, of course, the stiffness of the springs lies somewhere between these two extremes, which means that we get a certain amount of direct action on the control and a certain amount of servo assistance. As the air speed increases, the resistance to the pilot's input increases (with the square of the speed) so that the relevant spring compresses further, and thus more tab deflection is obtained and more aerodynamic balance is provided, just when needed.

Once or twice in this section we have made passing reference to power-operated controls, and this has proved to be the ultimate solution to the problem of aeroplanes outgrowing the handling capacity of pilots. Large slab tailplanes and substantial hinged control surfaces can then be used with impunity, without being constrained in their design by the physical ability of the pilot to cope. But this gives rise to a new and almost antithetical problem in that, rather than the pilot having too much physically demanded of him, he now merely has to transmit control commands to the power machinery to do the job for him. No longer does the pilot have to exert a force on the controls which he knows to be directly associated with the aerodynamic force on the flying surfaces, and consequently the pilot has been deprived of all *feel* in the controls. Feel, like the old cliché of flying by the seat of the pants, is one of the pilot's most important sources of information about the way that the aircraft is flying, and if denied this the situation is somewhat akin to presenting the pilot with an aircraft with unstable characteristics. It is so important that it has been found necessary to augment powered control systems with an additional system which automatically reintroduces an artificial resistive force to the controls, purely and simply to provide the pilot with the necessary feel.

This feel in the controls is often referred to by the term *q-feel*. We may recall (for example from the discussion of Bernoulli's principle at the end of Chapter 4 of *Flightwise – Principles of Aircraft Flight*) that the total pressure in the air consists of two component parts: the static pressure which we designate by the letter p, and the dynamic pressure (the additional pressure which would be available if the air's kinetic energy were converted into pressure energy by bringing it to rest) which is $\frac{1}{2}\rho V^2$. It is the latter, the dynamic pressure, which provides an indication of the magnitude of aerodynamic forces, as we found in the derivation of the aerodynamic coefficients C_L and C_D, and so it is the dynamic pressure that needs to be reflected in the feel fed back to the pilot. The other variable factor determining the force on a control surface is its angle of attack, and this is directly related to the *displacement* of the pilot's control rather than the force exerted. These two aspects of the operation of pilot's controls, the force and the displacement, need to be clearly distinguished from each other in one's mind. Since feel must relate to dynamic pressure, it might have been given the name $\frac{1}{2}\rho V^2$-*feel*, but clearly this is a little clumsy. Instead, the letter q is chosen to represent $\frac{1}{2}\rho V^2$, being a natural alphabetic partner for p, the static pressure, with which it is so closely associated.

Powered controls were originally introduced for the sake of providing sufficient control force in the face of growing aircraft size and speed. But once they were well established and accepted as safe and reliable, they opened the door to many other refinements of the way in which an aircraft could be controlled. Such progress was also greatly enhanced by the phenomenal rate of development of data processing, at first using analogue computers (crude by today's sophisticated standards) and then by means of the digital computer. By the incorporation of such systems powered controls can be called upon to perform feats that would be way beyond the capacity of any human pilot to perform at sufficient speed.

The subject of the human pilot interface, as discussed in this chapter, will never be outmoded as long as aircraft have human pilots, but we can now move beyond this discussion and look (particularly in Chapter 13) at the way in which aircraft development has been, and is, progressing through the integration of pilot, computer and powered controls in collaboration with each other.

CHAPTER 12
Manoeuvrability and Agility

INTRODUCTION

There are certain words bandied about by aeronautical writers which, despite being potentially the key to the most engaging of discussions, are so carelessly used that they tend to make me (and, I suspect, many other enquirers) switch off before knowing whether the writer has anything worthwhile to say or not. At the start of Chapter 2 we stripped one such hackneyed word, 'stability', of its mystique, and another candidate, although not specifically our concern in *Flightwise*, is the term 'performance'. Now we come across the catchword 'manoeuvrability', which I have seen being passed off as an 'explanation' for all sorts of aerodynamic features of aircraft!

There is usually nothing *wrong* with people's use of this word since, as a glance at any good dictionary will show, it conveys a profusion of shades of meaning. But herein lies precisely the problem: without being specific, the user is saying virtually nothing beyond defining a general concept. It goes without saying that an aircraft must be manoeuvrable, but what does *more* or *less* manoeuvrable mean? Without some attempt at definition and quantification, it is totally meaningless to assert, for example, that canards, or relaxed static stability, make an aircraft more manoeuvrable.

Our initial approach to aircraft control in this book was to start from the premise that there are three dimensions of space within which we would like to have total liberty of movement, and that an aircraft has six degrees of freedom through which to achieve this goal. But very quickly certain overriding constraints such as minimum flying speed and the physiological limit of a human's endurance of acceleration clouded this ultimate goal, so that we have had to content ourselves with passage of an aircraft through the air more resembling the flight of a steered arrow than that of a moth or a dragonfly. Are the darting, impulsive movements of 'flying saucers' for ever to be confined to the realm of the science fiction devotee or ufologist? Must real human-carrying airborne vehicles always be constrained to high speeds and gentle curves, always pointing in the direction of motion? Must we humbly accept that perhaps the 'chauffeur' school of the pioneering days were ultimately closer to the realities of flight than were their 'airman' contemporaries?

Apart from the mere esoteric attractiveness of the idea, there are two distinct and identifiable areas of need, or of potential usefulness of the aircraft, which have provided the urge for aeronautical visionaries and inventors to struggle to overcome some of the constraints on an aircraft's controllability. In the first place, the need for hovering flight without forward speed, and the ability to move and rotate in any direction under precise control, has spawned enormous inventive effort since the very earliest days of flight. The helicopter has undoubtedly come of age today, and also, as we saw in the last chapter, the hovercraft has come and has not yet gone, but the research and development into better ways of achieving these goals in aircraft which are also useful in other ways goes on unabated. This side of the coin is characterised by the primary requirement of hovering flight, having achieved which the search goes on for ways in which the craft may be developed to do as many as possible of the other things which conventional aircraft, with their predominant forward air speed constraint, are generally better at.

The alternative approach is to start with the conventionally forward-flying aircraft, and then to investigate ways in which its manoeuvrability may be enhanced to give it as much as possible of the versatility of motion associated with the hovering type. It may rightly be supposed that an aircraft which is primarily conceived as a means of high-speed transportation would have little need for the gimmicks of extreme manoeuvrability, and in general this is indeed the case. It is only in the arena of combat that such requirements have become evident. Just as throughout the history of armoured warfare better armoured and better armed tanks have been developed to increase their survivability and lethality in combat, so throughout the history of aerial combat the need to attack a target (on the ground or in the air) without succumbing to the actions of the airborne enemy has brought great ingenuity to bear in developing more and more versatile aircraft.

Thus in the development of combat aircraft the need for greater manoeuvrability has become one of the chief driving forces. This need manifests itself in a number of different mission requirements. First of all, in aerial combat with an airborne adversary the basic rule is 'shoot the enemy or get shot', and the most effective stance for a good shot is to fly towards the enemy aircraft from behind – which of course is exactly what the opponent is trying to do to you. Superficially the aircraft which can perform the tightest turn would appear to have the advantage, but also small differences in maximum speed, ability to alter speed rapidly, and most particularly the quickness with which a turn or a pull-up can be initiated or modified or terminated can make the difference between being the vanquisher or the vanquished. Secondly, there is the ground-attack rôle, in which a diving aircraft must within a very short time aim itself accurately at a target on the ground, release its weapon and then rapidly change course to escape from the scene. Thirdly, whilst approaching the target zone behind enemy lines, today's tactic for avoiding detection by enemy radar or ground observers is to fly in at high speed so close to the ground as to be concealed from view by the surrounding features such as rising ground, trees and buildings. Clearly the need for rapid changes in course to avoid collision in such circumstances is paramount.

It is in this context that the word 'manoeuvrability' has tended to become so overused as to have become obscure in its precise meaning. Initially, in the context of aircraft control, the word was invoked to mean the tightness of turn or pull-up that an aircraft was capable of, and we will take it that this is still the 'correct' meaning of the word. (We shall define tightness in two alternative ways a little later on.) But if tightness of turn were the only criterion of an aircraft's mission effectiveness, the contest might long since have reached a stalemate, since ultimately (in many combat situations) the tightness of turn is constrained by the physiological limitations of pilots and crew to enduring acceleration, which is the same (about eight times the acceleration due to gravity) regardless of colour, race or creed. Manoeuvrability, then, means tightness of turn, but this is not the whole story.

Given the aircraft's assumed capability of carrying out maximum rate turns and pull-ups compatible with crew physiology, the winning edge today is found to depend on the quickness with which an aircraft can *alter* its state of motion, in as many ways as possible, and over as wide a range of flying conditions as possible. Thus it is no use just being fast; it is also necessary to be able to change speed rapidly from very fast to very slow (the slower the better) and back again. And it is inadequate merely to be able to pull $8g$ turns, since as we shall shortly see, it is frequently the aerodynamic stalling of the wing which limits the turn before the maximum permissible load factor is achieved, so that stalling limits need to be pushed back. Also one needs the ability to roll into and out of the turn faster than the opposition, and to be able to initiate a pull-up (either when entering a turn or when climbing or looping) without being penalised by a pitch transient during which the aircraft actually moves the wrong way and wastes precious time. Such needs have given rise to the additional word *agility* in the aviation vocabulary. Indeed the new Eurofighter 2000 started its development life bearing the name or title 'Agile Combat Aircraft', since agility was the fundamental rationale underpinning its design philosophy, as it is with many of the present and upcoming generation of combat aircraft.

We shall start this chapter by looking closely at the limitations and constraints on manoeuvrability with which the designer must be familiar and within which the pilot must operate, and we shall then look at one or two additional phenomena ready to trap the unwary pilot if he sails too close to the wind. Then we shall move on to consider ways in which the agility of an aircraft may be enhanced, both by increasing the quickness and effectiveness with which manoeuvres may be initiated, and also by considering ways in which developers are attempting to push back the traditional manoeuvre boundaries. We shall close the chapter with a brief departure from the mind-set of conventional control thinking by looking into the possibilities offered by using direct force control.

MANOEUVRE LIMITATIONS

Although we have asserted that the maximum turn rate ultimately depends on the aircraft's structural strength which is dictated by the physiological limitations of the human crew, there are situations in which other limitations make this ultimate structural limit unattainable. The rate of a turn depends not only upon the lift-force that the wings are producing but also on their angle of bank and the air speed, and these factors are also intimately linked with the smallness of radius of the turn which, in some circumstances, may be a more important criterion than how long the turn takes to execute.

There are quite a few interrelated parameters rearing their ugly heads here, and they are linked together by three distinct equations: (i) the general lift formula, (ii) the equilibrium of vertical forces on the aircraft according to Newton's First Law, and (iii) Newton's Second Law applied to the centripetal acceleration of the aircraft. It is not usually our practice in *Flightwise* to explain features by reference to mathematics, but if a complex set of interrelationships such as this were to be fully explained using only words, it would be extremely difficult to focus on the significant features, and we would probably lose sight of the wood for the trees. Therefore we *will* use a few equations, but I promise that we shall only introduce them one at a time as and when they are applicable, since it is the juggling of a multiplicity of equations all at once which can be distressing, even to the hardened mathematician. Nothing (with one exception) will be involved beyond basic algebraic formulae involving simple products and fractions. The exception will be a brief passing reference to trigonometric functions of the bank angle, which a few paragraphs further on we will eliminate again, but we will guide the uninitiated by the hand at these points.

Since wing lift is at the heart of turning performance, we will first of all consider what factors place limitations on how much lift a wing could produce, quite independently of the circumstances in which it is doing this. In practice, as we know[1], there are no sustained circumstances in which wing lift exceeds the weight of the aircraft other than during turns, and even during pull-ups the required lift-force is usually far lower than that for maximum rate turns. Therefore studying maximum lift-force in isolation from the turn is rather an abstract exercise having little direct application to aircraft flight. This is, however, an easier approach than trying to deal with everything at once.

Maximum Lift

We will start by using the first of our three equations, the standard 'lift formula' $L = C_L \frac{1}{2}\rho V^2 S$ in which L stands for the lift-force, C_L is the coefficient of lift which is a measure of the lifting effect of the wing and is directly related to its angle of attack, $\frac{1}{2}\rho V^2$ is the dynamic pressure of the air and tells us all we need to know about the flight condition – V being the air speed (or 'true air speed' as explained below) and ρ its density at the particular height at which the aircraft is flying – and S is the planform area of the wing, a measure of the size of the aircraft[2].

First of all we will carry out a simplification by which we can reduce the number of variables by one to make it more manageable. The dynamic pressure $\frac{1}{2}\rho V^2$ depends on both the speed and height at which the aircraft is flying, and it is important to us as a composite entity which tells us about the force-producing effect of the airflow. This dynamic pressure is actually the quantity that the pilot's air speed indicator measures, even though the display shows just the value of a speed. We recall[3] that the pressure difference measured by a pitot-static probe gives directly the dynamic pressure $\frac{1}{2}\rho V^2$, so that if the air density ρ were constant the air speed indicator could be calibrated to tell the pilot the aircraft's air speed directly. In fact ρ is not constant but decreases as altitude increases, continuously throughout the entire atmosphere until it reaches zero in outer space. Consequently the measurement of $\frac{1}{2}\rho V^2$, depending on two changing variables, cannot be used directly for calibrating the air speed indicator. The solution adopted is to use a fixed value for ρ, and the value chosen is that of

---

[1]This is discussed fully in Chapter 2 of *Flightwise – Principles of Aircraft Flight* in the sections headed 'The Forces Acting on an Aircraft', 'Forces in Curved Motion' and 'Transitional Flight'.

[2]The derivation of this equation and a full explanation of its terms is given in Chapter 3 of *Flightwise – Principles of Aircraft Flight*, in the subsection 'Coefficient of Lift' of the section on aerodynamic coefficients.

[3]This topic is introduced and discussed in Chapter 4 of *Flightwise – Principles of Aircraft Flight*, under the heading 'Static Pressure and Dynamic Pressure'. The paragraph containing this footnote and the following two paragraphs are substantially copied from the section headed 'So What?' in Chapter 11 of *Flightwise – Principles of Aircraft Flight*.

the internationally agreed standard sea-level air density, denoted by ρ_0. The speed V which the formula now gives is the only variable quantity, and it is denoted by V_e and called the *equivalent air speed*, or EAS. For our purposes, we can take it that the equivalent air speed and the indicated air speed (called the IAS, the actual reading of the air speed indicator) are exactly the same as each other, although in practice a couple of corrections have to be made to the IAS to give the EAS. (These are relatively small compared with the conversion between indicated air speed and true air speed.)

Having calibrated the air speed indicator as if operating at the fixed air density ρ_0, it can now be thought of as measuring $\frac{1}{2}\rho_0 V_e^2$ rather than $\frac{1}{2}\rho V^2$. As a result, regardless of altitude, the instrument gives the value of V_e, which is the speed that the aircraft *would be flying at* if it were at sea-level air density at a speed giving the same pitot-static pressure difference. Both expressions $\frac{1}{2}\rho V^2$ and $\frac{1}{2}\rho_0 V_e^2$ are equal to the same pressure difference, that between the total pressure and the static pressure as measured by the pitot-static probe, and so the two expressions are equal to each other. Based on the resulting equation $\frac{1}{2}\rho V^2 = \frac{1}{2}\rho_0 V_e^2$, if the pilot needs to convert from EAS to true air speed (TAS) (for example, for navigation purposes), then he may calculate his true air speed from the formula $V = V_e\sqrt{\rho_0/\rho}$.

Since ρ is always less than ρ_0 (except at or below sea-level), the square root in this formula is always greater than 1, and so the true air speed is always greater than the equivalent (or indicated) air speed. Looking at this the other way round, an air speed indicator always (except at or below sea-level) reads a lower value than the actual speed at which the aircraft is flying through the air, and the difference becomes greater and greater as altitude increases, until if the aircraft were a space vehicle and left the atmosphere altogether at a very large true air speed, its equivalent air speed once there was no more atmospheric pressure to measure would fall right off to zero.

Using the fact that $\frac{1}{2}\rho V^2 = \frac{1}{2}\rho_0 V_e^2$, let us rewrite the original lift formula as it now applies to a given aircraft in straight level flight at *any* altitude. By this means we replace the variable ρ by the fixed value ρ_0, and hence reduce the number of variables by one, which was our aim. Assuming straight and level flight, we may also include the fact that the lift equals the aircraft's weight W. To help in understanding what the equation tells us, each quantity that is constant under the given conditions has been underlined.

$$\underline{W} = \underline{L} = C_L\underline{\tfrac{1}{2}\rho_0}V_e^2\underline{S}$$

Hence we can clearly see that the two non-underlined quantities C_L and V_e are uniquely linked by the equation, and so it expresses the

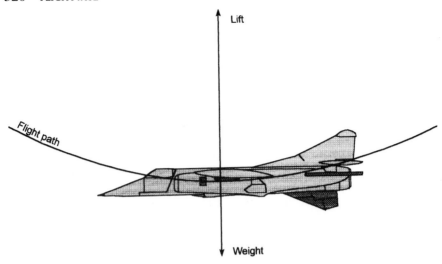

Figure 12.1   Aircraft in accelerated non-turning constant-speed flight

fact with which we are familiar that, the slower you fly in straight level flight, the more coefficient of lift (and hence angle of attack) you need to maintain a constant lift to balance the weight. Incidentally, if required we could use this formula to find out the lowest possible speed that the aircraft could fly in steady level flight, often called the stalling speed, by putting into the equation the maximum attainable lift coefficient – but more about this maximum C_L value in a moment.

Let us now alter the scenario a little, such that the aircraft is still flying level (at the instant in question) and in a vertical plane (not banked or turning) but its lift is no longer equal to, but is greater than, its weight, so that the aircraft is flying in a vertical circular path and accelerating towards the centre of the circle which is directly above it. It is doing a pull-up. This situation is depicted in Figure 12.1, and is only instantaneous since immediately beforehand and afterwards the lift and weight are not in line with each other so that things become more complicated. Now the lift is no longer equal to the weight and so, as when discussing Figure 8.1, we define the *load factor* as the ratio of the lift to the weight, and denote it by the letter n. If, say, the lift is four times the weight, the load factor n equals 4, and we say colloquially that the aircraft is 'pulling 4g'. It is convenient to write nW in place of L in the lift formula since the weight W is constant, and so we have

$$n\underline{W} = C_L \tfrac{1}{2}\underline{\rho_0} V_e^2 \underline{S} \qquad \textbf{Equation 12.1}$$

in which the constant values have again been underlined, and the additional quantity n makes a total of three variable parameters altogether.

But we are interested in examining the *limits* of manoeuvrability, and any one of the three variables n, C_L and V_e may potentially impose a limit on how tightly the aircraft may be pulling up. Let us take these three possibilities one at a time. First of all, there is a maximum attainable value of C_L, which is achieved at the stalling, or *critical*, angle of attack. Bear in mind by recalling the shape of a typical lift curve (graph of C_L against α) that at the stall the lift does not suddenly disappear or even necessarily fall off very abruptly (although it may do so in the event of a leading edge stall), and so the stalling condition is that of *maximum*, rather than little or no, lift, as some people seem to believe. In practice the pilot would normally leave a margin of error and not regard this stalling point as a working maximum, since the region immediately beyond may in some aircraft be very hostile, and also since pure symmetrical flight cannot be guaranteed and a stalling wing-tip could result in a spin. However, for mathematical purposes the highest attainable value of C_L is $C_{L_{\max}}$, and for a given aircraft in a given configuration (e.g. excluding the use of devices such as flaps) this is a constant value. We can thus rewrite our equation for the limiting situation as $n\underline{W} = C_{L_{\max}}\underline{\tfrac{1}{2}\rho_0}V_e^2\underline{S}$ which relates the only two remaining variable quantities $\overline{n}$ and V_e.

The lift equation can now be easily rearranged to show that $n = (\text{constant}) \times V_e^2$, a quadratic equation, and so the graph of V_e against n will be a parabola passing through the origin. The best way now to investigate the manoeuvrability limitations of the aircraft is by recourse to a diagram incorporating this graph, and such a diagram is shown in Figure 12.2 and is called a *manoeuvre margin* diagram. The letters A to G have been included simply as arbitrary labels by which we can refer to the various points and regions of the diagram, and the thicker black line bordering the grey area defines the limits within which the aircraft can safely fly.

Let us walk and talk ourselves around Figure 12.2 starting at point A, the origin, and moving through B towards C. This curve through ABC is the parabola of the quadratic equation $n = (\text{constant}) \times V_e^2$, and points on it give the load factor n which will be attained at any equivalent air speed when flying with the aircraft's angle of attack set to the critical angle. Thus we see that at speeds from zero up to the point C, the load factor is not restricted by the structural strength of the wings, because the aircraft would have stalled before that load factor were reached. Point B is the point at which the aircraft's load factor is 1, and so the speed at point B is the aircraft's level flight stalling speed. Flight is possible only in the grey area under the curve from A

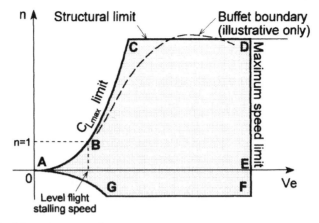

Figure 12.2   Manoeuvre margin

to B if the aircraft is bunting[4], like driving over a hump-backed bridge, and the lift is less than the weight, but in fact sustained flight is not a practical proposition at speeds less than that at B. Later when we are investigating the possibility of increasing agility it may well be worth-while to ask whether there could be ways in which this minimum speed limitation may be overcome, and whether the manoeuvre boundary between A and B could be pushed up.

The horizontal line from C to D is at the value of the load factor that the aircraft designers have decreed to be its maximum safe value, and this may be about 8 for a combat aircraft (since the maximum 'g-force' that the average human pilot can tolerate whilst remaining conscious is about 7g), but very much lower at about 2g for airliners. (Thus the proportions of the manoeuvre margin diagram will be very different for such different types of aircraft, which is why no numerical values have been given in the figure.) This structural limit usually has a 50% safety margin built in, before any catastrophic failure will occur, but at any load factor exceeding the specified structural limit it is likely that minor damage may occur such as rivets popping and panels coming off.

The manoeuvre limit imposed by the curve BC has been determined by consideration of the maximum lift coefficient available in relatively low speed flight where the airflow may be regarded as incompressible. Since our concern in the present context is particu-

---

[4]A bunt is another name for a push-over. It is discussed in the section headed 'Transitional Flight' at the very end of Chapter 2 of *Flightwise – Principles of Aircraft Flight*.

larly with aircraft that are to be expected to operate at least in the transonic flight regime, if not at supersonic speeds, we must consider now what effects the compressibility of the air has on the manoeuvre limitations. To be able to understand these effects properly, you may find it valuable to refresh your memory on the nature of high-speed compressible flow and of shock waves, matters that were discussed thoroughly in Chapter 10 of *Flightwise – Principles of Aircraft Flight*. But our major concern now is the situation in which only *parts* of the flow around the aircraft are supersonic, and this was dealt with extensively in Chapter 11 of the same book which dealt with transonic flow. In particular, shock waves were found to be generated behind parts of the wing where the airflow was speeded up most, and this was seen to be on the upper surface some way behind the leading edge. Increasing the angle of attack towards the critical angle increases this speeding-up tendency, and consequently the formation of a shock wave can pre-empt the onset of the conventional stall. Furthermore, in the section headed 'So What?' of Chapter 11 it was shown that shock waves could be experienced on an aircraft at equivalent air speeds very much lower than the speed of sound in air, for a number of reasons. Such shock waves can cause a 'shock stall' to occur, which bears many similarities to a high-angle-of-attack stall at lower speeds, and the effect of this is to modify the curve BC of Figure 12.2 downwards to a lower limit indicated by the dashed line in the figure, labelled the 'buffet boundary'. This modification becomes more significant as altitude increases, so that at high altitude it may well bring the manoeuvre margin down below the upper line CD of the manoeuvre margin diagram. The dashed line is merely illustrative of the possibilities at an example altitude rather than being definitive in shape, but it does demonstrate that, for a combat aircraft, the manoeuvre boundary may well be dictated by compressibility effects before the structural limitation is reached.

The right-hand boundary DE of the safe operating zone demarcates another limiting criterion specified by the designer, this time the maximum equivalent air speed (often denoted V_{NE}, standing for the *never-exceed speed*). This is the greatest speed that the aircraft can be safely flown at before aircraft stability problems are known to start occurring, or beyond which aerodynamic flutter or control reversal or instability or other problems are known to be liable to arise. Sometimes the never-exceed speed may be dictated by structural considerations, as the load imposed by high dynamic pressure may overstress certain parts of the structure. The V_{NE} value is usually set with about a five to ten per cent safety margin below that at which anything catastrophic will happen.

One of the great advantages of using equivalent air speed rather than true air speed for manoeuvre margin diagrams such as Figure 12.2 is that the same diagram applies for all altitudes of flight (except for the buffet boundary), whereas if true air speed were used a whole series of such diagrams would be needed for flight at different heights. Furthermore, as we have seen, the pilot's air speed indicator shows the equivalent air speed directly (give or take a couple of relatively small corrections) whereas he usually has no direct read-out of the aircraft's true air speed. Therefore the pilot only needs to know and remember one V_{NE} value, and one level flight stalling speed, rather than a range of values for different altitudes. The never-exceed speed is determined by considerations of aerodynamic loading on one part or other of the airframe, and since aerodynamic force is always proportional to dynamic pressure and the air speed indicator effectively measures dynamic pressure, the air speed indicator is in fact a far more useful instrument for a pilot to have than a true air speed gauge would be. It is an essential flying instrument, whereas a true air speed gauge (if installed) is useful only for navigational purposes.

In addition to a never-exceed speed, a never-exceed Mach number M_{NE} is also likely to be specified by the designers, for other aerodynamic reasons such as shock buffet or control reversal or other limitations. Whereas V_e is independent of altitude, Mach number is the ratio of *true* air speed to the speed of sound, and so it is dependent on the air temperature at the operating height, as well as on the true air speed. Thus V_{NE} and M_{NE} do not normally coincide. No M_{NE} boundary is shown in Figure 12.2, since the graph has been plotted against equivalent air speed and not against Mach number.

The region AEFG of Figure 12.2 may seem a little strange and surprising, but all aircraft must be designed to have at least a small capability for negative-g flight. In the case of an aerobatic or combat aircraft an ability not just to fly inverted but also to carry out manoeuvres whilst inverted will be essential, and any aircraft, even a large transport aircraft, is liable to be subjected to negative-g sometimes, such as during an emergency bunt or in rough air conditions. This is why passengers are asked to secure their lap straps when turbulence is anticipated. Combat aircraft are typically designed to withstand negative-g loads of about $-4g$, but large transport aircraft are typically limited to $-\frac{1}{2}g$. The value of V_{NE} is unaffected, so that the straight line DEF is continuous at E, and the changes to the other boundaries reflect the inverted wing shape and different g limitation.

We have now seen how the maximum usable load factor depends not only on the structural limit of the aircraft but also, at lower speeds, on the maximum available lift coefficient and sometimes, at higher speeds, on the Mach number. We must now examine how these limitations influence the turning performance of the aircraft.

Manoeuvrability in a Level Turn

At the beginning of Chapter 8 it was shown (by reference to Figure 8.1) that there is a direct connection between the angle at which an aircraft must be banked to execute a balanced level turn and the load factor of the lift-force being generated by the wings, and that this relationship is completely independent of the weight, size or flight condition of the aircraft. Now that we have examined the limitations which apply to the lift-force, we must look more deeply at the circumstances of the banked level turn, because so far we have said nothing at all about the 'tightness' of the turn. Tightness is not a very scientific or precise word, but by it we might mean one of two things, depending on the operational requirements. Either we would like to know how *small* a circle the aircraft could turn in – in other words, what is the least possible radius of the turn – or we might be more interested in how *quickly* the aircraft could be turned round from flying in one direction to flying in another at, say, 180° to the first. Shortly we will look closely at these two questions, one at a time, but in preparation for doing so we must take a look at the other two equations that we shall need to call upon.

Let us first of all write down the second equation referred to on page 317, obtained from equating the vertical forces and components in Figure 12.3. It gives us the relationship between the load factor and the bank angle. This angle ϕ[5] has to be just the right size for the vertical component of the lift-force to be exactly the same magnitude as the aircraft's weight, so that no height is gained or lost during the turn, and thus we have the upper triangle of the force vector diagram in Figure 12.3. Now those who are familiar with trigonometry will need no explanation of the fact which emerges from this right-angled triangle, which is that $W = L \cos \phi$, where W is the weight and L the lift, and I suggest you jump straight to the next paragraph whilst I briefly explain this to the others. As far as vector triangles are concerned, the word 'cos' (short for 'cosine') is simply a tool that works out the proportion (i.e. fraction) of a vector that is exerted in one of the two component directions, when the vector is split into two perpendicular components. There is also another tool, 'sin' (short for 'sine' and pronounced like 'sign' with which it must not be confused) which gives the proportion of the vector that acts in the other component direction. In trigonometry these proportions are defined as the ratios of the lengths of certain pairs of sides of a right-angled triangle, but really you don't need to worry about learning all that for the present purpose. All you need to know can be summed up in three statements as follows:

---

[5]Don't worry if you spotted that ϕ is actually negative in this case because the aircraft is coming towards us. Its sign is not important in the present situation.

(i) Being tools, cos and sin need raw material to work on, and their raw material is an angle. Without an angle they are meaningless. Thus we have cos ϕ above, which means the cosine of the angle ϕ. Although the raw materials of the cos and sin tools are angles, their outputs are simply numbers without any units.

(ii) If you imagine standing on a vector triangle facing out along the resultant vector direction, and if you have to turn *through* the angle labelled ϕ in order to face along the component that you want to work out, then you must use the *cos* tool on ϕ to find out what proportion of the resultant is acting in the required component direction. You then multiply the magnitude of the resultant by this proportion to find the magnitude of the component. Thus in the present situation the proportion of lift acting in the vertical direction is given by cos ϕ, and so the magnitude of the vertical component equals the total lift times cos ϕ. To find the proportion of the resultant which acts in the direction of the *other* component,

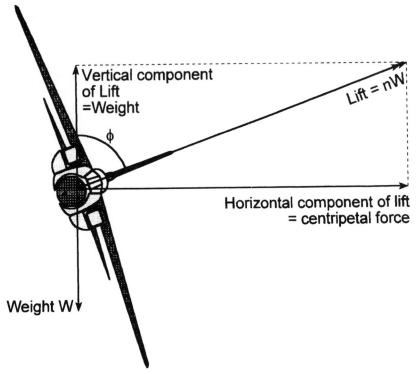

Figure 12.3   Aircraft in a banked turn in level flight

i.e. the horizontal component in the present case, you do *not* rotate through the named angle, and so you use sin φ instead. We will need to use this shortly.

(iii) The values of (i.e. the proportions given by) cos and sin of all angles between 0° and 90° are always between 0 and 1. (You can't have an angle bigger than 90° in a right-angled triangle, and we always get a right-angled triangle when we resolve a vector into two perpendicular components.) If φ were very small indeed (i.e. the aircraft were scarcely banked at all), the vertical component would be virtually equal to the lift so that cos φ would be almost one, and there would be practically no horizontal component so that sin φ would be scarcely more than zero. If on the other hand the aircraft were banked extremely steeply so that φ were not far short of 90° – it couldn't actually reach 90°, or there would be no vertical component left to balance the weight, and height would be lost during the turn – then cos φ would be very close to zero since only a tiny proportion of the lift would be acting vertically, and sin φ would be approximately one since the lift would almost all be being used as centripetal force. Values of cos and sin for angles between 0° and 90° vary smoothly but not uniformly, and cannot be worked out without resorting to advanced mathematics, which nobody actually does. Instead, you get them simply by entering the angle on a scientific calculator and pressing the cos or sin key, or looking them up in a table.

As earlier we would prefer to use the load factor n rather than the lift as a variable, so we will substitute nW for L in the equation $W = L \cos \phi$, giving $W = nW \cos \phi$. Dividing both sides by W and by $\cos \phi$ gives us

$$n = \frac{1}{\cos \phi}$$ **Equation 12.2**

which reminds us of the fact already observed that bank angle and load factor are directly related to each other without any dependence on any other quantity at all. A large bank angle ϕ (approaching 90°) means that cos φ is very small, so that its reciprocal, which gives us n, is very large. Conversely, a small bank angle corresponds with a small load factor (but never less than one in a level banked turn).

Equation 12.2 above was found by considering the balance of the vertical components of force in Figure 12.3. To relate this to the turning performance about the centre of the circle (way out to the right), we must now make use of the third and last equation, the one which relates the force component in the horizontal direction to the centripetal acceleration it produces. From either right-angled triangle (or the rule given in the explanation of sin and cos on page 327) we can immediately write down that

$$CF = L \sin \phi \qquad \textbf{Equation 12.3}$$

where *CF* is the centripetal force. Now the nearest we have come to finding a way of calculating the magnitude of the centripetal force was in Chapter 2 of *Flightwise – Principles of Aircraft Flight*, in the section headed 'Forces in Curved Motion', and there it was shown that there exists a centripetal acceleration towards the centre of the circle, but we stopped short of actually working out its value because it inevitably involves a small amount of calculus. Rather than getting distracted into a discourse on calculus now, let us behave somewhat out of character for *Flightwise* and merely quote without proof the formula for the centripetal acceleration *a*, which is $a = V^2/r$, where *V* is the aircraft's true air speed and *r* is the radius of the turning circle. From Newton's Second Law the centripetal force must be the product of the aircraft's mass and this centripetal acceleration. We have so far been dealing with the aircraft's weight as a force rather than its mass. Instead of introducing an additional variable *m* for mass let us use the fact (from Newton's Second Law applied vertically downwards to a falling object) that $W = mg$, so that instead of the mass *m* we may write $\dfrac{W}{g}$. Thus multiplying mass and acceleration in accordance with Newton's Second Law applied horizontally gives:

$$CF = \frac{W}{g} \times \frac{V^2}{r} \qquad \textbf{Equation 12.4}$$

We may now equate the right-hand sides of Equations 12.3 and 12.4 and replace *L* with *nW*, giving

$$nW \sin \phi = \frac{W}{g} \times \frac{V^2}{r} \qquad \textbf{Equation 12.5}$$

There is now no point in having both *n* and ϕ in this equation, since they are uniquely related together by the relationship of Equation 12.2. When flying we may think either in terms of limiting the number of *g*s being pulled (which applies in pull-ups as well as banked turns) or of the bank angle in a turn, and since the first is of more general applicability and relates directly to the aircraft's performance and structural strength, we shall choose to retain *n*, corresponding to our earlier discussion when we used *n* as the vertical axis of the graph in Figure 12.2. The answer that emerges when we eliminate ϕ from the pair of Equations 12.2 and 12.5 is:

$$W \sqrt{n^2 - 1} = \frac{W}{g} \times \frac{V^2}{r} \qquad \textbf{Equation 12.6}$$

and this may be derived either by using the well-known relationship that $(\sin \phi)^2 + (\cos \phi)^2 = 1$ or, more simply without reference to trigonometry, by referring to the upper triangle in Figure 12.3. If we scale that triangle down by a factor of W, the length of the hypotenuse becomes n, the length of the vertical component is one, and by using Pythagoras's Theorem it immediately follows that the length of the

horizontal component is $\sqrt{n^2 - 1}$. Scaling back up by W gives the

centripetal force, which can then be slotted into the left-hand side of Equation 12.4, from which Equation 12.6 follows straight away. No more trigonometry!

Minimum Radius Turn

Let us rearrange Equation 12.6 so that the turning circle radius r is its subject:

$$r = \frac{W}{g} \times \frac{V^2}{\sqrt{n^2 - 1}} \times \frac{1}{W} \qquad \textbf{Equation 12.7}$$

From this we see that the Ws immediately cancel out (and g is constant), so that r depends on the two variables speed and load factor, which we may look at one at a time. If we take the load factor to be fixed, e.g. the maximum available in the prevailing circumstances according to our earlier discussion, then r is directly proportional to V^2. Thus to obtain as small a turning circle as possible (a particularly important need in close air-to-air combat in order to outmanoeuvre the enemy) the aircraft must fly at as low an air speed as possible. Referring back to the manoeuvre margin diagram in Figure 12.2, this clearly means operating as close as possible to the curved C_L limit line between points B and C. (The fact that Figure 12.2 uses equivalent air speed whereas the V in equation 12.7 is true air speed does not invalidate the *principle*.) Hence tremendous research and development efforts are today made to extend this low-speed manoeuvre boundary further and further to the left, and this will be a major theme of Chapter 14.

The other way of looking at Equation 12.7 is to apply it to a particular flight condition of an aircraft, so that V may be regarded as a constant, and to see how the turning circle radius is related to the load factor or g being pulled. (Bear in mind that the g in Equation 12.7 is a constant, the acceleration due to gravity, and must not be confused with our colloquial use of 'pulling gs', where the number of gs is actually the n of the equation.) But this does not give us any new insight beyond confirmation of the obvious, that as n increases so the turning circle radius decreases.

We may usefully draw together our thoughts about the manoeuvre margin and the turning circle radius by considering once again the lift formula and applying it directly to the turning situation. Replacing *just the final W* in Equation 12.7 by L/n (since $L = nW$) gives

$$r = \frac{W}{g} \times \frac{V^2}{\sqrt{n^2 - 1}} \times \frac{n}{L}$$

(n.b. L/n is inverted because W appeared on the bottom of the equation). Tidying up slightly into a more suitable form, this may be re-written as:

$$r = \frac{W}{g} \times \frac{V^2}{L} \times \frac{n}{\sqrt{n^2 - 1}}$$

If we now substitute for L in this equation by using the lift formula $L = C_L \frac{1}{2}\rho V^2 S$, which we will keep in the form using true air speed so that the air density ρ is a variable depending on altitude, we have:

$$r = \frac{W}{g} \times \frac{V^2}{C_L \frac{1}{2}\rho V^2 S} \times \frac{n}{\sqrt{n^2 - 1}}$$

Interestingly V^2 very conveniently cancels out on the top and the bottom, which means that the radius of turn appears not to be directly dependent on the aircraft's air speed after all. But we have already drawn the important (and correct) conclusion from the simpler equation 12.7 that for a given load factor r is indeed proportional to V^2. What has happened here is that by using the lift formula we have introduced the alternative quantities C_L, ρ and S, which are themselves related to the speed. We are simply looking at things in another way. By cancelling the V^2s and judiciously rearranging the remaining terms of this equation, we can rewrite it in a form which will enable us to see clearly what factors will in practice determine the radius of a turn:

$$r = \frac{W}{S} \times \frac{1}{\rho} \times \frac{2}{g} \times \frac{1}{C_L} \times \frac{n}{\sqrt{n^2 - 1}} \qquad \textbf{Equation 12.8}$$

In this equation $2/g$ is constant and so we can ignore it for our present purpose. Once again let us decide to use a fixed load factor n. From the other factors we may immediately deduce that for an aircraft to turn with the least possible turning circle radius, as well as flying as slowly as possible, the following additional requirements must be met:

(a) The first factor W/S must be a minimum. The weight and

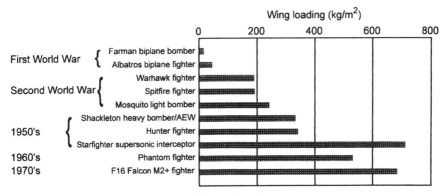

Figure 12.4   Wing loadings of some military aircraft

wing area of an aircraft are very frequently grouped together in this way, and the fraction W/S is referred to as the *wing loading*. It is a measure of how much weight is supported by each square metre (or other area unit) of wing area in level flight, and it thus gives a measure of how effective the wing is at producing lift, independently of the overall size of the aircraft. The wing loading is fixed at the design stage and, apart from varying weight by, for example, burning fuel, the pilot has no control over it. In the early days of flight when the theory of aerofoil sections and wing structures was in its infancy, wing loadings were very low, which augured well for small turning circles. But over the decades wing loadings have become very much higher, as is illustrated by the chart in Figure 12.4, and today's extremely high wing loadings, whilst advantageous for other design requirements, actually militate against performing tight turns. Thus today's drive to make combat aircraft more manoeuvrable is in some respects a desire to get *back* to the tighter turns which were possible on the more leisurely aircraft of yesteryear.

(b) The second factor $1/\rho$ must also be a minimum, which means that the density of atmosphere must be as high as possible. This is achieved at the lowest possible altitude, and therefore the smallest radius turns can be executed at sea level.

(c) C_L, being on the bottom of a fraction, must be as high as possible. In general this simply means that the aircraft must ideally fly at $C_{L_{max}}$. However, flying in a turn at minimum altitude using maximum angle of attack is clearly highly danger-ous, since these are ideal conditions for entering into an unrecoverable spin, and so in practice a smaller angle of attack limit must be used to provide an adequate safety margin.

We have so far worked on the assumption that the aircraft is turning at a fixed load factor (and its related bank angle), but we will complete the investigation by looking at the effect that varying n has on the turning circle radius. It is not obvious how the factor $\dfrac{n}{\sqrt{n^2 - 1}}$ in Equation 12.8 affects the value of r, and so let us look at a table of values covering the likely operating range.

n	1	2	3	4	5	6	7	8
$\dfrac{n}{\sqrt{n^2 - 1}}$	∞	1.155	1.061	1.033	1.021	1.014	1.010	1.008

As we would expect, at $n = 1$ the factor has the value of infinity, which simply means that the radius of turn is infinite since the aircraft is not in a turn at all. Between $n = 1$ and $n = 2$ its value clearly falls very rapidly indeed down to 1.15, but if we are looking at *smallest* turning circles we shall not be interested in load factors as low as this. We notice that at the other end of the table the factor is levelling off towards a limit of 1, and it will never drop below 1 even as n approaches infinity. We may thus say that, in any reasonably tight turn (only a 3% error at $n = 4$, and getting better as n increases above that value), to a good approximation this factor equals 1, which is its upper limit, and it could therefore be completely omitted from the equation without undue detriment to the value of r. Hence for any given aircraft there is a minimum-size turning circle which is independent of the load factor or the bank angle being applied. As an arbitrary example, for an aircraft with a wing loading of 400 kg/m² (i.e. 3924 N/m²) and a maximum lift coefficient of 2.5, flying at sea-level where the air density is 1.225 kg/m³, the minimum possible turning radius from Equation 12.8 (regardless of bank angle or load factor) is $\dfrac{3924 \times 2}{1.225 \times 9.8 \times 12.5}$ which equals 261 metres.

How does this new insight into the behaviour relate to the manoeuvre margin diagram of Figure 12.2? Assuming that the pilot will use maximum available coefficient of lift (allowing a margin of safety), there are two parameters open to him to vary in order to achieve the smallest turn: the air speed and the load factor. Minimising air speed means moving to the curved left-hand boundary of the manoeuvre margin diagram, and since B is further to the left (i.e. lower speed) than C, B would be the best point to operate at if minimum speed were the only consideration. But at B n only equals 1, at which no turning is possible at all, and so it is necessary to move up the curve from B towards C as load factor increases. How far up? The answer to this must be decided from the table of $\dfrac{n}{\sqrt{n^2 - 1}}$ against n, from which we see that there is very clearly a law of diminishing returns. At a glance it would look as if $n = 4$ might be a sensible figure, since for any value of n greater than this there is scarcely any reduction at all in turn radius. Thus values of n greater than about 4 will only give very marginal improvements in turning circle radius, making it not worthwhile to try to get near the structural limit or the buffet boundary of Figure 12.2. We may conclude that, *for small radius turns*, it would be advantageous to find ways of extending the C_L range to a higher maximum value, so that the curve BC would be pushed up and a higher load factor could be attained at the lower speeds, but there is scarcely anything to be gained by pulling more than about 4g.

Maximum Rate Turn
As well as the size of the turning circle, we could also be interested in *how long* it takes to perform a complete turn, or perhaps more usefully in practice, half a turn, to face back in the direction that the aircraft came from. To investigate this, we need to consider the angular rate at which the aircraft is progressing round its turning circle. Here it is more convenient to talk about angles in *radians* rather than degrees. A radian is an angle measurement which is derived as the ratio of two lengths, so that it is conveniently absolute and dimensionless, whereas the size of a degree has been initially arbitrarily chosen. In Figure 12.5 the angle θ in radians is *defined* as the circular arc length s divided by the radius r of the arc. If we think of a point object moving along the arc from the top to the right, its speed V is the time rate of change[6] of s, which we can write as $\dot{s}$. Now the angular speed, which we will denote by ω, is equal to the time rate of change of the angle, or $\dot{\theta}$, which is the rate of change of s/r. Since r is constant, this may be written as $\dot{s}/r$, or V/r. Thus we can very simply express the turning rate ω, in radians per second, by the equation:

$$\omega = \frac{V}{r} \text{ radians per second} \qquad \textbf{Equation 12.9}$$

[6]Rates of change are explained in Chapter 6 of *Flightwise – Principles of Aircraft Flight*, under the heading 'Rates of Change'.

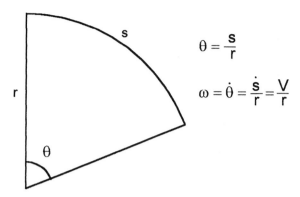

$$\theta = \frac{s}{r}$$

$$\omega = \dot\theta = \frac{\dot s}{r} = \frac{V}{r}$$

Figure 12.5   Angles and angular rates in radian measure

Aircraft usually have a rate-of-turn indicator amongst their flight instruments, incorporated into the same instrument as the slip indicator which we looked at in Figure 9.9. The two devices together are sometimes known as a *turn coordinator* since in conjunction with each other they assist the pilot in coordinating the controls during banked turns. Some rate-of-turn indicators show a view of an aircraft from the rear, which banks as the aircraft banks and whose wing-tips move over one or more calibration marks each side. For example, in a Cessna Skylane light touring aircraft, the only calibration mark each side indicates that the aircraft is in a turn which, if sustained, would take the aircraft through a complete 360° in 2 minutes. Others have a vertical needle which deflects to left or right to give a reading of the turn rate. In either case the instrument is driven by a gyroscope which responds to the aircraft's yawing and/or rolling motion.

A pilot is not usually concerned with what units the rate of turn indicator is calibrated in (if any), and in fact (as in the Cessna example mentioned above) the time taken for the aircraft to complete a full circle is of more practical value than the angular speed. We would therefore like to transform Equation 12.9 into a form which gives the time taken for one complete 360° turn (the periodic time, which we will call *T*), but before we can do this we need to convert the equation from one giving radians per second to one giving revolutions per second. In Figure 12.5, if we sweep the right-hand radius line further clockwise until it has gone round a full circle and back up to the top, the angle θ is 360° – but what is that in radians? By definition, it is the arc length of a full circle divided by the radius, or in other words the circumference of the circle (which is $2\pi r$) divided by *r*, or 2π. Thus 360° equals 2π radians (or a bit more than 6 radians). So if we want to turn the angular speed ω from radians per second to revolutions per second, we must *divide* by 2π (because the answer must be smaller). Thus:

$$\omega = \frac{1}{2\pi} \times \frac{V}{r} \text{ revolutions per second.}$$

To find the period T we wish to know how many seconds per revolution this is equivalent to, and so we simply require the reciprocal:

$$T = \frac{2\pi r}{V} \text{ seconds.}$$

We can replace the r in this equation by using the expression for r which was derived from the lift formula and is given at Equation 12.8:

$$T = \frac{2\pi}{V}\left(\frac{W}{S} \times \frac{1}{\rho} \times \frac{2}{g} \times \frac{1}{C_L} \times \frac{n}{\sqrt{n^2 - 1}}\right)$$

and after extracting the constant terms to the front this becomes:

$$T = \frac{4\pi}{g} \times \frac{1}{V} \times \frac{W}{S} \times \frac{1}{\rho} \times \frac{1}{C_L} \times \frac{n}{\sqrt{n^2 - 1}} \text{ seconds.} \quad \textbf{Equation 12.10}$$

Using this equation we can now answer the question 'what must the designer or pilot do to make sure that the time taken to complete a turn is as short as possible?' Comparing Equation 12.10 with Equation 12.8, we see that the only difference (apart from a change in the constant factor from $2/g$ to $4\pi/g$) is the inclusion of the additional factor $1/V$. We thus conclude that to minimise the time taken for a complete circle depends as before on having the lowest possible wing loading and flying at sea level air density, but beyond this the answers are not so straightforward. The remaining parameters C_L, V and n are all interrelated, the first two by the lift formula and the last two by the manoeuvre margin diagram. It is therefore no longer obvious (and in fact it is *not* a requirement) that $C_{L_{max}}$ should be used, since the requirement to raise V pushes the operating point towards the right on the manoeuvre margin diagram. All we can say (without going further into the mathematics) is that the product of $\frac{1}{V}$ and $\frac{1}{C_L}$ and $\frac{n}{\sqrt{n^2 - 1}}$ should be a minimum. Bearing in mind the weak dependence of the last factor on n at values above about 4 that we observed earlier, we may say in the first instance that it is required to achieve the maximum product of V and C_L, and then to modify this by increasing n if found to be advantageous.

Referring back again to the manoeuvre margin diagram at Figure 12.2, since the operating point has now moved away from the extreme left-hand side of the grey area, the curve BC is less likely to be a constraint preventing the point moving *up* the diagram to higher *n* values. Thus for maximum turn rates it is much more likely than for minimum radius turns that the upper margin CD (modified by buffet considerations) will become the effective boundary. Furthermore, the very high induced drag experienced at high angles of attack means that very often the available thrust is not able to sustain the high speeds which are required, and so a considerably reduced upper speed limit may be forcibly imposed for sustaining very high rate turns.

Departures – Inertia Coupling

We have been dealing with flying right up to the extreme limits of the manoeuvre margin in turning flight, and so we should take a look at what lies just the other side of the fence. In Chapter 9 in the section headed 'Stalling and Spinning' we discussed the features of stalling that were control related, as well as looking fairly closely at how a spin occurs and what it consists of, and so we will not repeat those topics here. But there is an additional way in which many high-speed combat aircraft are prone to departing from controlled flight, which is known as *inertia coupling*. Although this is not a purely aerodynamic phenomenon, it is certainly a very serious constraint on the controllability of many aircraft in tight manoeuvres, and, anyway, the book title says nothing about aerodynamics only!

Inertia coupling is an unwelcome consequence of the way in which the shape, and hence the mass distribution, of high performance aircraft has evolved. The traditional aircraft form when seen in plan view gives the approximate appearance of a doubly symmetric cross with wings of roughly the same proportions as the fuselage. Frequently the wings will be heavily loaded with fuel and may also support two or four engines spaced out along their span, and this lateral mass distribution very approximately corresponds with the fore-and-aft mass distribution of the fuselage plus its contents of systems, passengers, cargo and crew. As a result, the moment of inertia (which we introduced in the section 'Building the Model' of Chapter 5 under the subheading 'Newton's Second Law and Moment of Inertia') about the x-axis on such aircraft is of the same order of magnitude as that about the y-axis. But, particularly in combat aircraft, the pursuit of high speed combined with the need to withstand very large load factors has gone hand in hand with the requirement for ever more space to house engines and a plethora of other systems. This has resulted in wings becoming smaller and shorter, whilst the fuselage has grown ever longer, in order to accommodate all these systems in addition to the fuel (which can no longer be stored in the very small thin wings), without an undue increase in cross-sectional area. An extreme example of

Figure 12.6   Mitsubishi F-1 – large ratio of pitching:rolling moment of inertia

this process can be seen in the Lockheed F-104 Starfighter shown in Figure 6.16, although its interception mission requirements did not allow it to be optimised in design for extreme manoeuvrability. But, slightly less pronounced, these characteristics are typical of the majority of today's high-speed and high-performance combat aircraft, and are strongly exemplified by the older Japanese Mitsubishi F-1, a single-seat supersonic close-support fighter which is shown in Figure 12.6. The resulting mass distribution means that the pitching moment of inertia of the fuselage about the lateral axis (I_y) is very much greater than the rolling moment of inertia of the wings about the longitudinal axis (I_x). This feature of a pitching moment of inertia that is large compared with the rolling moment of inertia gives rise to a variety of behavioural oddities that we will now examine, and which may be experienced in different aircraft types to varying degrees when performing tight manoeuvres in certain flight conditions.

Yaw divergence
Yaw divergence is something that the aircraft does because it thinks it is a gyroscope, and so we must first of all spend a few moments looking at what a gyroscope is and how it works, by reference to

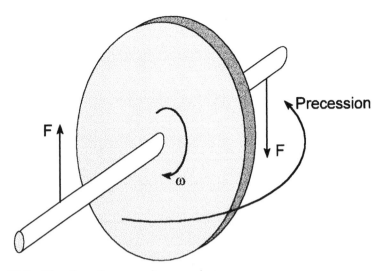

Figure 12.7   Direction of gyroscopic precession

Figure 12.7. The figure shows a flywheel spinning clockwise (as viewed in the figure) about its axis, which is horizontal. A moment is exerted on the axle by means of the couple consisting of the two forces F, and the axis about which this couple is being applied (not shown) is also horizontal, but at right-angles to the axis of the flywheel. For example, the couple of the forces F could be provided by the hands of a person supporting the spinning flywheel by its axle, by applying a greater upward force through the left hand (as viewed in the figure) than the right.

Anyone who has handled a gyroscope knows that the way that it responds to this situation is far from what is expected, and it feels very odd. Rather than the gyroscope tipping over in the way that the applied couple would lead one to expect, it does indeed rotate, but in another direction altogether. The motion is called *precession*, and it is a rotational rate about the one axis we have not yet considered, the vertical axis. If the person holding the gyroscope (in the previous paragraph) were to be standing on a small turntable, he or she would start rotating anticlockwise on the spot, as viewed from above. Although the behaviour is unexpected, it is certainly very real, and the direction of the precession can quickly be predicted by the following simple rule. Imagine that the same applied moment as in the figure were produced instead by a pair of forces, one on the top of the flywheel acting away and to the right, and an equal and opposite one acting at the bottom to the left and towards you. Now if this pair of forces were carried round through 90° with the rotation of the flywheel, what was the top one will be acting away and to the right on the point nearest to you, and the force that was previously at the bottom will be acting towards you and to the left on the furthest back point from you. Now the precession occurs in the direction of this new couple, which is the direction indicated by the arrow labelled 'precession'. To summarise, we may state the precession direction rule as follows:

> **The direction of precession is as if the couple causing it were acting 90°**
> **further round the flywheel in its direction of rotation.**

Gyroscopic precession is used to very great effect in many flight instruments and systems, but it also presents a problem on some propeller-driven aircraft, which was particularly acute on old tail-draggers using massive radial piston engines which rotated with the propellers. When sufficient speed was attained during the take-off run the tail had to be lifted from the ground to the normal flying attitude, which meant that a fairly large and rapid nose-down pitching rotation occurred. Assuming that the propeller(s) rotated anticlockwise (as viewed facing forwards), the nose-down pitching moment on them would effectively be carried round through 90° in the direction of spin, and this would result in the aircraft yawing strongly to the right. The same effect (to a lesser degree) is experienced by most propeller-driven aircraft whenever they pitch nose-up or down, and this presents an additional requirement for the rudder, which must be used to compensate. Multi-engined aircraft *could* have an equal number of engines rotating in each direction to counteract each other, but the problem is not serious enough to justify the very great manufacturing cost that would be incurred in building two opposite-handed versions of the same power plant.

The long thin combat aircraft has a very substantial moment of inertia about the lateral (y) axis, and this combined with the nose-up pitch rate that occurs during any pull-up manoeuvre (such as during a sustained turn) means that the aircraft behaves very much like a gyroscope rotating in the x–z plane about the y-axis. Of course the rotational rate, the pitch rate q, is relatively low compared with that of a flywheel, but the moment of inertia is large, and it is their product $I_y q$, the angular momentum (to be discussed shortly), which is of significance. The situation is illustrated in Figure 12.8, in which all conventions correspond with those introduced in Chapter 2 under the heading 'Aircraft Stability Parameters'. However, in addition to following the argument by reference to this figure, I suggest that you dust off your aircraft model and keep that to hand, since we will be looking at a very three-dimensional situation.

During a sustained pull-up at a pitch rate q, the pilot applies right roll control to produce a rolling moment of L; both q and L are positive in accordance with our conventions. According to the rule by

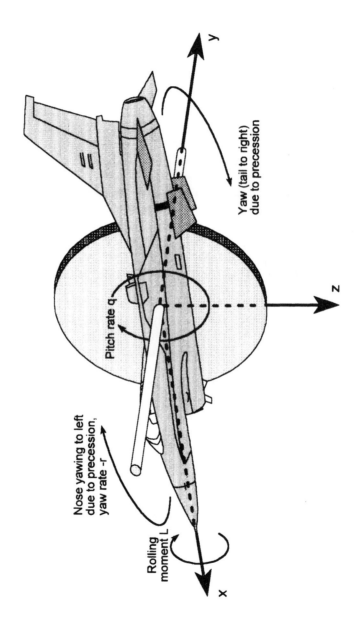

Figure 12.8   Gyroscopic effect on combat aircraft in pull-up, viewed from below

which we can determine the direction of precession, instead of the rolling moment effectively pushing the top of the flywheel to the right and the bottom to the left, we must think of it as if acting 90° further round in the direction of rotation of the flywheel – or fuselage. Consequently it is as though there were a couple acting to the right at the back of the flywheel and to the left at its front – in other words, a yawing moment – and this will have the effect of yawing the nose to the *left*, a negative yaw rate. It is likely that the pilot would have wished for a yaw to the right to accompany the bank following the roll input, and so a yaw to the left would be very disconcerting. Furthermore, it is exactly the same effect as adverse aileron yaw which we discussed in Chapter 9 in the section 'Cross-coupling in Normal Flight', although produced by a totally different cause. If the aircraft is prone to adverse aileron yaw the problem will be exacerbated by the gyroscopic effect.

We need not leave an explanation of this strange phenomenon in the realms of mystery, since we have already covered all the necessary concepts to enable us to analyse gyroscopic precession, and even to find a quantitative relationship between the pitch rate and the precessional yaw rate. Just to refresh your memory on a couple of points, we shall first of all need to call upon the fact that rotational vectors (except for angular displacements) may be fully represented and treated as vector lines drawn in the direction of the axis of rotation. They can then be added by the normal procedure for combining vectors.

We shall also require a slight modification of Newton's Second Law, which for rotational motion is $M = I\alpha$ (where M is the moment, I the moment of inertia and α the angular acceleration) corresponding term by term with the linear version $F = ma$. We will write the acceleration a of this linear motion equation as $\dot{V}$ where V is the particle's velocity, so that the equation can be written $F = m\dot{V}$. It makes no difference to the right-hand side if we find the rate of change[7] of the velocity first and then multiply by the mass, or do it the other way round, i.e. multiply the velocity by the mass first and then find the rate of change of the resulting product. This is because mass is a scalar quantity, so that when it multiplies a vector quantity such as velocity it merely alters its magnitude and not its direction. Doing the operation in the alternative order (multiplying first) means that we actually have a more versatile and general form of Newton's Second Law, and it gives rise to a new quantity which needs a name. The quantity is mV, the product of mass and velocity, and it is called *momentum*.

[7]If you need any help with rates of change, there is a section on this in Chapter 6 of *Flightwise – Principles of Aircraft Flight*.

[8]Although we have only been discussing the magnitude aspect of it here, **V** is a vector (as we know), and so m**V** is also a vector in the same direction as **V** but with m times its magnitude. As we said above, after multiplying we must take the rate of change of the resulting new quantity in order to satisfy Newton's Second Law. So we may rewrite Newton's Second Law in the new form as follows:

> **Force equals rate of change of momentum, where momentum is the product of mass and velocity.**

In the gyroscope situation we are involved with rotational quantities, and so we need the rotational equivalent of this new formulation. Replacing term by term the linear quantities with their equivalent rotational quantities, we have:

> **Moment equals rate of change of angular momentum, where angular momentum is the product of moment of inertia and angular velocity.**

We are now ready to apply these ideas to the gyroscope, and we will do so using the usual aircraft conventions and notation, so that afterwards we shall be able to apply the result directly to the aircraft situation without more ado. Figure 12.9 shows an extract of the relevant parts of Figure 12.8, together with a vector triangle that we will develop. If you find it a little difficult to relate to the figure, remember that you are looking upwards from below. It is the rate of change of angular momentum that we are eventually interested in, and so we must examine how the angular momentum itself behaves. The angular momentum of the flywheel, by the definition above, is I**q**, and it is a vector in the direction of the y-axis, as shown in the vector triangle on the lower right. The result of applying a rolling moment **L** is that the flywheel precesses according to the rule we looked at earlier, which means that the entire gyroscope with its x and y axes rotates about the z-axis, anticlockwise when looking down from above so that the vector **r** is upwards. After a very short period of time which we will call dt, the angular momentum vector I**q** has rotated with the y-axis through a corresponding very small angle dψ, (ψ being the conventional symbol for yaw angle) to a new position also drawn in the vector diagram, labelled as I**q**′. The angular momentum has changed in direction only. Now this new vector I**q**′ must be the resultant of adding a little angular momentum vector d(I**q**) to the original vector I**q**, forming an isosceles triangle which lies in the horizontal plane as shown, with the arrowheads following the circus-elephants rule of vector addition. This is another example in which vector 'addition' does not increase the magnitude of a vector but merely changes its direction.

[8]We will now revert to using bold symbols for the vector quantities, as **V** here, since their directions are important as well as their magnitudes.

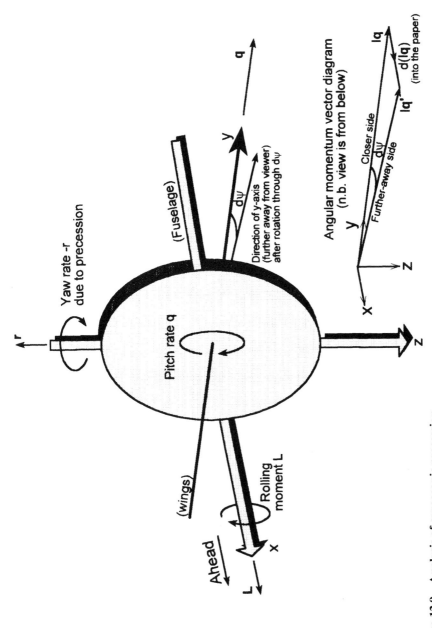

Figure 12.9   Analysis of gyroscopic precession

There is an important point to notice here, and it is that the direction of the vector d(I**q**) is exactly the same as the direction of the vector of the rolling moment **L**, i.e. parallel to the x-axis. (Don't forget that moments must also be rotational vector quantities, just as forces are linear vector quantities.) This confirms that Newton's Second Law for rotational motion really does apply in the way that we have presumed, since it says that the moment vector is a scalar (the moment of inertia) times another vector, the rate of change of angular momentum. Furthermore, the *rate* of change of angular momentum must be in the same direction as the *actual* change of angular momentum, since we only multiply or divide by a scalar (time) to change one to the other. Therefore these two vectors **L** and d(I**q**) cannot be other than in the same direction. This revelation also mathematically confirms our rule about the direction of precession.

We now want to express the new little vector, representing the amount of angular momentum that has been added, in terms of the angle dψ through which the vector I**q** has rotated, in order to find a relationship between the pitching angle and the yawing angle. The isosceles triangle is very thin so that its base is virtually the same length as a circular arc would have been, and so by the definition of an angle in radians we can state that:

$$d\psi = \frac{d(I\mathbf{q})}{I\mathbf{q}} \quad \text{or} \quad d(I\mathbf{q}) = I\mathbf{q} \times d\psi$$

Before we can apply Newton's Second Law, which says that the moment equals the moment of inertia times the *rate of change* of angular momentum, we must get this equation in terms of rates of change. We said that the little change that we have been considering occurs in a very short time dt, and so the rate of change of the quantities on each side of the equation is obtained simply by dividing by dt. Although this is only approximate for a little time period dt, it becomes exactly true if we then allow dt to shrink right down to zero – the basis of the method of calculus. Dividing both sides by dt we have:

$$\frac{d(I\mathbf{q})}{dt} = I\mathbf{q} \times \frac{d\psi}{dt}$$

Now the left-hand side of this equation is the rate of change of angular momentum, and so by Newton's Second Law it equals the moment being applied, which is the rolling moment **L**. Furthermore, the term $\dfrac{d\psi}{dt}$ on the right is the yaw rate **r**. We can therefore rewrite the equation in terms just of quantities with which we are familiar, as:

$$\mathbf{L} = I\mathbf{qr}$$

We have reached the end of our quest. Apart from making it possible to understand the apparent mystery of precession, we have finished up with a quantitative statement which tells us that, if a certain fixed rolling moment is applied to a given aircraft (i.e. constant L and I_y), the rate of yaw divergence r is *inversely* proportional to the pitch rate q. This surprising result means that, if yaw divergence is going to occur, it is in fact a more threatening phenomenon at lower than at higher pitch rates! So if we thought that it was a bit far fetched to consider a pitching-up aircraft as a gyroscope, how wrong we were!

In practice the problem of yaw divergence is best overcome by providing the aircraft with adequate directional (weathercock) stability, and a solution which has frequently been applied is to increase the size of the tail fin, which is liable to become somewhat shielded during a pull-up. Beyond this, restrictions which disallow pilots to roll continuously through more than 180° have often been imposed, since the yaw divergence and sideslip effects resulting from a continuous roll have been known to be catastrophic.

Pitch divergence

By comparison with yaw divergence, pitch divergence is much easier to understand. It used to be a rare occurrence which was normally only encountered at very high altitudes, but today with the emphasis on manoeuvring at extremely large angles of attack it has become commonplace. Rather than complicated diagrams this time, all you will need is your trusty model in your hand. Once again this is a feature of those combat aircraft which have the majority of their mass distributed fore-and-aft along the longitudinal axis.

At very high altitudes the density of air (one of the factors in the lift formula) is very low, so that a considerable lift coefficient, and thus angle of attack, will be required to achieve sufficient lift. Take your model and 'fly' it across in front of your face at a very large angle of attack. Whilst doing so, imagine that the pilot applies a rolling moment to the right with the controls. Because of the large angle of attack, the resulting roll will not occur purely about the aircraft's longitudinal inertia axis as we usually assume, but to a much better approximation the aircraft will roll about its velocity vector – in other words, about the line of its flight path. Because the nose is well above this line (and the tail well below it), it follows that the nose (and tail) will swing in a fairly wide circle about the velocity vector line. This is a situation in which the centripetal force required to restrain nose and tail in circular paths is not available, and both the nose and the tail will tend to swing out further from the roll axis, resulting in the nose pitching up strongly. If the longitudinal static stability of the aircraft is insufficient to take care of this, an unpleasant departure from normal flight can follow.

Autorotation

We have already considered (in Chapter 9 under 'Stalling and Spinning') the purely aerodynamic cause of autorotation, in which a dropping wing can cause the wing to stall and hence lose, rather than gain, lift. But there is another rather peculiar and unusual way in which autorotation may occur, which results from the concentration of the aircraft's mass along its longitudinal axis in a fuselage which is very long compared with the wing-span. For this reason it is classed as an inertial coupling effect, but its cause is really aerodynamic. Once again, models at the ready, please.

First of all, let us consider a long thin combat aircraft flying straight and level at a moderate speed and angle of attack, so that the fore-and-aft line of the fuselage, which we will call its inertia axis, is inclined a little upwards from the flight path direction, the stability axis. When a pure rolling command is input through the roll controls, we may assume with good justification that the rolling takes place primarily about the inertia axis, so that the inertia x-axis virtually stays in the same orientation that it starts from. Now hold your model in front of you flying wings-level in this attitude, and roll it to the right about the axis of the fuselage through to a full 90° of bank. The wings are now vertical, but the fuselage is still pointing upwards relative to the flight path as it was before the roll. Consequently there is now a side-flow coming at the aircraft from its right-hand side, (due to a yaw angle and not to sideslip, since the centre of gravity is still travelling along the original flight path). The aircraft's L_v or rolling stability will consequently be stabilising in its influence, providing the lower wing with more lift (to the right), thus opposing the initial roll and tending to roll the aircraft back to where it came from. Because of the high I_v value compared with the low I_x value, the directionally stabilising effect of the fin will take considerably longer to take effect, whereas there is very little inertial resistance to rolling.

Some aircraft are so designed, on the other hand, that the angle at which the wing is attached to the fuselage, (to be precise, the angle between the wing mean chord and aircraft's inertia axis) is large, so that when cruising at a moderate speed and relatively low angle of attack, the longitudinal inertia axis is actually inclined downwards below the velocity vector. If you set this situation up on your model, and then as before roll the model through 90° to the right about the inertia x-axis as happens in practice, you will find that the side-flow is now coming from the aircraft's left side, so that the L_v or 'dihedral' effect will be to try to roll it further. Thus the roll tends to be self-per-petuating rather than self-limiting, and it is in such circumstances that autorotation can occur.

Although for simplicity we postulated level flight just now, the circumstances leading to autorotation are in practice more likely to occur when roll is demanded during low-*g* manoeuvres, such as push-overs or bunts. There is a particular combat (and aerobatic) manoeu-vre which is in effect a very quick way to lose forward speed and commence flying in the opposite direction. It consists of pulling up into a half-loop, and when inverted at the top rolling through 180° to end up flying back in the direction one had come from. At the top of the loop the load factor will be low and may frequently even be nega-tive, with the nose of the aircraft pointing up above the tangent to the flight path, i.e. outwards from the circle of the loop. The subsequent roll is then being executed in just the conditions which can precipitate the autorotation. Although we said that autorotation is primarily an aerodynamic phenomenon, the high roll rates that can result from it may be conducive to pitch divergence, especially if the roll continues to 180° and the roll axis modifies itself to being closer to the velocity vector.

TOWARDS GREATER AGILITY

So far we have been concentrating on manoeuvrability, the tightness of turns, but now we turn our attention to considering ways in which the agility of an aircraft may be enhanced, both for the purpose of outmanoeuvring an adversary in aerial combat and also for improving the ability to aim at a ground target which the aircraft is rapidly approaching in a hostile environment. There are basically two facets to this pursuit of agility. On the one hand, we will be interested in *how quickly* an aircraft can change from one manoeuvre state to another; how rapidly it can roll into a balanced turn, and how a pitch-up (or down) can be achieved with minimum adverse pitch transient. On the other hand, we will investigate whether the manoeuvre boundaries can be extended, and if there are any useful *new ways* in which we can do things that conventional approaches to control have not previously bothered with on the premise that 'if it ain't broke, don't fix it!'.

Rapid Manoeuvre Entry

Let us go back first of all to the subject of pitch transients that we first discussed in Chapter 10. In Figure 10.3 the problem was illustrated by reference to an old biplane, but it is just as topical with today's fight-ers. Let us suppose that a fighter pilot wishes to shake off an enemy aircraft which is menacingly pursuing him close on his tail. There are a number of evasive actions he could try, but in order for us to deal with just one thing at a time, let us suppose that he decides on a pull-up into a half-loop, at the top of which he may roll out to reverse his direction of flight, or do something else. Now the two aircraft are flying at the same speed (which close pursuit would imply) and are at the same altitude and hence air density. Let us furthermore assume for the sake of argument that they both have the same wing loading W/S and are capable of achieving the same manoeuvrability limits, whether it be the maximum C_L value attainable or the structurally limited load factor. Again for simplicity of argument, let us suppose that the time taken for the pursuing aircraft to cover the distance between them is exactly the same as the rear aircraft pilot's mental reaction time between observing and mimicking the manoeuvre of the front aircraft, so that they both start the manoeuvre at the same place. If all these conditions are precisely true, the two aircraft would be equally manoeuvrable, and neither would have any advantage over the other. The second could follow the first round the loop and the front aircraft could not shake it off.

It is in situations such as this that agility may provide the key to having the upper hand, and in this instance the pitch transient response may make all the difference. A conventional tailplane exerts a down-load to achieve a pull-up before the lift of the wings has increased to the required amount, and so the net lift is initially reduced. Consequently the two aircraft, if conventionally tailed, will both move downwards a little before pulling up into the loop – scarcely noticeable since they are both doing it together. However, if the front aircraft were equipped with canards instead of a conventional tailplane for pitch control (and with no other difference), the pitch transient would be favourable since the canards exert an upward force to pitch the nose up, and so the aircraft would move up immediately and into the loop more quickly. This may well give the front aircraft enough of an edge in the engagement to be able to shake off the pursuer, or even to loop round and fly in behind it, so swapping rôles with it. The situation is illustrated in Figure 12.10.

Exactly the same advantage is had by the canard aircraft over the tailplane one in a turn, but in this case the rate of roll and the quickness with which a roll can be commenced and arrested must also be taken into account. The aspect ratio of the wings will effect their roll damping (L_r), but the chief consideration here is the effectiveness of the roll controls (L_ξ). We have looked earlier at the problems associated with ailerons, and have seen that tailerons have the drawback of having a very limited moment arm, as well as having to share their authority with pitch trimming and control. We have also seen that dif-

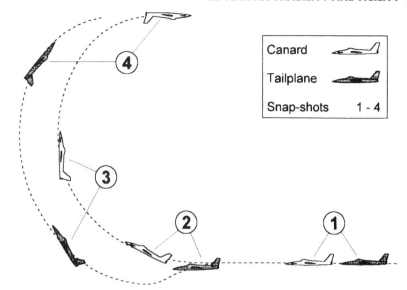

Figure 12.10   **Advantage of canards to a pursued aircraft in an evasive pull-up**

ferential canards are usually a non-starter for providing roll control, because of the downwash that they generate over the wings. Therefore probably the most effective solution in most cases is the use of spoilers, especially since they also overcome any propensity to adverse aileron yaw. If adverse aileron yaw is a feature of the aircraft, it will have a similar disadvantage (in the lateral plane) to the pitch transient problem which we have just considered, since the rudder force needed to compensate for it will be outwards from the centre of the proposed turn.

Extending the Manoeuvre Boundaries

Conventionally the centripetal force for all manoeuvres (turns, pull-ups and any combination of these) is produced by wing lift, and as we have seen the limitations of this occur as often due to meeting the $C_{L_{max}}$ boundary of the manoeuvre margin diagram as the structural limit. The question of enhancing $C_{L_{max}}$ suggests the possibility of using the aircraft's high-lift devices such as trailing edge flaps and leading edge slats and slots in order to tighten up turns. Indeed, these can be and sometimes are used for this purpose, but it means that their design has to be approached in such a way that they are not constrained by their structural strength to be used only at low speeds, as landing flaps usually are, or that they are too slow and inconvenient to deploy or retract.

Today very extensive research is going on into more extreme ways of extending the $C_{L_{max}}$ boundary, and designers and developers are busily experimenting with aircraft that are capable of fully controlled flight at extremely large angles of attack of around 70°, and in some cases even more than 90°. Clearly at such angles a conventional aerofoil is way beyond its stalling angle, and furthermore lift (which is defined as the component of the aerodynamic force perpendicular to the free stream airflow) is now nearer to being parallel to the wing chord line than normal to it, and engine thrust plays a most important part in providing lift. Drag is also extremely high in such manoeuvres whilst little thrust remains in the flight direction, so that the aircraft slows down very dramatically to extremely low speeds, and this deceleration in the flight direction can produce high load factors on the aircraft structure and crew.

So how are such seemingly impossible feats to be contemplated? Many ingenious approaches are being studied and tried, but chiefly they depend on three separate lines of enquiry. Firstly, much greater use is being made of the thrust of the jet engine(s) than traditionally in the past, by 'vectoring' it. The simplest approach to *vectored thrust*, as the technique is called, is simply to deflect the jet engine efflux by special thrust-vectoring 'paddles', independently either upwards or downwards relative to the aircraft, or to one side or the other. This approach can be and is being used by modified existing aircraft whose jet efflux emerges at the rear. They essentially work like aerodynamic surfaces, in that they deflect an airflow and hence receive a reaction force in the opposite direction, but the forces are substantial since they are in an extremely high-speed airflow which the paddles can deflect through quite large angles.

Being at the tail, as well as producing a body force on the aircraft these paddles produce strong pitching and yawing moments about the centre of gravity when deployed, which is not always desirable, although it can be made use of in some circumstances. But thrust vectoring could be very useful if the vectored force could act through the centre of gravity. There is one combat aircraft that has precisely this facility (in the longitudinal plane only), and that is the British Aerospace Harrier jump-jet which first flew in 1960, and it and its derivatives such as the GR5 and AV-8B have been in operational use ever since. Being designed initially and primarily for its vertical take-off and landing capability, its four thrust nozzles are uniformly distributed around the centre of gravity, so that it lifts and hovers rather like a four-legged table. Because of this central position of the thrusting nozzles, it was soon discovered that its potential for vectoring its thrust during forward flight gave it tremendous agility as a combat aircraft. This technique of *vectoring in forward flight* is affectionately known as *VIFFing*, and it was put to the test and was found invaluable in the Falklands conflict of 1982. If the Harrier is being pursued by another aircraft, the pilot can vector the thrust nozzles downwards (i.e. the thrust upwards), thus providing lift both to compensate for the lift lost due to the rapid reduction in speed as the drag exceeds the residual horizontal component of thrust and to raise the aircraft above the pursuer's flight path. The pursuing aircraft then has no choice but to overtake, whereupon the Harrier pilot can simply recover to the normal flight speed, being now in an ideal position to attack the enemy aircraft from behind.

Although the vectoring of thrust relative to the aircraft's longitudinal axis with nozzles or paddles offers far-reaching possibilities, the very action of inclining the aircraft itself at a large angle of attack to the airflow automatically vectors the thrust in a most marked way, without any use of adjustable paddles or nozzles. In any conventional tight turn, there is a component of thrust acting centripetally, which we have tended to overlook, but when angles of attack of around 70° plus are being contemplated, by far the major component of the thrust is acting towards the centre of the turning circle. But two caveats must be borne in mind. Firstly, there is very little forward component of thrust left in such situations (which may be an advantage or a disadvantage), and secondly, at such extreme attitudes (and possibly very low forward air speeds) gas turbine engines are in very great danger of failing because of the disturbed airflow into the intake, and it presents the engine developers with an enormous challenge to produce gas turbine engines which will operate reliably and consistently under such conditions.

After vectored thrust, the second line of enquiry towards flying at very large angles of attack is to investigate and make use of the modified features of the airflow around the stalled aircraft. The conventional aerodynamics of smooth attached flow is largely replaced by separated flow with a great amount of turbulence, but as was shown in Chapter 13 of *Flightwise – Principles of Aircraft Flight* under the heading 'Leading Edge Vortices – The Plus Side', separation can also give rise to the formation of highly ordered and stable vortices, within which the pressure is very low. If such vortices can be generated in the correct places on demand, they can produce very significant aerodynamic forces, not only on the wings but also on the fuselage and other flying surfaces.

But on their own these two lines of enquiry would not be powerful and versatile enough to cope with the extreme and outlandish requirements of flying safely at very large angles of attack. The third, and the unifying, feature is the extension of the old ideas of aerodynamic control surfaces to provide the aircraft with full control under all the extreme conditions to which it is to be subjected. This necessitates the universal use (in pitch) of all-moving slab control surfaces, placed where they will not experience aerodynamic interference from other parts of the aircraft, and which can be deflected under power through extremely large angles very rapidly indeed so that they are always pointing with an appropriate angle of attack into the local relative airflow. The management of such demanding high-speed systems is well beyond the capability of a human pilot, and so it is only the arrival and maturity of digital computer technology, coupled with sophisticated actuators, that make such systems possible. Additionally, the use of such high-speed, computer operated control systems means that the traditional requirements of stability need no longer be a constraint. This gives a further substantial boost to the drive towards greater agility, since it and stability are by their very nature not good bedfellows.

Direct Force Control

In pursuing ultimate manoeuvrability and agility, it seems that no holds should be barred, and that the preconceived conventions of aircraft control should be no deterrent to trying completely new ideas. It was this philosophy that made the investigation of the ideas of *direct force control* become fashionable some time ago, and like most fashions there will be some useful legacies for the future, whilst other ideas will be relegated to the dustbin as gimmicks.

The idea is actually based on the resolution of the fallacy or misunderstanding that we elucidated at the start of Chapter 8. Controlling an aircraft does not imply reorientating it – this is primarily a function of stability during a manoeuvre – but of applying a direct force through the centre of gravity to give the aircraft, regarded as a particle, the required centripetal force. The phrase direct force control has been coined to refer primarily to extending this idea to translating (moving) an aircraft upwards or sideways *without* reorientating it. VIFFing as applied to the Harrier is an example, in which the aircraft as well as slowing down may be moved bodily upwards to a higher flight path parallel to the first, and to do this a pitching moment is also required to oppose the natural pitching up tendency caused by the aircraft's longitudinal stability. The same effect might be obtained by other means of lift augmentation such as the use of flaps, provided again that a nose-down pitching moment be provided to prevent the aircraft from adopting a circular path. The additional upward force need not be great, since it is not required to produce an acceleration (except when starting the manoeuvre) but an upward velocity that will be balanced by the 'downwards drag' (a Z_w effect) that the movement generates.

Such a manoeuvre (or the opposite, a reduction in lift to drop to a lower flight path) may be found useful in getting out of the way of an aircraft pursuing from behind, such as when VIFFing as described earlier. But the chief application which has motivated such thoughts is the repositioning of the aircraft when trying to line up with a ground target (either an enemy position to be fired at, or a runway on which it is proposed to land) without having to pitch the aircraft into an unsuitable attitude. This could be much quicker than the traditional pull-up and subsequent push-over (with accompanying pitch transients), and would also obviate the risk of losing sight of a target which has already been visually acquired. It would also remove the hazard of an adverse pitch transient (on a tailplane aircraft) during a pull-up near to the ground.

If this idea is viable vertically, why not horizontally? Is there any way in which the aircraft could be slid crabwise from one flight path to a new parallel one, whilst keeping the longitudinal axis parallel to the flight path throughout the movement? This would save considerable time by avoiding the convoluted blending of rolling and yawing motions that is otherwise required to achieve the same effect, whether primarily using ailerons or rudder (as discussed in Chapter 9), and would certainly be a boon in both of the aiming situations mentioned above.

Conventionally the main agents producing side-force are fin and fuselage, in the form of Y_v, but this merely resists a sideslip, and so cannot be used to achieve the required effect. A side-force (from 'rest', i.e. without any sideslip) may be generated by the rudder, and would be represented by the derivative Y_ζ, the left rudder pedal giving a force to the right, but the dominant effect would be a yawing moment due to N_ζ, which we do not want. Ideally we require a matching side-force to be produced on the nose at the same time, but if an additional fin were added there it would negate the directional stabilising effect of the aft fin, and that would be totally unacceptable.

A possible solution is to use the previously discussed lifting effects of deliberately generated vortices. If asymmetrically sized vortices can be produced in the airflow around the nose, they will create a side-force which can be matched by a balancing side-force on the fin in the same sideways direction, produced by deflection of the rudder, and the two opposing yawing moments will cancel out. At least two ways have been hit upon for achieving such asymmetric nose vortices. The first is being seriously explored at the time of writing, and it is to use vectored nozzles a little way behind the tip of the nose to blow compressed air from the engine in a swirling direction, making use of what is known as the *Coanda Effect*. Provided there is some angle of attack, a nose-cone naturally generates a pair of vortices in its wake as the flow separates on the two sides, and by directing the compressed air jet to one side or the other the vortices become asymmetrical in size and effectiveness as required. This use of the Coanda effect produces a side force by means of the Magnus effect which was discussed in the section headed 'Cylinder Lift in Real Flow' in Chapter 7 of *Flightwise – Principles of Aircraft Flight*.

Another way of producing the same effect was discovered by accident when investigating the use of canards for roll control. Although opposite deflection of canards did not turn out to be useful as a means of producing roll control, it did produce the unexpected result of a direct side-force on the fuselage. Canards have become well established for the other advantages that they bestow, and so it is possible that this bonus may be harnessed in the future.

*   *   *

So there are many things that could be done to enhance the manoeuvrability and agility of an aircraft, but they all require to be effectively managed if they are to be of value. Although man's ingenuity for thinking up new devices may be far from its limit, the pilot of a combat aircraft already has more than enough to do to occupy his mind and limbs in flying and managing the aircraft whilst carrying out a complex and demanding mission. This is where the computer comes into its own, and in the next chapter we shall look at what may be on offer from the advanced digital technology of today.

CHAPTER 13
Control-Configured Vehicles

INTRODUCTION

Despite the timelessness of Newton's Laws, their application in the field of aircraft control and stability has leapt forward by enormous bounds since the faltering efforts of the airmen and the chauffeurs of the nineteenth and early twentieth centuries. In its progress from Chapter 1 to Chapter 12 this book has loosely reflected the advances from the work and insight of George Cayley and the Wright brothers to the speed and almost inconceivable agility of today's and tomorrow's combat aircraft. But the physiology of the people who have to fly these fast and versatile machines is virtually unchanged from that of their forefathers, and the human pilot's ability to cope is now being overtaken by the demands of managing the recent advances in control concepts. If the potential is to be realised, the pilot needs considerable help.

Whether it is the inevitable consequence of the way that technology has matured, or mere good fortune, one cannot say, but this need is today being matched by the emergence of sophisticated digital computer technology. This has given rise to the now well-established concept of the *control-configured vehicle* or CCV, in which computers working in harmony with the pilot make decisions based on information received from flight data sensors, and on the strength of those decisions make adjustments to the aircraft's controlling mechanisms, thus directing certain aspects of its flight. This technology, which is known as *active control technology* or ACT, allows the designer to incorporate many ingenious ideas, some of which we have already looked at and others that we will review below. Thus the capability of the aircraft may be greatly extended in ways that, without ACT, would give an unaided pilot a totally unmanageable overload and would therefore be completely impracticable.

Active control technology is the product of a coalition of aerodynamics, electronics and control engineering. It is one aspect of a relatively new branch of aeronautical engineering known as avionics (an elision of aviation and electronics) incorporating all aspects of aeronautical technology which draw on electronics. Avionics is perhaps better known for its great impact on the more visible developments in the fields of aircraft instrumentation, guidance and navigation. Because of active control technology's great dependence on electronics and control engineering, it would be inappropriate for us in this book to attempt to discuss *how* it may be implemented in terms of the workings of its electronic, hydraulic and electro-mechanical black boxes. Rather, we will concentrate on *what* such systems may be expected to achieve, and how these possibilities extend the scope of the designer to produce an aircraft with superior stability and control features.

By the 1980s electronics and computer technology had already reached such a degree of sophistication that there was an air of smugness emerging amongst some of its protagonists. Computers, they were saying, had become so smart that, if you used enough appropriate electronic black boxes, you could make a brick s***-house fly! In other words, computers and electronic wizardry were actually becoming capable of *replacing* old-fashioned aerodynamics. This was a dangerous fallacy which, perhaps because of the few tragic accidents that have befallen CCV aircraft, seems fortunately to have faded from prominence. But as we look at some of the benefits that active control technology may bestow, we must bear firmly in mind that ultimately the flight and manoeuvrability of an aircraft is still utterly dependent on aerodynamic forces and moments, and that Newton's laws make no concessions whatsoever to clever electronic black boxes. Thus when the active control technologist gets an idea in his head, it is a *sine qua non* that the aerodynamicist must provide aerodynamic control surfaces or devices with sufficient authority and reliability to put it into effect.

POSSIBILITIES
Artificial Stability
Artificially providing an aircraft with stability to augment or even substitute for deliberately downgraded, or relaxed, static stability is one of the most important and influential capabilities of active control technology. At the end of Chapter 4 we considered at some length the benefits of relaxing an aircraft's longitudinal static stability, and we also considered the nature and the complexity of the task that a computer-operated pitch control surface would have to be able to cope with. Active control technology enables the pitch control surfaces to be operated very rapidly indeed in response to sensors sending the computers information about imminent nose-up or nose-down departures, so that even a very unstable aircraft can seem to be stable to the pilot. For example, in the case of the Grumman X-29A, an experimental aircraft with forward-swept wings and canards that was built to explore the suitability of this configuration for a high agility fighter, the centre of gravity was placed no less than 35% of the wing mean chord length *behind* the neutral point, making it extremely unstable in pitch. To cope with this, sensors monitor the pitch and the computers

and actuators adjust the aircraft's control surfaces 40 times in every second.

Stability Augmentation

During our investigation into lateral/directional dynamic stability in Chapter 7, we looked very closely at the causes and nature of the two principal lateral dynamic modes, the Dutch roll and the spiral dive mode. We were able to show that there is a direct conflict between the amount of dihedral stability L_v that is desirable for these two modes – too much, and the Dutch roll will be divergent, and too little and there will be an unstable spiral mode. If the necessary compromise cannot be struck, the more crucial Dutch roll has to take precedence since the slowness of the spiral mode means that it is controllable by the pilot.

However, on many aircraft (both large and small) it is found that when flying at high speed a satisfactory compromise value of L_v cannot be found, even granted the above concession. In such cases, priority in aerodynamic design is given to the higher L_v demands of the spiral dive mode, which on its own would mean that every rudder input by the pilot would result in an oscillatory yawing motion coupled with some rolling, and at worst the Dutch roll mode would be divergent, a totally unacceptable state of affairs. The solution is to force the Dutch roll into submission by means of tackling its dominant yawing oscillations, and this is achieved by applying a periodic rudder input to reinforce the fin's natural yaw damping. To illustrate, with model in hand, consider the aircraft yawing clockwise, the nose swinging from left to right across the flight path. The yaw damping derivative N_r of the fin is providing an anticlockwise moment $N_r r$ which is opposing the yawing motion, but is not on its own sufficient to subdue the oscillations, particularly because I_z (which is approximately the sum of I_x and I_y)[1] is large. It must be augmented by a rudder deflection ζ to the left which produces a tail fin force to the right and consequently an anticlockwise yawing moment $N_\zeta \zeta$ as required. If the yawing motion still overshoots the central position, this rudder input must be reversed to damp down the yaw back the other way, until the motion stops.

Theoretically it would be quite possible for the pilot to do this by pressing with the left foot when the nose is swinging to the right and with the right foot when swinging to the left. But for a start the pilot has got better things to do, and secondly, since the Dutch roll is a relatively high frequency motion, the pilot might marginally mistime his rudder inputs, and the timing wouldn't need to be very far out for the rudder applications to reinforce the oscillations rather than oppose

[1] This was explained in Chapter 7, under 'Equations of Motion and Aerodynamic Derivatives – The Inputs'.

them. This would result in the Dutch roll diverging more rapidly than it otherwise would if left to its own devices, a case of *pilot-induced oscillations*.

The answer is for an automatic system to sense the need for these rudder inputs, and to apply them without reference to the pilot at all. Such a system is called a *yaw damper*, and is the most common of a number of such *stability augmentation systems* (abbreviated SASs – sorry, this subject is peppered with acronyms!) in use. The term was coined in around 1950 by the American manufacturer Northrop, during the development of their flying-wing bomber aircraft, the YB-49. It was well appreciated that the stability derivatives, and hence the flying qualities, of a tailless aircraft such as this could not be satisfactory through natural aerodynamics alone, and so Northrop proposed a system that they at first called a 'stability derivative augmentor'. However, the draughtsman doing the installation drawings found that the space for the title on the standard drawing form was not wide enough for this long name, and so he abbreviated it to 'stability augmentor', and all similar systems have been called stability augmentation systems ever since[2].

The original name would have been preferable in that it describes such a system more lucidly. Although we have here concentrated on the yaw damper, any deficiency in an aircraft's dynamic stability characteristics is amenable to improvement by augmenting the aerodynamic stability derivative which is the cause of the unsatisfactory behaviour. In modern aircraft, stability augmentation systems are also used for pitch rate damping (to improve the short period pitching oscillation characteristics) and roll rate damping, as well as relaxed static stability as we considered a little earlier.

Stability augmentation systems in aircraft are not new. In 1894 Hiram Maxim used a longitudinal stability augmentor on his enormous 3600 kilogram steam-driven biplane test-rig. This system, which consisted of a gyroscopic sensor and a steam-driven actuator to deflect the 'horizontal rudder', closely resembled in principle the SASs of today, except for its power source and the fact that it weighed over 130 kilograms! However, by 1912 a father-and-son team, the Sperrys, had built a gyroscope-and-compressed-air system that was fully capable of maintaining both pitch and bank angles simultaneously. Lawrence (the father) spectacularly demonstrated the system in operation by holding his arms above his head in the open cockpit of a Curtiss float-plane, whilst the aircraft was flying hands-off, straight and level, with a mechanic standing on top of the starboard wing-tip!

[2]D. T. McRuer and D. G. Graham, 1981. *Eighty Years of Flight Control: Triumphs and Pitfalls of the Systems Approach.* Journal of Guidance and Control 4(4).

Systems such as the Sperrys' gave rise to the term 'autopilot', and were the precursors of the *automatic flight control systems* (AFCSs) of today, a generic term covering the entire system that manages the flight controls of an aircraft. When an aircraft is being designed as a control-configured vehicle, the computers, sensors and actuators of the aircraft's automatic flight control system are very capable and versatile, and so yaw damping and a number of other stability augmentation systems can readily be incorporated within it.

Configuration Management

The design of an aircraft's wing is fraught with compromise. In Chapter 13 of *Flightwise – Principles of Aircraft Flight* it was shown that a good lift coefficient distribution for coping with a large overall angle of attack may be obtained by twisting, or washing out, a wing, but that this means that the wing-tip regions are underutilised (or even negatively loaded) in a high-speed cruise. A large amount of sweepback (for reducing high-speed drag) implies a much lower aspect ratio than if the same wings were unswept, but a high aspect ratio is desirable for reducing induced drag in the cruise and hence for extending the range. It has also been shown, in Chapter 14 of *Flightwise – Principles of Aircraft Flight,* that the lower aspect ratio associated with a swept wing, together with the sweepback itself, provides a much less bumpy ride for the pilot on a low-level flight beneath enemy radar cover, than would a high aspect ratio, unswept wing. Flaps and leading edge slats and slots are almost indispensable for producing the high lift coefficients needed at landing speeds, and may be used for providing direct lift at higher speeds in manoeuvres, but they tend to be very draggy and therefore are unsuitable for use in normal flight.

Some of these compromises have been overcome to a limited degree by providing the pilot with manual control over adjustable features. Variable sweep combat aircraft such as the Tornado and F-111 allow the pilot to select the most appropriate wing sweep angle (and hence also aspect ratio) according to the requirements of each phase of the mission, and high-lift devices are invariably deployable and retractable. But in both cases the mechanisms are relatively cumbersome and the movements are therefore very slow in comparison with the rapid variations of attitude that the aircraft is capable of in flight. Such systems are therefore normally set and left in a required configuration for an extended period of the flight, and are not regarded as instantly adjustable flight controls.

Ideally the aerodynamic features of an aircraft such as those mentioned above (and perhaps others) would be fully and instantly adjustable at every moment during an aircraft's flight. The results of the optimisation calculations so painstakingly and accurately carried out at the design stage would then actually be realisable in flight, and would not have to be sacrificed to one compromise or another at almost every instant during a flight as is the case in practice. The problem has always been, however, that even if all the necessary systems were to be installed, it would be more than a full-time job for the pilot to manage the controls for such a plethora of adjustable systems, setting aside the highly complex analytical task of actually deciding what their optimum settings should be at every instant. Such a concept has always been an unrealistic flight of fancy for the aerodynamicist.

Today active control technology has actually turned this dream into a realistic possibility, although we must be cautious before jumping to conclusions that the fully articulated bird-like aircraft is just around the corner. The concept, which has been given the name of *configuration management*, is that, given virtually unlimited computer power, one can make anything and everything adjustable that traditionally has had to be designed to a fixed compromise solution, and can then control all the adjustable surfaces and devices with actuators (behaving rather like the muscles of a bird) continuously and at high speed, according to the instructions of the computer which is constantly updating the flight data and optimising all the parameters.

A significant application of this concept is the *mission-adaptive wing*, in which a wing is fitted with multiple leading and trailing edge hinged surfaces for adjusting the camber, flexibly covered for smooth and uninterrupted airflow. If the hinge lines of these surfaces were to be arranged in the manner suggested in Figure 13.1, it would also be

Figure 13.1 Mission-adaptive wing

possible to optimise the spanwise C_L distribution for all flight conditions by varying the amount of washout, thus avoiding the need for compromise in resolving the conflict between negative lift at the tips in the cruise and satisfactory handling characteristics at high angles of attack that we mentioned just now. The mission adaptive wing will also allow the induced drag always to be kept to a minimum compatible with the overall C_L requirement, giving improved range in the cruise and better performance in manoeuvres, whilst the pilot will be free to concentrate on the primary task. The concept of the mission-adaptive wing, combined with variable sweep, has been investigated by NASA on a modified General Dynamics F-111 strike aircraft, and is used to a substantial extent on the Eurofighter 2000. Perhaps by the centenary of the Wright brothers' first flight 'wing warping' may once again be the order of the day!

The mission-adaptive wing is one way of obtaining direct lift-force control which we discussed at the end of Chapter 12. All of the ideas of direct force control that we looked at there for the purpose of increasing an aircraft's agility, including the use of thrust vectoring, pose a completely new problem. They present the possibility of manoeuvring the aircraft in ways which are not even conventional enough to be managed by the usual cockpit controls. They actually provide the pilot with new alternative ways of achieving certain effects, and for this reason the pilot must interface with them in a manner such that he is in command, since it would be far-fetched indeed to conceive of the AFCS being responsible for making such mission-sensitive decisions. For example, the pilot might wish to use direct lift force in order to get a better over-the-nose view of the ground beneath and ahead, (i.e. better than the aircraft provides in conventional handling mode), either during landing or in a battle zone. Or he may wish to translate the aircraft sideways without any yaw whilst approaching a ground target, and there is no conventional aircraft control that ever had such a function. The automation of active control technology will certainly be used to coordinate these and other special modes such as lateral nose-pointing, and enable them to work effectively, but a major rethink of the pilot interface is needed before all possibilities can be implemented. Beyond the one additional lever that the pilot of a Harrier jump-jet already has for controlling the vectoring of the engine's thrust, work on achieving the most satisfactory approach to pilot interfacing is still very much in an investigatory stage, since not all the dynamic possibilities are yet properly understood.

Carefree Handling

The work of a combat aircraft pilot is at its most demanding when performing tight manoeuvres, especially when engaged with an enemy who is watching for every mistake and searching for any opportunity to destroy him. As we saw in the previous chapter, it is at just such moments that our pilot is having to push his own aircraft as close as he dares to its limits, whether it be the stalling limit at a high angle of attack with the serious risk of entering a spin, the buffet boundary beyond which dangerous stability departures may occur, the maximum load factor that he can withstand without blacking out, or the never-exceed speed beyond which the aircraft may be in danger of suffering severe structural damage. At the same time, his concentration has to be centred on successfully pursuing and outwitting his opponent. Victory and defeat (by the enemy or by his own errors) are precariously balanced.

It is to tackle such situations that active control technology has been challenged with its most daunting test, to provide the aircraft with *carefree handling*. By this is meant that the computers are programmed to detect through the flight data sensors when the aircraft is approaching any limiting situation, and then to input control commands that will actually override those of the pilot to ensure that the bounds cannot be exceeded under any circumstances. If such a system can be perfected, it means that the pilot would be free to use the aircraft controls with abandon, totally unhampered by concern for the consequences to the aircraft of any mistakes he might make, (although the term 'carefree' is perhaps not the most apt in view of the stressful nature of the situation), so that his concentration can be applied one hundred per cent to the task in hand.

In view of the very complex nature of the aircraft's dynamics and aerodynamics in extreme situations, such a system makes enormous demands of the computer software writers. There are so many ways in which an aircraft could conceivably be behaving at any moment, and so many difficult-to-predict parameters to take into account, that one must ask whether it can ever be possible for a programmer to anticipate and cater for every conceivable eventuality. Nevertheless, enormous strides have been made in the development of carefree handling, especially during the 1980s in an experimental unstable active control technology SEPECAT Jaguar. The Jaguar is prone to wing rock at very large angles of attack, (a combination of a divergent Dutch roll mode and inertia coupling effects) which can lead to a very sudden departure in roll. In addition, when a Jaguar enters a spin, its motion is very erratic and the two-seater version cannot be recovered from the spin at all without the deployment of a spin parachute. But in the experimental aircraft the carefree handling facility was refined to such an extent that the pilot was unable to get the aircraft into trouble whatever extreme control demands he made. The new generation of far more agile aircraft than the Jaguar will make even greater demands on carefree handling, and it will be crucially important to get it right.

The ideas of carefree handling have also been carried over into some recent civil transport aircraft, such as the European Airbus A320. However, following two accidents, it is still regarded as highly debatable whether such an idea is appropriate, and whether it can ever be totally foolproof. The concept of carefree handling is still very much in its infancy, and its progress is something to be watched with interest.

Gust Alleviation

The effect of turbulence in the air is to create gusts on a wing which briefly alter its angle of attack and hence its lift coefficient. This means that in all but very smooth airflows there is a constant fluctuation of the lift-force that the aircraft structure has to withstand. The first part of Chapter 14 of *Flightwise – Principles of Aircraft Flight* was given over to discussing the reasons why this is of concern, and it was there shown that it is very significant both to large transport aircraft and to combat aircraft in high-speed low-level flight, for very different reasons. It was explained that the combat aircraft pilot cannot perform his mission properly if the aircraft is providing a very hard and bumpy ride; and that the fatigue life of a transport aircraft tends to be mainly used up by the continual stressing and unstressing of the components resulting from gust loads.

The basic idea of a *gust load alleviation* (GLA) system appeared straightforward, and as early as 1949 it was applied to the Bristol Brabazon, then the largest aircraft in the world.[3] If a gust could be detected early enough, before it had imposed its sudden load on the wing, appropriate control surfaces could be deflected in order to cancel out the effect of the temporary change in angle of attack. In the case of the Brabazon, a gust vane was mounted on the aircraft's nose to detect gusts before they had reached the wings, and the signal from this was used to cause the ailerons to be deflected symmetrically to compensate.

Unfortunately, this and all other attempts throughout the 1950s and 1960s to design a GLA system were unsatisfactory, for a number of reasons. One reason was that the symmetrical deflection of the ailerons altered the pitching moment of the wing, and this interfered with the aircraft's longitudinal stability. Other problems were the over-simplistic modelling of a gust in the pitching plane only, the

---

[3]A fuller account of the history of gust alleviation control, as well as much more about the other subjects we are discussing here, may be found in the chapter on 'Active Control Systems' in Donald McLean's book *Automatic Flight Control Systems*.

downwash effects on the tailplane, and the time delay between the gust reaching the wings and the tailplane. The core of the problem was that, instead of using the time-honoured control engineering approach of providing feedback from an event, the use of a gust vane was depending on feed-*forward*; it was trying to anticipate the effect of the gust before it had been experienced.

With the great improvements in speed of detecting an event and activating a response that are available with today's active control technology, gust load alleviation is now a practical possibility, and is commonplace, but it is still a very difficult type of system to design properly. Accelerometers are normally used in place of vanes. These detect very quickly and directly when a gust load has *just begun* to occur, and aerodynamic compensation is immediately applied not with the conventional control surfaces but with auxiliary surfaces provided for this purpose. Thus the CCV has sprouted yet more control devices!

Such a gust load alleviation system bestows a benefit for a variable sweep combat aircraft on a low-level mission. If the pilot can depend on the system to provide a sufficiently smooth ride, the wings need no longer be swept back to reduce ride hardness as described in Chapter 14 of *Flightwise – Principles of Aircraft Flight*. Thus the need for the compromise of having to sacrifice the low induced drag of high aspect ratio wings for the sake of providing an acceptable ride is obviated.

Since transport aircraft are designed to a very much lower load factor limit than combat aircraft, a gust load that would merely be an inconvenience to a fighter may actually stress the structure of the transport aircraft to a substantial proportion of its design limit. These loads are continuously counted by accelerometers for the purpose of fatigue life monitoring, and if the count can be kept low by the use of a gust alleviation system, the fatigue life of the aircraft can be enormously extended.[4]

Active Flutter Suppression

One of the great benefits of a control-configured vehicle is the fact that its structure may be made substantially lighter than its conventional equivalent. A reduction in aircraft weight is one of the major advantages to be gained by relaxing the aircraft's longitudinal static stability, and furthermore the use of a gust alleviation system may allow structural components to be designed using lower stress limits, and hence to be lighter. But the sting in the tail is that the flying surfaces will consequently be more flexible than on the conventional equivalent aircraft, and therefore more susceptible to aeroelastic flut-

---

[4]Fatigue is discussed in Chapter 14 of *Flightwise – Principles of Aircraft Flight*.

ter. If nothing were done about this, the aircraft's never-exceed speed might well be restricted to a lower value than that of the equivalent conventional airframe, which is clearly undesirable.[5]

Here is an opportunity for active control technology to come to its own rescue. Because of the very high response rates that ACT can achieve, it is possible for accelerometers to sense when flutter is about to occur, and to activate the appropriate aerodynamic surfaces (usually auxiliary surfaces, as with gust alleviation systems) so that they apply aerodynamic forces in anti-phase. Such systems are referred to as *flutter mode control* (FMC). Not only can FMC allow a restoration of the hoped for flutter speed, but it may even enable higher flutter speeds to be achieved, so that the maximum safe flying speed may be increased.

Alternatively to capitalising on this opportunity to raise the flutter speed, perhaps the most significant benefit of FMC in fighter and ground attack aircraft is the resulting increase in the permissible wing-mounted stores (weapons) load that can be carried, within the same speed limitation. But for bombers (carrying their stores internally) and transport aircraft, the possibility of reducing the structural weight is likely to be the most important benefit.

Autopilot

Although the function of 'George', the old automatic pilot, may have been subsumed into the all-embracing automatic flight control system, there are still certain functions which an automatic system may actually be capable of doing better than any human pilot because of the human's comparatively slow speed of reaction and the limited acuteness of his senses. We will look at two particular situations in which active control technology has made it possible for the AFCS to take over from the pilot: terrain-following radar and automatic landing.

Terrain-following Radar

The concept of carefree handling that we considered earlier need not be limited to tight manoeuvre situations. Another facility which is now well established is *terrain-following radar* (TFR), which enables an aircraft on a low-level interception mission (typically at 50 feet above the ground during hostilities, but generally at about 250 feet during peacetime training) to follow automatically the undulations of the ground, pulling up when necessary in time to avoid ground obstacles, and descending rapidly the other side. The pilot is very fully occupied

---

[5]Flutter was discussed in a section under that heading near the end of Chapter 9. We are here talking about structural flutter rather than that of control surfaces, since the control surfaces are powered and are firmly constrained under the thumb of the automatic flight control system.

with following the course (especially over unfamiliar enemy territory) and directing the mission, so that being able to leave the terrain-following task to an automatic system is not a mere optional extra but a boon which may make the difference between the mission being accomplishable or otherwise.

Automatic Landing

Most large modern transport aircraft are equipped with such a sophisticated automatic flight control system, linked with the navigational and other avionics systems, that they are capable of doing automatically almost the entire job of the pilot without any input from the pilot, once he or she has keyed in the necessary data to the various systems. For example, a Lockheed L1011 TriStar, as converted to its tanker rôle for the Royal Air Force, can be programmed to carry out every aspect *bar one* of an entire flight, including taxying from the terminal building to the runway, the take-off run, the climb, the cruise including all navigation, the approach to the destination airfield, the landing, taxying to the final terminal, and coming to rest parked in the right place.

So what is the one action that the pilot still has to do? He has to pull back on the pitch control in order to make the aircraft rotate at the moment of take-off. It is certainly not beyond the wit of avionics and control engineers to automate this relatively trivial task, interrogating the appropriate air speed and other data sensors, making the crucial 'go/no go' decision, and acting upon it. But the fact that this is not done reflects the depth of feeling underlying a very old and thorny dichotomy between pilots and engineers. The pilot has, since the earliest appearance of automation on the flight deck, jealously upheld and fought to maintain the fact that he is the captain, that he is ultimately responsible for the aircraft's safety and achievement of its task, and that ultimately he must therefore make the crucial decisions.

This one operation of deciding whether it is safe to proceed with, or whether to abort, the take-off, and having made that decision to act upon it by manually rotating the aircraft into its take-off attitude, may be seen as a symbolic token of the captain's ultimate authority over the progress of the entire flight. With mixed feelings of reluctant reservation combined with gratitude that many aspects of their job have been made easier, pilots have today come to accept the inevitable march of technology. This even includes an acceptance of the fact that, in some situations, automatic landing systems can do a job in difficult circumstances with higher precision than a human pilot can accomplish with his slower reactions and somewhat more *ad hoc* judgement.

But things have moved on. With the arrival of the all-embracing philosophy of active control technology, the pilot has once again found himself being subjected to what he sometimes sees as emotional blackmail. You see, now that automatic landing systems are possible, there would be very substantial advantages to be gained in the design of aircraft if *all* landings were to be carried out by the automatic landing system! For a start, the maximum impact-loading of the undercarriage at the moment of touch-down could be reduced, since the undercarriage would no longer need to be designed to absorb the worst of heavy landings carried out by human pilots. This would mean that the undercarriage, which is a useless dead-weight during flight, could be made very much lighter, together with that part of the aircraft's structure that transmits the undercarriage loads to the airframe.

As well as being lighter, the undercarriage could also be provided with very much softer suspension, because it will not have to be designed to absorb the occasional heavy landing. Although this would offer little benefit for combat aircraft, about half the fatigue life of some transport aircraft is used up just during taxying because of the hard suspension of the undercarriage, and so great savings in aircraft life costs could be made here.

There has been little incentive to develop automatic landing systems to the higher specifications and level of reliability that would be demanded if they were to be used for all landings, largely because of the unacceptability of the idea amongst the flying fraternity – and perhaps a fear, with some justification, of redundancy. But there is no doubt that great advances could be made. The use of direct lift-force and side-force control under the management of the AFCS could be used to make approach and landing paths very much smoother and more direct than at present, and direct lift-force could overcome the pitch transient problem of an aft-tailplane aircraft. Furthermore, systems would have to be developed that were self-contained and completely independent of airfield installations. I wonder whether we shall ever see the day ...

Artificial Intelligence

All the features of a control-configured vehicle that we have considered so far have consisted of handing over control of aerodynamic features (that are either conventional or already well understood in principle) to the computers, because they can do the job much more quickly than a human pilot, and can cope with many more things at once. In every case, the control laws for the AFCS have to be developed and implemented in software before the aircraft can use them in flight. But that was so because computers could until recently only obey instructions.

Recent advances in *artificial intelligence* have opened up a completely new possibility: that an aircraft would be able to limp home and land itself safely after suffering serious in-flight damage to some of its control systems and aerodynamic surfaces. By the use of 'neural network' software, it is hoped to be able to design an AFCS that will be capable of comparing the data about what is actually happening to the aircraft with stored data on how the aircraft ought to fly, and then modifying the flight control system's control laws to take account of any mismatch. For example, if sensors show that a rule is being violated so that the aircraft is turning too abruptly, the neural network would rapidly learn, in less than 1 second, how to assist the pilot in the use of pitch and roll controls, engines, flaps, rudders and other control surfaces in ways that may be very unconventional, but will enable the aircraft to fly a recovery to its base and land safely.

NASA and McDonnell Douglas, who at the time of writing are jointly working on a project to develop such a system, hope to test the concept in an F-15 flying testbed in 1997, but believe that such systems are still five to fifteen years away from widespread use. However, the possibilities offered by the use of artificial intelligence open the door to unimagined possibilities, and this is clearly an area to be watched with great interest.

LIMITATIONS

We have seen that active control technology offers solutions to a very wide range of problems. But by solving such problems a new need for compromise has been introduced at the design stage. How far should the designer go in perfecting the aerodynamics of the aircraft? The additional actuators and related systems and structure which, for example, must be provided to implement the mission-adaptive wing, plus any other variable aerodynamic devices such as wing sweep, side-force control, vectored thrust and other auxiliary control surfaces, will all add considerably to the aircraft's weight, the minimising of which is always a fundamental and crucial requirement. Then there is the additional complexity of such systems, which must be miniaturised to a great extent to fit inside the very limited spaces, making considerable maintenance demands and presenting serious access problems. Ultimately, it is economics which determines to what extent what is possible is actually practical. A combat aircraft will have a certain specification, and the most economical design that meets this specification will normally be the one that wins the contract. In practice where the mission-adaptive wing philosophy is being experimented with, only fairly traditional types of leading and trailing edge devices are being used with fewer hinge-lines than are suggested in Figure 13.1, but these devices are being made active full-time under computer control rather than merely configurable by the pilot for phases of flight.

A chain is only as strong as its weakest link. Apart from economics, there are other limitations to be considered which apply ultimate constraints over what may be achieved by a control-configured vehicle. Whereas an aircraft controlled purely by a human pilot relies entirely on the pilot's senses as the basis of making decisions, a control-configured vehicle acts upon measurements of the state of the aircraft's motion which are made using a large number of mechanical *sensors*. These include accelerometers to measure the effect of forces and moments, gyroscopes for gaining information about attitude and rotational rates, and aerodynamic vanes or pressure sensors in the airflow for measuring the angle of attack and the sideslip angle. Also, radar altimeters and radar are used for such purposes as terrain following and for other systems dependent on features and events outside the aircraft itself. All these are in addition to sensors measuring the pilot's control inputs and the pitot and static pressure tappings needed anyway for altimeter, air speed indicator and Machmeter. Although such an array of sensors can be far more sensitive, versatile and wide ranging than the pilot's senses, the authority and reliability of the AFCS is ultimately dependent on the integrity of these sensors; and there are limitations.

Gyroscopes have been used for about 70 years to drive certain flight instruments such as bank, climb and turn indicators, providing them with a fixed frame of reference. They have proved reliable and accurate to within a few degrees, and may be adapted directly from the task of providing visual information for the pilot to that of feeding back working data to the AFCS. However, 'to within a few degrees' is not accurate enough for the precise requirements of today's systems, and very much greater precision is absolutely essential. (Furthermore, gyroscopes suffer from an inherent drift rate of about ten degrees per hour, which is an inconvenience that can be allowed for.)

Because of the need for very great accuracy, extremely high precision sensors have been developed. For example, the limited accuracy of the gyroscope has spawned the development of the much higher precision ring laser gyro. But the very precision of laser gyros and radar altimeters creates its own problem, that of *noise*. This problem arises from the fact that the system is so accurate and rapid in its response that it has exceeded the 'accuracy' of the very data that it is measuring. The small continuous fluctuations which in the very nature of the real world envelop the data signal coming from the atmosphere, from the outside world or in particular from the electrical system of the aircraft itself, render that signal 'noisy' or 'dirty'. Although by use of statistics and electronics this noise can be filtered out to a certain degree, ultimately it is one of the factors that imposes an overall limitation on what can be achieved in a control-configured vehicle.

For stability augmentation systems, accelerometers are used in conjunction with gyros to provide feedback signals. Often accelerometers are required to measure the linear accelerations of the aircraft regarded as a particle, and as such they must be placed exactly at its centre of gravity. If not, in addition to their prime purpose, they will not only read rotational accelerations due to the rotation of the mounting point about the centre of gravity, but will also be subject to spurious accelerations or corrupted readings resulting from the elastic deformation of the aircraft components to which they are attached. It is equally important to locate gyros for measuring rotational rates (especially pitch) at the centre of gravity and away from places where the output will be significantly affected by structural bending. However, there may well be good reason why it is physically impossible to locate all or any of these sensors at or close enough to the aircraft's centre of gravity, and therefore the misplacement of such sensors imposes a limitation on the integrity of the systems dependent on them.

Often the most appropriate type of sensor will be an airflow direction sensor, since many of the derivatives (such as M_w and L_v) have airflow direction as their independent variable.[6] By their very nature, such sensors (be they airflow-following swinging vanes or cylindrical probes normal to the airflow which measure the difference in the pressure at two static tappings on their surface) have to be located in the airflow on the outside of the aircraft, and as such they are highly vulnerable to contamination or damage by such events as bird-strikes.[7]

In addition to the limitations imposed by the placing and use of sensors, it must be remembered, as we commented at the beginning of this chapter, that ultimately the integrity of any automatic flight control system is dependent on the aerodynamic authority of the aerodynamic control surfaces and devices that it uses to achieve its aims. Only they, and not the sensors or black boxes, provide the necessary forces and moments to control the aircraft in the way that is required, and without exception all such control surfaces and devices have some limitation on their authority.

[6]This was explained in the section of Chapter 5 headed 'Angle of Attack Dependent Derivatives, Z_w and M_w'.
[7]I recall reading once of a young airman (not in the Royal Air Force!) who was bored during a night shift guarding several fighter aircraft on an airfield pan. For entertainment and exercise he decided to practise pull-ups by hanging on the pitot probe protruding from the front of one of the aircraft, but unfortunately as a result the probe suddenly developed a serious bend. Being rather alarmed and nonplussed, the airman then attempted to conceal the effect of his folly by systematically bending the probes of all the other aircraft under his care, so that no one would notice!

RISKS

When the idea of the control-configured vehicle using full-time active control technology was first conceived, many people (including hardened professionals in the field) were extremely sceptical about whether such an idea could ever become acceptable, let alone commonplace. A new buzz phrase, *fly-by-wire*, was entering the aeronautical vocabulary, by which was meant that no longer would pilots have any direct link with the aircraft controls, but would only be able to provide electrical signals, along wires, to a remote computer which intervened between the pilot and the aerodynamic controls. There would for the first time, it was maintained, be no physical mechanical connection between the pilot and the aircraft's controls. Safety considerations in the event of system failures would make this totally unacceptable.

Similar fears were almost certainly prevalent at an earlier period in the history of aviation, when hydraulic systems began to replace tried and trusted mechanical linkages, and when powered actuators supplanted aerodynamic balance for producing sufficient hinge moments. But the incorporation of fly-by-wire (FBW) and active control technology is actually a somewhat more significant departure than the conversion to hydraulic and power-operated controls. The reason for this is that, to gain the full benefit offered by the control-configured vehicle, one starts by designing an aircraft that cannot under any circumstances be flown by a human pilot unaided. Relaxing of the longitudinal static stability whilst retaining a reduced positive static margin was a step on the road towards much greater aerodynamic efficiency and will remain a valid thing to do in many situations such as transport aircraft, but the full manoeuvrability and agility potential of the control configured vehicle will only be achieved when the aircraft is designed from inception to be statically unstable in pitch.

At first, active control technology was tried out and developed using existing conventional aircraft (such as the SEPECAT Jaguar) as experimental test platforms, and it was possible in the event of serious system failure for the pilot to use an emergency mechanical linkage to operate the essential controls. This philosophy, known as *manual reversion*, also carried over to the first transport aircraft to contain a substantial number of active control technology systems, whilst confidence in such new and revolutionary systems was still being cultivated. But as it matured the experimental fly-by-wire Jaguar dispensed with its manual reversion system, and today there are a number of fully fly-by-wire airliners in passenger service which have no manual reversion at all.

Such a revolutionary idea inevitably carries with it some risks, and we would be dishonest to overlook this. But the awareness of this problem has spawned the growth of the new and very sophisticated science of reliability studies, which has meant that risk assessment and management has developed to a remarkable degree. The sort of reliability figures required today for a civil fly-by-wire airliner with no manual reversion are a probability of less than one in a thousand million that the system will totally fail in any one hour, or one in ten million for a combat aircraft. In practice it would be impossible to prove that it met the requirement, and verification is therefore provided by analysis using component reliability data collected over years of observation of similar components. Let us look at some of the areas of risk that have had to be addressed.

The use of active control technology has enabled aircraft to have flying qualities that are virtually faultless right up to the very brink of conditions of high incidence departure[8] or spin initiation. Thus the very successfulness of such systems is in danger of bringing about their own downfall, since the pilot no longer receives the traditional warning cues of impending danger. There is a narrow dividing line between the perfection of carefree handling systems and the pilot's ultimate authority.

Computers and electronic systems are by their nature susceptible to damage from outside causes such as lightning and radio transmissions. Not only must they be designed to be sufficiently resistant to such influences, but combat aircraft must be protected from deliberate enemy interference and disruption by means of radar or radio jamming. One way in which this potential problem is being tackled is by replacing fly-by-wire systems with *fly-by-light* technology, in which all control signals are transmitted around the aircraft, not using electrical signals travelling along metal wires, but rather by light signals transmitted through optical fibres.

One neat proposed idea for the incorporation of fly-by-light technology is to make major parts of an aircraft's body structure out of composite material built around a matrix of very long fibres that provide both structural strength and also thousands of possible optical paths from place to place around the aircraft. Then instead of installing the customary complex looms of electrical wiring that are very heavy and constitute a major part of the overall weight of conventional aircraft, it would simply be necessary to identify and expose the two ends of a structural fibre that reached from a signal input point to the required output location, connect into this fibre at each end and use it for transmission of optical signals. If one such fibre were to suffer damage, there would be an abundance of spare fibres within the structure which could be used to carry out a repair. Fibre-

---

[8]Sorry! Technical jargon for departing from conventional flight when the stalling angle is exceeded.

optic signals are not subject to electrical or electromagnetic interference in the way that electrical signals are, so the potential for ideas such as this are far-reaching.

When considering ultimate reliability and the likelihood of a total catastrophic failure, one must treat this as the result of failure of one or more of the subsystems that we have been looking at. This has given rise to the introduction of the term *availability*, which is broadly defined as a measure of how many major subsystem failures could be tolerated, after which the aircraft will still be able to continue to operate. For example, the availability of a naturally unstable and unflyable combat aircraft may be specified as one or two, and for a system in which the aircraft without stability augmentation is still stable, this number may be somewhat higher.

The availability requirement of a control-configured vehicle makes particular demands on the integrity of the computer systems used. Anybody who has used computer programmes will be aware that it is virtually impossible to guarantee any complex piece of software to be totally free from bugs. Even with the extreme care that must be taken in preparing software for flight control systems, the number of possible combinations of data that the computers will have to be capable of safely handling will be so large that it is totally impossible to guarantee that every eventuality has been anticipated and tested. As well as this, there is of course the reliability of the computer hardware itself to be taken into account.

To take care of the risks inherent in computer and software design, doubling, trebling or even quadrupling of systems is used. Each of the parallel lanes (for a particular system) is designed to be as far as possible totally independent of the alternative lanes, both in terms of the hardware and of the software. For example, a triplex system may have software for each of its three separate computers written by totally unconnected software designers, each being given exactly the same specification to work to.

If a duplex (i.e. two parallel lane) system were used, and one of the two lanes were to develop a fault, the control system would receive two conflicting commands as to what to do next, and would have no way of knowing which of these was correct and which was corrupt. The only way for such a conflict to be resolved would be for a human pilot, on the basis of other information available to him, to make the decision and to switch out the offending lane. Therefore a duplex system can be used only in limited authority systems which are not critical to survival, and where failure simply downgrades the flying qualities of the aircraft with no more serious consequence. Duplex systems are therefore of very limited use in control configured vehicles.

The solution to this problem is to use a system of automatic *voting* between the computers themselves, and this can only be done with the minimum of a triplex system, which has three lanes in parallel. A special black box is incorporated which continuously reads the output commands of all three lanes, and does nothing about them unless one of the three figures received is different (by more than a small acceptable level of tolerance) from both of the other two, which agree with each other. A computer lane is deemed to have failed if its output does not agree with the other two, whilst those two still agree with each other, and in this event the black box will automatically switch it off, leaving just the other two to work as a duplex system. Of course there can be no such automatic voting between the remaining two, because if they disagree there is no way for the black box to know which one to believe. An automatically voted triplex system can therefore only survive a single failure. In situations where it is required to be able to tolerate up to two failures (i.e. where the availability figure is two), a quadruplex (4-lane) system must be used. In this case the same type of voting is used as before, but two failures (one at a time) can be detected and the lanes automatically deselected.

In these multiplex systems, it is important that as much of each lane as possible is independent of the other lanes, and so the input sensors must also be multiplexed, and placed if possible far apart from each other on the airframe – a bit tricky if they should be at the centre of gravity! It would be unfortunate if a lane were deemed to fail and to be voted out simply because one of its designated sensors developed a small error from the others, and so another black box is used to provide *input signal consolidation* by which such an erroneous input signal can itself be voted out, leaving the other sensors to provide the signal for its lane.

Another possible source of failure is the power supply to the AFCS. Any amount of multiplexing would be totally wasted if there were only a single power supply to all lanes and it should fail. It is therefore usual to provide auxiliary generators for use in the event of engine failures, and once again multiplexing of power supplies will be necessary.

Finally, one other feature of automatic flight control systems is the way in which control surfaces behave in the event of a system failure. Rather than settling in a docile manner to a tidy and relatively inoffensive neutral position, the nature of many actuators is such that when control surfaces fail they go straight over to one extremity or the other of their movement. This is called a *hard-over failure*, and clearly if any one control surface were to fail in this manner the effect would be at best severe and at worst catastrophic. At the time of writing, it is thought likely that several accidents and incidents occurring to Boeing 737 airliners have involved hard-over failures of the rudder. At first aviation authorities used to insist that control deflections for such systems as stability augmentation should be limited to, say, ten per cent of the overall authority of the surface, so that a hard-over failure could be contained. However, restrictions of this sort severely limited the scope of such systems, and consequently much greater deflections, sometimes as great as 100%, have to be tolerated. The risk of hard-over failure is consequently something that designers have to take particular care to guard against.

CHAPTER 14
Where Next?

INTRODUCTION

We opened this book with a review of the early history of flight, paying particular attention to the way in which the pioneers had been influenced by the needs of stability and control. Let us close the sandwich by taking a look now at where the intervening years have led, and let us survey the way in which the aircraft scene is moving today. We have already seen that it is in the field of combat aircraft that the strongest drive for innovation in stability and control is to be found, and although transport aircraft development is still going on apace, the present-day advances in that field are not driven by any strong need to develop control and stability concepts. In this final chapter therefore we shall concentrate solely on the combat aircraft scene.

As early as 1972 moves were being made in Great Britain to address the perceived need for greatly improved manoeuvrability and agility in future fighter aircraft. A far-reaching experimental project was launched in which a SEPECAT Jaguar was used as a testbed for experimenting with and developing the facilities offered by active control technology, using the fly-by-wire concept, as discussed in the previous chapter. This led, in the 1980s and right through into the 1990s, to a considerable flurry of activity both in Europe and the United States of America, in which several experimental programmes were launched. During that period, the perceived nature of the military threat altered very considerably due to the demise of the Soviet Union and with hindsight of the various military campaigns of recent years, and this has given rise to changes in rôle for combat aircraft and to altered priorities in design specification. Furthermore, economic and political turbulence have led to a number of changes of direction among collaborating countries within Europe.

As a result, the fighter scene in Europe that is emerging today is of a single European fighter aircraft, the Eurofighter 2000, which, barring further serious problems, is expected to see military service at around the turn of the millennium. Whilst this project is maturing, the British aerospace industry is starting to develop its next-generation combat aircraft, the so-called 'Next Combat Aircraft' (or NCA) with twenty-first century technology, and a flight demonstrator of this is at present planned to appear in 2001. Meanwhile, in the USA the experimental and developmental bit has been firmly taken between the teeth, and there have been and are continuing to be a number of advanced pro-

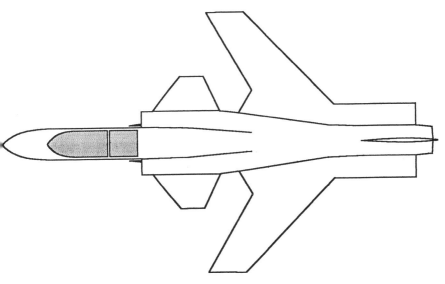

Figure 14.1 **Plan-view sketch of Grumman X-29A**

jects using existing combat aircraft and also completely new experimental ones. We will take a closer look later on at the Eurofighter
2000, but first we will look at three particular major United States projects.

GRUMMAN X-29A FORWARD-SWEPT WING AIRCRAFT

When the original idea for *Flightwise* was drawn up a few years ago, I
had pencilled in 'Forward-Swept Wing Aircraft' as the title of this
final chapter, since the concept was then seen as potentially an excit-
ing breakthrough in new aircraft design which might have had great
influence on the future scene. The Grumman X-29A (sketched in
Figure 14.1) was originally conceived in 1981 and built as a vehicle to
investigate the potential of the forward-swept wing (FSW) concept for
combat aircraft, but during its life it was overtaken by the new perceived need for very great agility, especially in performance beyond
the stall. Although this was not the rôle that the X-29A had been
originally designed for, it was realised that the aircraft in fact had
many features which would make it a good competitor with other configurations in the arena of agility, and so after its initial use for evalu-
ating forward-swept wing ideas it was pressed into service for further
tests at very high angles of attack.

Judging by the way aircraft design has moved on, it would seem
that forward-swept wings are not, after all, likely to feature strongly in

future combat aircraft design. However, the concept is so intriguing and apparently revolutionary that it will be valuable for us to reflect on some of the pros and cons that the forward-swept wing concept potentially offers. We will look not specifically at the particular results or features of the X-29A, but rather at the generic characteristics of a forward-swept wing aircraft in principle.

Forward-swept Wing Aircraft[1]

The main reason why forward sweep has never been very seriously considered as a viable alternative to the more conventional sweepback is that it possesses an intrinsic structural disadvantage, which is known as wing divergence. If you extend your arm forwards out of a moving car window with the palm flat, and raise it a little, it tends to move up further. Its position is unstable, since the further it rises the stronger the force still trying to push it up. If you extend your arm backwards, on the other hand, the aerodynamic force on your hand always tends to restore it to the horizontal when raised or lowered. In flight, in addition to the normal bending of a wing, a swept wing experiences a torque about a line called the torsional axis which extends over the length of the wing and, chordwise, is somewhere close to the maximum thickness position. This torque twists the wing and so modifies the angle of attack of aerofoil sections out towards the tip. A swept-back wing distorts so that the lift coefficient towards the wing-tip reduces. But if the sweep is forward, this distortion, combined with the bending of the wing, has the effect of increasing the angle of attack in the wing-tip region, and this in turn gives rise to a larger lift-force, which accentuates the twisting and bending and increases the stresses in the wing structure.

Using traditional constructional materials and methods, the weight penalty imposed by building a forward-swept wing strong enough safely to withstand this instability has always been so great that it would have outweighed any possible aerodynamic advantages there might have been. However, with the use of today's carbon-based composite materials, very strong thin structures can be designed and manufactured, so that the weight penalty can now be kept very small. It therefore becomes worthwhile to examine whether there are aerodynamic benefits to be gained from the use of forward sweep.

It was shown in *Flightwise – Principles of Aircraft Flight* that wing sweep serves different purposes in supersonic, subsonic and transonic wing design, and so we must investigate each of these separately. First of all we will show that for a supersonic wing forward sweep has a substantial disadvantage over backward sweep. It is the sweep of the *lead-*

---

[1]This section is substantially reproduced from Chapter 13 of *Flightwise – Principles of Aircraft Flight.*

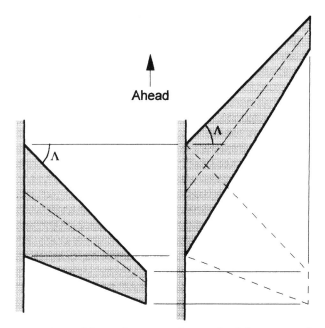

Figure 14.2 Comparison of forward sweep and sweepback for supersonic wings

ing edge of the wing that is significant for supersonic purposes[2]. Figure 14.2 depicts two supersonic wings each with the same root chord and tip chord and hence taper ratio, and also each with the same span[3]. Both have an equal leading edge sweep angle of Λ (the upper case Greek letter 'lambda', defined as the angle from the straight out, unswept position), being designed for flight at the same Mach number. Despite having the same leading edge sweep as demanded by supersonic considerations, it is immediately apparent that, because of taper, there is much more overall sweep in the forward-swept wing than in the swept-back wing. Let us examine a bit more closely what we mean here by overall sweep.

When a swept wing gets bent and twisted along its length due to lift, the parts near the leading edge get bent up more, or less, than those towards the trailing edge, and this accounts for the twist. It is reasonable to suppose that, somewhere between the leading and trailing edge, there should be a line along the wing's length that is only bent

---

[2]This is explained in the section 'Low Speed/High Speed Design Considerations' in Chapter 10 of *Flightwise – Principles of Aircraft Flight*.
[3]Remember that the span is measured normal to the longitudinal axis. It is the direct distance between the two wing-tips.

upwards by the amount due to the bending load, no more and no less. The long-and-short dashed chain lines represent these lines, which are the torsional axes of the wings. From a structural point of view, the length of these lines is a better indication of cantilever length than is the semi-span measured normal to the fuselage, and therefore we shall loosely refer to these lines as the structural axes, and their lengths as the structural spans of the two wing forms.

Looking at the figure, it is clear that the sweep angle of the structural axis of the forward-swept wing is greater than that of the swept-back wing. Also the structural span of the forward-swept wing is clearly greater than that of the swept-back wing, and both of these facts can readily be confirmed by measuring with a protractor and a ruler. These features magnify the already unfavourable structural characteristics of swept, tapered wings that were considered in *Flightwise – Principles of Aircraft Flight*, and this is in addition to the inherent structural instability of the forward-swept wing that we have already pointed out at the start of this section. If designing an aircraft mainly for supersonic flight, then a forward-swept wing would be a far worse choice than the equivalent swept-back wing.

On the other hand, we have seen that sweep can also be used to advantage in the design of high subsonic speed wings. Do the same disadvantages of forward sweep apply there? Let us examine this question. The first thing we need to clarify is how far back on the aerofoil chord of the wing we should measure the sweep angle. Just now we recalled that for a supersonic wing the sweep must be measured at the leading edge, since it is at the leading edge that we wish to control whether the flow is effectively subsonic or supersonic. However, when using sweep to raise the critical Mach number of a wing, a different criterion must be applied. It is at the point of maximum thickness of the aerofoil section that the greatest flow speed is achieved, and at which Mach 1 is first reached, and so it is reasonable that it should be the locus of such points that should be used as the reference line for measuring the wing sweep, and not the leading edge. The position of this point on the aerofoil depends on the aerofoil section shape, and it might typically be at about 35% of the chord from the leading edge, so that it roughly coincides with the structural axis of the wing. Consequently forward sweep for high subsonic purposes has virtually no effect on the structural span as compared with backward sweep, and so it is not ruled out on these grounds, but neither does it achieve any advantage.

A major outcome of transonic wing research has been the adoption for virtually all high-speed transport aircraft of supercritical aerofoils, and the acceptance of operating within the transonic regime, with a shock wave present on the upper surface of the wing towards the trail-

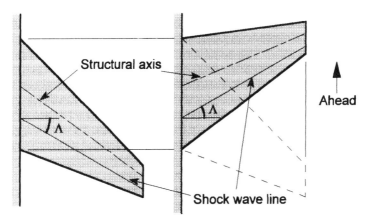

Figure 14.3   Comparison of forward sweep and sweepback for transonic wings

ing edge. Some American research in 1976 revealed that the transonic drag rise of a wing is in fact related to the sweep angle of the shock wave line, and not to the line of points of greatest flow speed as it is for high subsonic design.

A supercritical aerofoil is designed so that the shock is as near to the trailing edge as possible, and in practice this may be typically 70% of the chord length back from the leading edge. This best line for measuring the sweep angle is thus substantially behind the structural axis which we estimated to be at around the 35% chord position, so that sweeping the wing forward rather than backward, using the shock line as reference, will have the advantage of reducing the sweep angle of the structural axis, and of reducing its length which we have called the structural span. Figure 14.3 illustrates this phenomenon. On the left is the identical swept tapered planform that we started from in Figure 14.2, showing the structural axis as before but with the addition of the shock wave line, at about the 70% chord position. The sweep angle Λ has been redefined now as the sweep angle of the shock wave line. The right-hand drawing shows the effect of shearing the wing forward so that root, tip and semi-span lengths and hence aspect ratio all remain unchanged, until the shock line is swept forward by Λ rather than aft. The result is a wing with exactly the same aerodynamic sweep but less overall sweep and a much sturdier, squatter profile, in which the wing structural span is shorter for the same aerodynamic span. Overall then, the swept-forward transonic wing would be structurally superior for the same aerodynamic sweep, if it were not for the wing-tip divergence problem.

One of the primary aims of aircraft design is to minimise drag, and when considering planform shapes we are concerned especially with the minimisation of induced drag. How does the direction of sweep (fore or aft) bear on the induced drag? In Chapter 13 of *Flightwise – Principles of Aircraft Flight* it was shown that there exists a large C_L peak in the wing-tip region of a swept-back, tapered wing. Such a distribution is unfavourable for producing low induced drag since we ideally require the C_L value to be constant over the entire span. In both cases (sweepback and taper) the excess upwash in the tip region was produced by the vortices being shed from further inboard, but the reasons for the effect being strong were different in each case. The choice as to whether the wing should be swept forward or backward cannot have any influence on the effect of taper since the taper ratio is not affected and we have deliberately considered taper and sweep separately from each other. However, the tip region upwash due to sweepback was produced by the fact that the root region was upstream of the tip region and hence had a stronger effect on the tip region than the tip region had on the root region. Since the trailing vortices are anticlockwise (on the starboard wing viewed from behind), the root region produced strong upwash at the tip region.

If the wing is swept forwards instead of backwards, it is the tip region that will have the stronger effect on the root region, which means that there will now be a preponderance of downwash over the inner regions of the wing. But apart from making necessary an overall higher angle of attack to achieve the total wing lift coefficient required, this does not have any clear implications on the relative upwash and downwash on tip region and root region. There is still more upwash or less downwash (whichever way you prefer to look at it) in the tip region than in the root region, so no conclusion jumps out at us.

However, in the forward-swept wing there will in fact be some improvement in C_L distribution due to sweep and a consequent reduction in induced drag. This is because, for the sake of calculating induced drag (by the theory based on the Biot Savart law) we must take our lifting line as being at the 25% chord point, whereas we have already seen that for designing a transonic wing we should measure the sweep angle at the 70% chord point. If (as in Figure 14.3) the 70% line is swept forward by the same angle Λ as that by which it was previously swept back, then the 25% line is less swept than it was before. (If this is not obvious, it can be checked from the figure by sketching in the 25% line and using a protractor.) Thus on the lifting line we have less sweep, and hence less of the tip region upwash effect, than on the equivalent transonic swept-back wing.

In conclusion, forward sweep may be expected to have a favourable effect on the induced drag of the transonic aircraft. It will also bring the initial stall zone away from the wing-tip and towards the root, bringing with it improvements to the aircraft's stalling characteristics.

In Chapter 14 of *Flightwise – Principles of Aircraft Flight*, on gust response, it was explained that the lift curve slope of a wing decreases as the sweep increases. This is a true result for an infinitely long wing, and so it is not a finite wing downwash phenomenon. Consequently it makes no difference whether the wing is swept forward or backward, since no distinction can be made between the two 'ends' of an infinitely long wing. Such a swept wing is of uniform cross-section, and so the leading edge, the trailing edge and other reference lines (such as the line of aerodynamic centres at 25% chord) are all parallel to each other. We do not therefore need to specify at which line we measure the sweep angle. However, in the case of our tapered, swept wing it is appropriate once again to use the theoretical lifting line, the line joining the 25% chord points. As we saw above, for the same amount of sweep at the 70% chord line, the 25% chord line will be somewhat less swept on a forward-swept wing than on a swept-back one. Thus the transonic forward-swept wing, being overall less swept, has a greater lift curve slope than the equivalent swept-back wing. During manoeuvring this is a substantial advantage for combat aircraft, since a small increase in angle of attack produces a larger increase in lift coefficient than would be the case on the equivalent swept-back wing aircraft, and so changes in wing lift are more quickly achieved, and the aircraft is more agile.

There is another feature of the forward-swept wing which also contributes to the same advantage, and it lies in the flexible nature of the wing-tips. When the wings of a swept-back aircraft are producing a large amount of lift such as, for example, during a turn, the upward bending and twisting of the wing-tips makes the angle of attack in that region get smaller, so that the lift falls off there, with the result that even more overall angle of attack is required to compensate for this and produce the required total lift-force. If the wings are swept forward, however, the bending up and twisting of the wing-tips increases the angle of attack in that region, so that the lift actually increases more rapidly than would be the case without the flexing of the wing. If this is not clear, it can very easily be demonstrated by once again putting your arm out of a car window, palm extended flat, first in the forward-swept and then in the swept-back position, and experimenting by inclining the arm slightly upwards. This means that the structural flexibility of the wing, which lies behind the main objection to the use of forward-swept wings, actually turns out to provide a major benefit for agile combat aircraft, as long as the structural strength requirements can be met. The wing will be very much stiffer, so that the twisting up will be much less pronounced than the twisting up of the conventionally structured swept-back wing. Hence the major component of this effect is the elimination of twist on the swept-back wing.

Unfortunately, this same effect also has an influence on the bumpiness of the aircraft's ride in gusts, since it effectively increases the lift curve slope, which directly influences the hardness of the aircraft's response to gusts[4]. It has been estimated that the g-loading could be doubled by the use of forward sweep. However, if used in conjunction with relaxed or negative longitudinal static stability and canard foreplanes as in the case of the X-29A, this problem may be alleviated by the ability to use a smaller wing and hence a higher wing loading.

An aircraft's lateral and directional stability are directly affected by sweeping the wing forward instead of aft. Just as sweepback provides a strongly stabilising rolling moment derivative L_v due to sideslip, so forward sweep is destabilising for exactly corresponding reasons. We have seen that on combat aircraft with short swept-back wings there is often a problem of an excess of L_v, aggravated by fuselage shielding, which has to be compensated for by use of anhedral. Forward sweep can reverse this problem, and some dihedral may even be needed. But the most significant stability problem has been found to lie in the directional stability at high angles of attack. Since the stall starts closer to the wing roots and the distance between wing roots and fin is small, the fin quickly becomes immersed in the wing's separated wake, seriously downgrading the directional stability N_v derivative. We will see shortly the effect that this has had on the X-29A programme.

Structural strength, weight and aerodynamic factors are not the only considerations that an aircraft designer has to take into account, and forward-swept wings may sometimes offer solutions to other problems related to the layout of components. For example, a swept-back wing allows the wing main spar to cross the fuselage[5] further aft, thus releasing more unobstructed space further forward. It may also offer the opportunity for much better downward visibility, as in the cases of a Swedish light observation aircraft the MFI 15B, the tandem-seat all-aluminium Blanik glider and the very popular two-seat club aircraft the Avions Pierre Robin ATL Club (which also features a V-tail). In all of these cases forward sweep is very moderate, and is certainly not provided for achieving a high critical Mach number! In the case of the German forward-swept Hansa executive jet, all cabin windows are ahead of the wing.

The main undercarriage wheels of a nosewheel aircraft must be

---

[4]This is explained in Chapter 14 of *Flightwise – Principles of Aircraft Flight*.

[5]A wing main spar is the chief structural member that extends from wing-tip to wing-tip. Almost always it extends across the fuselage as a single member shared by both wings, since this provides greatest strength at the wing roots where the bending effect is greatest. If two separate wing spars were to be attached to the fuselage, the fuselage itself would have to be designed to withstand the very large bending loads at the roots, and this would make for a very inefficient fuselage structural design.

placed slightly behind the centre of gravity, which often necessitates stowing them in the thinnest part of a swept-back wing. Another major layout benefit of the forward-swept wing is that its root will be further back relative to the centre of gravity than the root of a swept-back wing. This means that the undercarriage may be stowed in the forward part of the wing, which is deeper and provides more stowage space. The Hansa referred to above provides a good example of this.

From this discussion about forward-swept wings, we can conclude that it is highly unlikely that we shall ever see any predominantly supersonic aircraft designed with forward-swept wings. Transonic transport aircraft will only use forward sweep if there are decisive benefits in this concept on other grounds, which appears unlikely on the whole. But for combat aircraft optimised for manoeuvring in the transonic regime (which are now becoming a rarity), the benefits available make the use of forward sweep appear somewhat more promising. This was basically the philosophy that lead to the experimental Grumman X-29A, which is where we came in. It would appear likely that the chief reason why the X-29A experiment, although by no means unsuccessful, is not being enthusiastically followed up with other forward-swept wing combat aircraft, is that today most fighters are required to be thoroughly at home at supersonic speeds, and it is at such speeds that forward sweep actually imposes a performance (or structural) disadvantage compared with backward sweep. From Figure 14.1 the leading edge sweep of the X-29A is about 30°, and this would only be sufficient for avoiding supersonic flow over the wing as long as the Mach angle were no less than 60°. Thus from the relationship $\mu = 1/M$ (where μ is the Mach angle) we find that this aircraft is only suitably swept for supersonic flight up to a Mach number of 1.15, scarcely out of the transonic regime. The X-29A is indeed a supersonic aircraft, but this analysis shows that the wings scarcely obtain any supersonic advantage due to sweep.

The X-29A Programme
The X-29A is not merely a forward-swept wing aircraft, but it incorporates many other novel aerodynamic features in its design. It is a fly-by-wire control-configured vehicle with a special facility incorporated into the digital flight control system whereby the pilot can 'dial-a-gain' during flight. Gain is the control engineer's word for the measure of how much compensation is applied by a particular control surface, per unit amount of feedback from a flight data sensor, and so the effect of adjusting various gains in flight is very similar to the idea of altering an aircraft's aerodynamic stability or control derivatives on demand. By this means the whole dynamic behaviour of the aircraft can be substantially altered at will, so that the airborne aircraft provides an ideal

platform for experimenting with different airframe configurations. It has been said that the 'dial-a-gain' feature enables the flying aircraft to simulate a flight simulator, which is somewhat ironic when one thinks that simulators were introduced to emulate the flight of real aircraft!

Not least of the X-29A's advanced features is the use of canard foreplanes close-coupled with (i.e. only a short distance in front of) the wings. But one of the chief drawbacks of the use of canards, especially if close-coupled, is that being of low aspect ratio and producing positive lift they create a strong downwash over the root region of the wings, and a corresponding upwash outboard of their tips which strikes the outer wing region. Thus they have an adverse effect on the spanwise lift coefficient distribution over the wings, biasing it outboard, so adding to the aircraft's induced drag and wing-tip stalling tendency. As we have seen, the upwash towards the wing-tips due to sweep is reduced substantially by the use of forward sweep, so it is a shame to have to reintroduce the problem by using canards.

Pitch control and trim of the X-29A is provided not only by means of the deflection of the all-moving canards (which both move together) but also by flaps on the trailing edges of the broad roughly rectangular strakes behind the wing roots. These strakes were originally installed to resolve and take advantage of an incompatibility between the mainly straight flow around the fuselage and the large amount of circulation over the heavily loaded wing roots, and they provided an excellent platform for additional pitch controls to be used with the canards. The leading edge root extensions at the junctions of leading edges and fuselage, which have swept-*back* leading edges, were provided to help resolve the same flow incompatibility problem, and they also conveniently provided the housing for tensional stays to hold the wings against being forced backwards by wing drag.

When towards the end of its life the X-29A found itself competing in manoeuvrability and agility at high angles of attack with newer purpose-designed aircraft, its features were put severely to the test. The major new innovation that the others benefited from but that the X-29A never received was thrust vectoring, so that the contest was in that respect something of a David and Goliath scenario, and the X-29A was found to be somewhat deficient in pitch control authority at very high angles of attack. Nevertheless, in the event the X-29A acquitted itself extremely well on account of the various manoeuvrability and agility-enhancing features of forward-swept wings and canards that we have been considering, although falling short of achieving some of the extremes of flight that the competitors attained.

In these high angle of attack situations the X-29A revealed a most unusual and unexpected directional asymmetry of flight. At about $\alpha = 43°$ the nose yawed to the right at the same time as a mild wing-rock was starting. At about $\alpha = 48°$ the nose swung across and pointed instead to the left, but at $\alpha = 53°$ it swung back to the right again as the wing-rock ceased. This behaviour, caused by the shedding of vortices around the nose, led to the experimental programme being followed by considerable further tests, and really opened up the subject of nose vortex shedding to wider investigation.

As late as 1992, the aircraft was brought back into service to investigate these phenomena in a new series of tests. The aim was to learn how to manipulate the vortices shed around the aircraft's nose so as to produce a controlled side-force at the nose for enhancing yaw control. Two nozzles were mounted on either side on top of the aircraft's nose, which could rotate from pointing straight aft to 90° to either side and could eject a high-speed jet of nitrogen into the airflow to modify the normal nose vortices by means of the Coanda effect. To yaw to the right, the right-hand nozzle with 60° deflection to the right was used to cause the right-hand vortex to cling closer to the nose, whilst causing the left-hand vortex to move higher and to the left, with the result of a lower pressure on the right and thus a force in that direction. (Note that this is the opposite direction from any side thrust that might have been produced by the nozzle flow on its own.) By this means, yaw rates of 20° per second (in the range of α between 15° and 50° at speeds ranging from 100 knots to 160 knots) were achieved, which was said to be an improvement of 50% over the yaw rate which could be achieved by use of the rudder alone.

Thus the X-29A had served well beyond its original design brief, and had been able to pave the way for much of the development work on the other high agility aircraft that were to follow, in which nose vortex control was (and is) to play a very important rôle. The X-29A was retired to moth-balls in 1992.

MCDONNELL DOUGLAS F-18 HIGH ANGLE OF ATTACK RESEARCH VEHICLE

Unlike the purpose-built experimental aircraft that we are primarily considering, the McDonnell Douglas F-18 HARV (standing for High Angle of Attack Research Vehicle) was an otherwise standard F-18 equipped with thrust vectoring nozzles and a special research flight control system. It was initially (from 1987 until 1992) the principle aircraft in NASA's 60 million dollar high angle-of-attack programme, in which new concepts for vortex control were to play an important part. The programme was broad based, and included parallel development work using wind-tunnels and computational fluid dynamics[6].

[6]Computational fluid dynamics is the designing of aerodynamic surfaces and the evaluation of aerodynamic loads by means of solving the full equations of motion using powerful digital computers.

Figure 14.4   McDonnell Douglas F-18 Hornet

A production F-18 Hornet, as shown in Figure 14.4, is a high manoeuvrability Mach 1.8 fighter with an aft tailplane, twin fins and slightly swept-back wings. The principle modification for the HARV was the addition of thrust-vectoring nozzles at the exhaust from the jet engine at the rear. In addition, the production aircraft leading edge high-lift devices were modified, and also the wing-tip missile launch racks were replaced by camera pods and booms which carried air data sensors. The cameras were particularly useful for photographing the yarn tufts that were attached all over the wings and fuselage, to indicate the nature of the airflow close to the surfaces and to show where it was breaking away or was flowing in unexpected directions.

Pitch control of the F-18 HARV is provided by a combination of stabilator (all-moving tailplane) and thrust-vectoring, but, as a safety measure to guard against the danger of a thrust-vectoring system failure, the thrust-vectoring facility is not relied upon to assist with longitudinal trim of the aircraft (in the engineer's meaning) except in the event of the stabilator reaching the limit of its authority.

Thrust vectoring is also used for yaw control, and this is particularly important for one of the chief aims of this and all the programmes, to investigate and extend the ability of the aircraft to point its nose to either side of the flight path whilst flying at very large angles of attack. The purpose of this is for effective launching of air-to-air missiles towards an evading enemy aircraft. At the extremes of pitch and yaw angles it was found that the limits of authority of the controls were beginning to be reached, but the aims of the tests were almost completely achieved. As with the X-29A, there was found to be some wing-rock (in this case at angles of attack between 38° and 48°), but once again the limitations were chiefly found to be in yaw. At very high angles of attack the rudders were found to lose all effectiveness.

This gave rise to the commissioning of a further series of tests on vortex control around the nose, which started late in 1994, but this time instead of using the Coanda effect induced by nozzle flow, specially designed adjustable strakes were to be installed on each side of the nose to generate the required vortex flow. Each strake was to be 1.2 metres long and 15 centimetres wide, and was to be hinged along its longer edge to the fuselage, the hinge-line lying parallel to the aircraft's longitudinal axis. New flight control laws were to be introduced into the flight control system, which would operate the strakes as well as the thrust-vectoring paddles and other control surfaces.

MBB[7]/ROCKWELL X-31A

The MBB/Rockwell X-31A project is by far the most extensive and far-reaching one into the agile combat aircraft field. It started in 1984 as a joint project between the United States and West Germany (as she then was), and the project is still very much alive at the time of writing. A plan and side-view of the aircraft are shown in Figure 14.5.

Prior to the launch of the project, Rockwell had been developing the X-29A (which was thereupon taken over by Grumman), and MBB in conjunction with British Aerospace had been involved with the Experimental Aircraft Project (EAP), from which MBB withdrew. Rockwell and MBB were therefore able to join forces on the new X-31A undertaking which in 1985 became a joint NATO project. Rockwell's motivation to branch away from the non-vectored-thrust X-29A project and become involved with X-31A stemmed from an earlier project of their own known as SNAKE (for SuperNAtural Kinetic Enhancement) from which they had realised that vectored thrust would be an essential feature.

Two X-31A aircraft were designed to be built, as cheaply and as quickly as possible, and consequently 43% of their weight comprised parts cannibalised from production aircraft. These included the F-18 (for the canopy, ejector seat, instruments and cockpit controls), the F-16 (which provided the nosewheel), the Cessna Citation III executive

[7]MBB is the name of the German aircraft company Messerschmitt-Bölkow-Blohm.

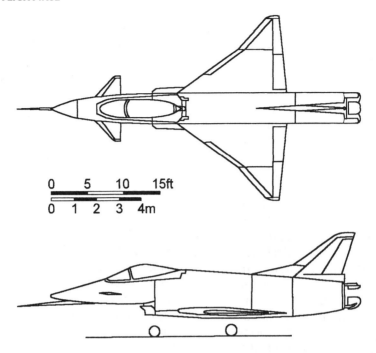

Figure 14.5   MBB/Rockwell X-31A

jet (for the main landing gear), the Corsair A-7 single-seat attack aircraft (for the main wheels) and many others. As a result, the cost of these two experimental aircraft was only about the same as the cost of two production F-16s, despite the economies of bulk buying of materials in the latter. One of the ironies of transatlantic collaboration was that MBB designed and built the wings using the SI metric system, whereas Rockwell used Imperial units throughout their design and construction of the fuselage, but when the parts were brought together the mating of the wings with the fuselage was perfect.

The configuration (based on MBB's experience with the European Experimental Fighter Aircraft) was to be a subsonic/supersonic compromise. It was to have a clipped double-delta wing with washout, and long-coupled canard foreplanes to reduce some of the interference effect on the wing airflow experienced with close-coupled types like the X-29A and to provide a greater moment arm and hence a smaller canard area. Although initially to be subsonic, the project was planned to be developed later up to Mach 1.3. The wings therefore used a transonic (yet only 5% thick) aerofoil, with as large as possible a leading edge radius (within the thickness constraint) for flow attachment at high angles of attack, and all fuel and systems (except for wing control surface actuators) were housed in the fuselage. The fuel tank was placed at the centre of gravity in order to maintain constancy of stability margin as fuel was used up.

The aircraft was to have a compromise between negative longitudinal static stability (a subsonic static margin of -5% of mean aerodynamic chord[8]) at normal angles of attack, and positive pitching stability at very high angles. If you are wondering how this could be achieved in view of our assertion that the stability depends only on the position of the centre of gravity, you should bear in mind that our theory was developed on the basis of linear aerodynamics. It was assumed that the lift curve is a straight line, and that consequently the $C_M(cg) - C_L$ graph would also be straight, but at high angles of attack beyond the stall such linear behaviour ceases to operate, and the rules become type dependent.

The wing was designed to be mission adaptive by the incorporation of fully active leading and trailing edge flaps. The leading edge flaps were scheduled to respond both to angle of attack and Mach number. The outer pair of the trailing edge flaps act both for varying wing camber and as ailerons, i.e. as flaperons, and their design was crucial, since the thrust vectoring nozzles, being located on the aircraft's longitudinal axis, provide no roll control at all.

Lift is so distributed that the canards are normally only lightly loaded. Although they are used in conjunction with the trailing edge flaps for providing pitch control, the primary use of the canards is in stabilising the aircraft in pitch during unstable flight and in restoring normal pitch from high angles of attack. Being normally lightly loaded, the canards have a very good margin of authority, which enables them to handle the aircraft's tendency to pitch up due to inertia coupling when rolling at high angles of attack. They also cope well with the additional nose-up pitching moment created by the ram effect of the air entering the engine intake under the front of the fuselage at high angles of attack. Since the intake is well ahead of the centre of gravity, the drag force on it (which in normal flight acts below the centre of gravity and therefore produces a nose-down pitching moment) moves above the centre of gravity at high angles of attack, and thus produces a destabilising nose-up pitching moment.

[8]The Mean Aerodynamic Chord (MAC) is a very precisely defined average chord length that is used in aerodynamic stability and control calculations. Its definition is based on the wing planform and area, and includes not only the chord *length*, but also its fore-and-aft *position* relative to the aircraft's fuselage. Its precise definition need not concern us here. A static margin of -5% of MAC means that the distance of the aircraft's centre of gravity *behind* the neutral point is 5% of the length of the MAC, making the aircraft substantially unstable, but very much less so than the X-29A, whose static margin was -35% MAC.

This engine intake has received special design attention, to cope with the serious problem during manoeuvring flight of the air entering the engine in a direction far removed from the axial ideal. Disturbed intake airflow can be very deleterious to gas turbine engine performance and can even cause total engine failure in some cases. The General Electric F404-100 engine used in all three of the aircraft we are looking at is fairly tolerant of airflow distortion – a factor which influenced the choice of this engine – and this feature has been augmented in the X-31A by providing a moveable lower lip on the intake, with the result that the engine can operate at maximum power even at extreme angles of attack.

At the rear of the engine are attached three thrust-vectoring paddles, providing the chief new experimental feature of the aircraft, its thrust vectoring ability. The paddles that were chosen had been developed during a United States Navy development programme on the Grumman F-14 Tomcat variable-sweep aircraft. They were made of carbon composite material for low weight (being far behind the centre of gravity) and so as to withstand the very high temperatures experienced when reheat[9] was being used, although they are never immersed in the very hot gas for more than brief periods. Their primary purpose is for thrust vectoring, and they can also be hinged outwards to double up as speed brakes.

In the case of the X-31A, as with all the high angle-of-attack programmes, control at very high angles of attack obviously presents great practical challenges, but it also requires a rethink of our control ideas. We have been content throughout this book so far to take it that there is not much difference between the direction of the aircraft's longitudinal inertia axis and that of the stability axis which coincides with the flight path, and this made it fairly easy for us to take on board the ideas of pitching, rolling and yawing. However, now that we must contemplate angles of attack of $70°$ or more, it is obvious that such a simplification completely fails us, since the aircraft's inertia z-axis is now much closer to the direction of the velocity vector than is the inertia x-axis. How, then, do we define the terms yaw and roll, and what is their effect?

In answering this question, let us first look at how the flight control system is configured as seen by the pilot. Remember that the pilot no longer directly operates particular aerodynamic controls – that would be far too complicated – but instead he has to use the cockpit controls to signal his manoeuvre *requirements* to the computers, and these con-

---

[9]Reheat, or afterburning, is the process of burning additional fuel in the already fast and hot jet exhaust gas at the rear of the engine, so as to expand and speed it up even more and thereby produce additional thrust.

vert those requirements into the appropriate combination of control deflections. But ideally these signals must still bear a close resemblance to the control inputs and responses with which the pilot has become thoroughly familiar during flying training and subsequent experience in conventional aircraft.

When the pilot moves the control column to the right, he expects the aircraft to roll to the right – but what does that mean if the nose is pointing almost straight up in the air, whilst the aircraft is still flying in a horizontal flight path? Or what does it mean if the nose is pointing sideways towards a target on one side of the straight-ahead flight path direction? The answer decided upon for the X-31A is that roll demands by the pilot are interpreted as a requirement to roll the aircraft, not about its longitudinal inertia axis, but rather about its velocity vector, i.e. about the line of the flight path. In fact this is no different from the conventional thinking, since the flight path is the stability axis, but it certainly needs emphasis since it is perhaps not what one would expect.

If an aircraft is flying with its longitudinal inertia axis roughly parallel to its velocity vector (i.e. conventionally), roll is produced just by ailerons and (ignoring secondary effects) no other control surface is involved. Now, with your aircraft model in hand please, 'fly' the model across in front of you, but this time with an angle of attack of 90°, ie with the nose pointing straight upwards. Its velocity vector is now parallel to its inertia z-axis, and so, if the pilot demands a roll by moving the control column sideways, the aircraft must respond by doing what we would previously have thought of as a yaw. No aileron deflection is appropriate, but the yawing controls (provided they work under these conditions) must be brought into play.

Now let us be a little more moderate, and fly the aircraft across at an angle of attack of about 70°. (Kebab skewer or knitting needle is handy here to give you the velocity vector reference line.) If you now roll your model about the velocity vector (X-31A control law style) you will see that the motion is a combination of 'roll' and 'yaw' (both in the conventional sense), and that the yaw rate is actually greater than the roll rate since the angle of attack is greater than 45°, at which angle they would break even. Using the vector representation of rotational rates as we have done before, the conventional roll rate and yaw rate vectors may be added to give the resultant rotational rate about the velocity vector line, which by proper definition is called a roll rate. To achieve this resultant motion, the flight control system will have to apply some aileron for conventional roll, and some rudder (or alternative control) for conventional yaw, and it is clear that the need for aerodynamic authority in yaw is now very appreciable, and increasingly so as the angle of attack increases. Yawing has become a primary control mode. There will also be a need for pitch control, to overcome the pitch-up tendency due to inertia coupling, and so all three rotational controls are required in response to the pilot's simple demand for roll by moving the control column to one side.

Let us now look at the alternative scenario in which the aircraft is flying along at a conventional angle of attack (so that its velocity vector lies roughly in the plane of its inertia x and y axes), but a substantial yaw angle is being maintained so that the aircraft is pointing to one side, let us say to the right. If now the pilot inputs a roll demand to the right with a sideways control column movement, the effect is that the flight control system provides some right rolling moment *and some nose-down pitching moment*, since the resultant roll about the velocity vector must be a combination of a nose-down pitch rate and a roll rate to the right. No yawing moment (other than that to maintain the constant yaw angle against the directional stability) is required. If on the other hand the pilot demands a pitch-up by pulling back on the control column, the resultant pitch-up must occur about a line perpendicular to the velocity vector, and your model will help you to be convinced that to do this not only is a pitching up required about the aircraft's inertia y-axis, but also the aircraft must roll clockwise about its inertia x-axis, which involves the ailerons. If you find this unconvincing, exaggerate the initial orientation of the aircraft by 'flying' it at a very large fixed yaw angle of, say, 80°.

How does the X-31A achieve the required components of rotational control about its three inertia axes? We have already seen that the aircraft's trailing edge flaps in conjunction with the canards are used to provide primary pitch control about the y-axis, but this can be augmented by deflecting the thrust-vectoring paddles upwards or downwards to produce a nose-up or nose-down pitching moment respectively. Despite the impression possibly given by the lower view in Figure 14.5, the three paddles are equally distributed around the nozzle, and in combination with each other can deflect the flow up to 10° in *any* direction away from the longitudinal axis, ranging around a complete cone. This achieves about 17% of the total engine thrust in the plane normal to the x-axis, in whichever direction around the cone the thrust is pointed. Being so far aft, this clearly provides a very substantial range of yawing and pitching moments about the centre of gravity, with which to augment the conventional controls. But it must be remembered that thrust vectoring can provide no rolling moment at all, since the vectored thrust force always acts through the longitudinal inertia axis.

Out of safety considerations, the designers have ensured that the aerodynamic pitch control surfaces (together with positive longitudinal stability) have sufficient authority to recover the aircraft from high angle of attack to conventional flight in the event of a thrust-vectoring system failure, but clearly the thrust vectoring in pitch enormously enhances the aircraft's agility.

Because of fin shielding at high angles of attack, the demands made of yawing moment are the hardest to achieve, even with directional thrust vectoring. It is this that has given rise to the increased determination to solve the problem by managing the nose vortices effectively, since the potential that these offer for side-force is substantial, and the forward position of the nose makes such forces ideal for producing yawing moments. Furthermore, one of the advantages of the control-configured vehicle, the ability to translate sideways without centripetal acceleration and without altering the direction in which the aircraft is pointing, depends on being able to produce equal moderate side-forces at both the front and the rear simultaneously, and this is not yet possible on the X-31A.

At the same time as trying to tame the vortices to provide side-force on the nose, the X-31A programme has also investigated the real need for a tail fin at all. Since a fin is thoroughly ineffective when it is most needed, and since it adds very appreciably to the weight and drag of an aircraft, would it be possible to dispense with it altogether? Essentially this implies following the lead of relaxed and negative longitudinal static stability, which is now well established, and applying the same principles to directional static stability. At present the stabilising yawing moments would have to be supplied just by thrust vectoring nozzles – which must be capable of being activated at very high rates to respond to an aircraft's natural directional instability – but later this could be augmented by controlled vortex-induced side-forces on the nose.

In 1994 the X-31A was flown 'tailless'. The tail was not physically removed, but the flight control system was set up in such a way as to produce a combination of deflections of the other aerodynamic control surfaces that would effectively cancel out the tail fin's directional stabilising effect. Whilst flying with this fin-cancelling system active at up to Mach 1.2 – it is in supersonic flight that a fin is most needed for directional stability – full directional stability was maintained by means only of thrust vectoring in the yawing plane under the control of the flight control system. The concept was thus proved, and a further test programme was launched to develop this and other related concepts using a production McDonnell Douglas F-15 Eagle fitted with thrust-vectoring nozzles. The aim was to reduce the area of the twin fins of the F-15 by 50%, in order to enable the aircraft to have a greater range on account of the weight and drag savings that would result. An additional benefit is to reduce the radar signature of the aircraft, making it more stealthy. By comparison, the Northrop B-2 'Stealth' bomber shown in Figure 5.7 is an aircraft in which fins have been totally dispensed with in the interests of achieving a low radar signature. The B-2 is a subsonic aircraft, with the directionally stabilising feature of a highly swept high aspect ratio wing, and directional stability is less difficult to achieve at subsonic than at supersonic speeds.

Other aircraft have also been used in the quest for perfecting agility and manoeuvrability at high angle of attack flight. In 1993 a General Dynamics F-16 Fighting Falcon, fitted with thrust-vectoring nozzles, flew at a sustained angle of attack of 80° and transiently during a manoeuvre achieved an angle of attack of 110°, which means that it was actually flying slightly backwards at that instant! It has demonstrated its ability to perform some weird and extravagant low-speed high angle of attack manoeuvres such as the 'cobra', earlier seen demonstrated by a Russian Sukhoi Su-27, and a manoeuvre called the 'hammerhead' in which the aircraft performs something resembling a complete vertical loop in not much more space than its own length, thus forcing a pursuing aircraft to overtake it. It has demonstrated a powerful capability to point its nose sideways for weapon aiming even at high angles of attack, and it can track an opponent *inside* its own turning circle. Yawing stability at moderate angles of attack has proved to be its greatest problem, and so it has been equipped with chines (longitudinal plates) either side of the nose. In this case they were fixed and not adjustable by the flight control system, being intended to solve an instability problem rather than to generate side-force as a flying control.

The X-31A programme is still very much alive at the time of writing, and is being supported by the findings of many of the other programmes discussed or mentioned above. At the 1995 Paris Airshow, the X-31A demonstrated its pedigree and future potential by giving a remarkable display of agility which delighted the Paris crowds. The display routine included a series of aerobatic manoeuvres, each of which consisted of tight loops in the fully stalled condition combined with supple rolling and yawing motions. One of these routines is illustrated in Figure 14.6.

EUROFIGHTER 2000

In the opening paragraphs of this chapter we painted the scenario within which the Eurofighter 2000 project is now nearing fruition. As with any combat aircraft of today, before its specification can be drawn up, the threat which it is intended to be able to defend against has to be carefully assessed. This threat has substantially changed in nature since the project was launched in the 1980s, and today it has been learned through the experience of the unexpected military engagements of recent years that flexibility has to be the name of the

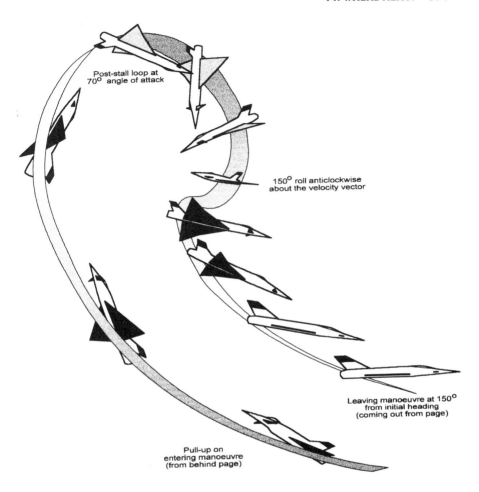

Figure 14.6 An X-31A manoeuvre at the 1995 Paris Air Show

Figure 14.7   Eurofighter 2000

game. Whilst no longer conceived as an air superiority fighter for operations over central Europe, such a rôle is still considered essential, both for escorting bombers and for long endurance combat air patrols in which it might be required to fight at a considerable distance from base. The other major rôle is as an air-to-ground attack aircraft, including the need to be able to defend itself.

This dual-mission capability requirement of air defence and air-to-ground attack dictated that agility, at both supersonic and subsonic speeds, was to be the primary design consideration, and the priority was to be given to the air-to-air rôle. As a result, and after a number of modifications during its development, the final configuration arrived at was that shown in Figure 14.7. It resembles the X-31A in that it is a canard delta aircraft, and the main differences are that the wing leading edges are straight (swept at 53°), the canards are slightly closer to the wings (but not close-coupled like the X-29A and most other earlier canard fighters), there are two engines rather than one, and there is no thrust-vectoring facility. Despite the twin fins of the earlier Agile Combat Aircraft from which it was derived, the Eurofighter 2000 has a single fin. It is capable of take-off and landing in a few hundred metres, so that it can operate from damaged or makeshift airfields.

By dint of providing the pilot with state-of-the-art avionics including a head-up display, the aircraft is single-seated, thereby reducing size and cost. Being fully fly-by-wire, the aircraft has a quadruplex flight control system, negative longitudinal static stability, gust alleviation for low-level flight, and carefree handling including a 'panic button' which the pilot can press if an unacceptable flight condition arises, causing the aircraft automatically to resume conventional steady flight.

The Eurofighter 2000 has a relatively stealthy radar signature compared with earlier aircraft, although at the time of its conception stealth was not given as much emphasis as it is today, and so the aircraft's stores, a major contributor to an aircraft's radar signature, are all externally mounted. This was a compromise brought about by the need for cost cutting.

As well as having a head-up display, the pilot is equipped with a helmet-mounted sight for missile aiming, using which he turns his head rather than the aircraft to aim missiles, and of course this leaves much of the onus for manoeuvrability in the care of the missile's aerodynamics and guidance rather than that of the aircraft. The pilot-control interface is designed around the philosophy of allowing the pilot to keep one hand on the control column (a small side-stick) and the other on the throttle nearly all the time. To facilitate this, these two hand controls have no less than 24 additional knobs and buttons to be operated with thumbs and fingers, by which the pilot manages aspects of the weapons and defensive systems as well as flight handling functions.

Although it is indeed extremely agile by 'conventional' standards, without thrust vectoring the agility of the Eurofighter 2000 is clearly constrained by comparison with those aircraft which have proved the value of this technique. Consequently in mid 1994 plans were announced for a mid-life upgrade to the Eurofighter 2000, which would include providing it with the thrust-vectoring system developed on the X-31A, and for this project the German involvement both in the X-31A and Eurofighter 2000 projects will prove especially useful. However, the idea is not as straightforward as might be supposed, since the American and European flight control system designs have been based on different philosophies. The Eurofighter flight control system is relatively conservative, being based on the outcome of the fly-by-wire Jaguar experiments which were conducted at a time when the technology was new, untried, and was arousing very serious concern over safety in the event of system failures. But the X-31A uses a more recent approach which is called 'Optimal Control Theory', and the two systems are not compatible with each other. The Eurofighter project team will therefore have to modify the flight control system substantially in order to be able to integrate vectored thrust with the existing system.

BEYOND AGILITY

With all the flurry of investigating and developing a very agile and highly control-configured aircraft to meet urgent defence needs, one might suppose that the combat aircraft designers would have their hands full with satisfying the present demands. But as ever the ruthless 'kill or be killed' competition to maintain the upper hand in the face of potential enemies and against stringent economic constraints goes on apace, and so today governments and aircraft industries are very intently and seriously planning for the subsequent generation of fighter aircraft.

The emphasis appears to be changing in two major ways. Firstly, the next generation of highly agile supersonic combat aircraft will have to be very much stealthier than the currently emerging generation; and secondly they must also be capable of vertical, hovering flight. Ideally, all these features should be combined in the same multi-rôle aircraft, together with having a useful operating range, but the design requirements for achieving vertical lift, high mission performance and stealth are so distinct from each other that substantial compromise appears to be absolutely inevitable in seeking such an aim. It is for this reason that so many concepts are presently on the drawing boards.

On the stealth front, Lockheed-Martin and Boeing are together working on a new combat aircraft, the F-22, for production and entry into service in the near future. It is expected to have diamond-shaped wings because of their stealth advantage (with the possibility of an alternative variable-sweep version for naval use), and it will incorporate much of the new agility technology including vectored thrust. Interestingly, however, it is moving away from the canard philosophy of recent years and will have an aft close-coupled tailplane. In the United Kingdom, one of British Aerospace's plans is for a successor to the Eurofighter 2000, which has appeared under the uninspiring codename of NCA, standing for 'Next Combat Aircraft', a stealthy subsonic interdictor[10] whose proposed configuration is shown in Figure 14.8. Its hallmark is undoubtedly its stealth, with all weapons being carried internally to avoid the substantial radar signature that externally carried stores present.

---

[10]To interdict is to prohibit. An interdictor's mission is thus to intercept and deter or disable an enemy aircraft, usually engaged on a ground-attack mission.

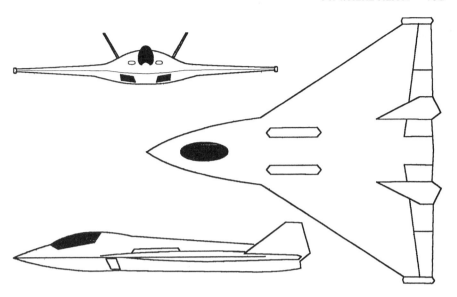

Figure 14.8 British Aerospace's 'Next Combat Aircraft'?

Throughout the 1990s interest has been strong in the development of the so-called ASTOVL aircraft, which stands for 'Advanced Short Take-Off and Vertical Landing'. Even the latest STOVL Harrier is not supersonic: a proposed supersonic STOVL aircraft based on the Harrier concept, the P1154, was cancelled in 1965 on the grounds of cost and for other reasons, but this opened the way for the first sub-sonic vertical take-off and landing Harrier, the GR1, to enter service with the Royal Air Force in 1969. Russia also built a VTOL fighter, the Yak-38 Forger, first seen in service in 1976, but it has now been withdrawn. And so a new ASTOVL aircraft which is supersonic, stealthy and agile with a sophisticated flight control system is needed.

If the additional aircraft control requirements of hovering flight and transition are to be added to those of what is becoming accepted as 'conventional' flight, all the questions that we posed earlier about the pilot interface become even more demanding. Even with the relatively simple operating system of the Harrier, the pilots have to be given special training for the task of handling the additional thrust-vectoring control, and this can still be extremely demanding of pilot skill espe-cially when, for example, landing on a heaving aircraft-carrier deck at sea, and the proposed ASTOVLs will be very much more demanding than that.

To tackle these problems, scientists at the United Kingdom's Defence Research Agency have been working on a project to design suitable flight control laws and pilot interface, using a converted Harrier as a testbed. The project is known as the Vectored Thrust Aircraft Advanced Flight Control programme, with the acronym VAAC (VTAAFCP really would have been too much of a mouthful!), and this has given rise to a complete rethink of flight control laws and pilot interfacing, even to the extent of requiring some alternative terminology. Instead of an AFCS we now have an IPFCS, standing for 'Integrated Flight and Propulsion Control System'. The pilot's hand and foot controls are now called 'inceptors', and those things which actually make the airframe or the engine do something (such as ailerons, throttle valve, variable-angle nozzles etc) have become 'motivators', all of which must be integrated and coordinated by the IFPCS to carry out the pilot's demands.

Meanwhile, throughout the 1990s, parallel studies which have been cooperatively sponsored by the United Kingdom and United States governments have been investigating the thorny problem of finding the best configuration and mechanical layout of airframe and powerplant for a future ASTOVL aircraft to fulfil all the conflicting requirements. This could easily make the subject for a whole new book, and even an additional chapter here could not do justice, in the *Flightwise* manner of tackling basic concepts from scratch, to the whole of the current ASTOVL scene. However, there is little doubt that this scene will provide the next chapter in the history of controlled manned aircraft flight, and so let us watch with interest, and now with much greater insight, as the story continues to unfold.[11]

*   *   *

[11]A very thorough synopsis of the future aircraft scene at the time of writing may be found in the following references:

- John Farley: *Thrusting Forward.* Flight International, 2–8 February 1994, page 22. (Article about the VAAC Harrier project.)
- Neville Beckett: *Beyond Eurofighter: UK Combat Aircraft in the 21st Century.* Journal of Aircraft, Volume 47 No 4, October 1994, page 377.
- Douglas Barrie, Guy Norris, Graham Warwick: *Short Take-Off, Low Funding.* Flight International, 29 March–4 April 1995, page 32. (Article about the US ASTOVL programme, including a number of proposed layout drawings.)
- Guy Norris and Graham Warwick: *Taking Shape.* Flight International, 13–19 December 1995, page 26. (Article on three design concepts within the US Joint Advanced Strike Technology (JAST) programme.)
- Graham Warwick: *Joint Endeavour.* Flight International, 3–9 July 1996, page 25. (Article about commonality and affordability of the Joint Strike Fighter programme, the new name of the US JAST.)

EPILOGUE

Aircraft stability and control has moved on a long way in 100 years. In *Flightwise – Aircraft Stability and Control* we have reflected these advances, hopefully not just by talking *about* them, but rather by thoroughly familiarising ourselves with the whys and wherefores of aircraft control and stability. If *Flightwise – Principles of Aircraft Flight* was the trunk of the tree, pushing out roots to draw in from all around it the nourishment of the basic concepts of the subject, then perhaps *Flightwise – Aircraft Stability and Control* has been the branching head of that tree, with all its vigorous and lush growth of leaves and fruit. We have seen that stability and control is very much the fruition of the principles of aircraft flight, since an object which can merely travel in one straight line through the air can scarcely be credited with the name of 'aircraft', and would be virtually useless.

Now our *Flightwise* journey is over for the time being, but the growth of the tree continues unabated. Sustained by the nourishment of a firm grasp of basic principles, I am confident that you will be able to add to your knowledge and develop your understanding of aircraft flight, by reading the wealth of books and articles on the subject with new insight. I trust that you will now feel qualified to count yourself amongst those who are 'flightwise'.

Index